# ROY CLARK

Deluxe

# Big Note Guitar

## Song Book

ISBN 0 8494 0160 7

45853

## Index of Keys

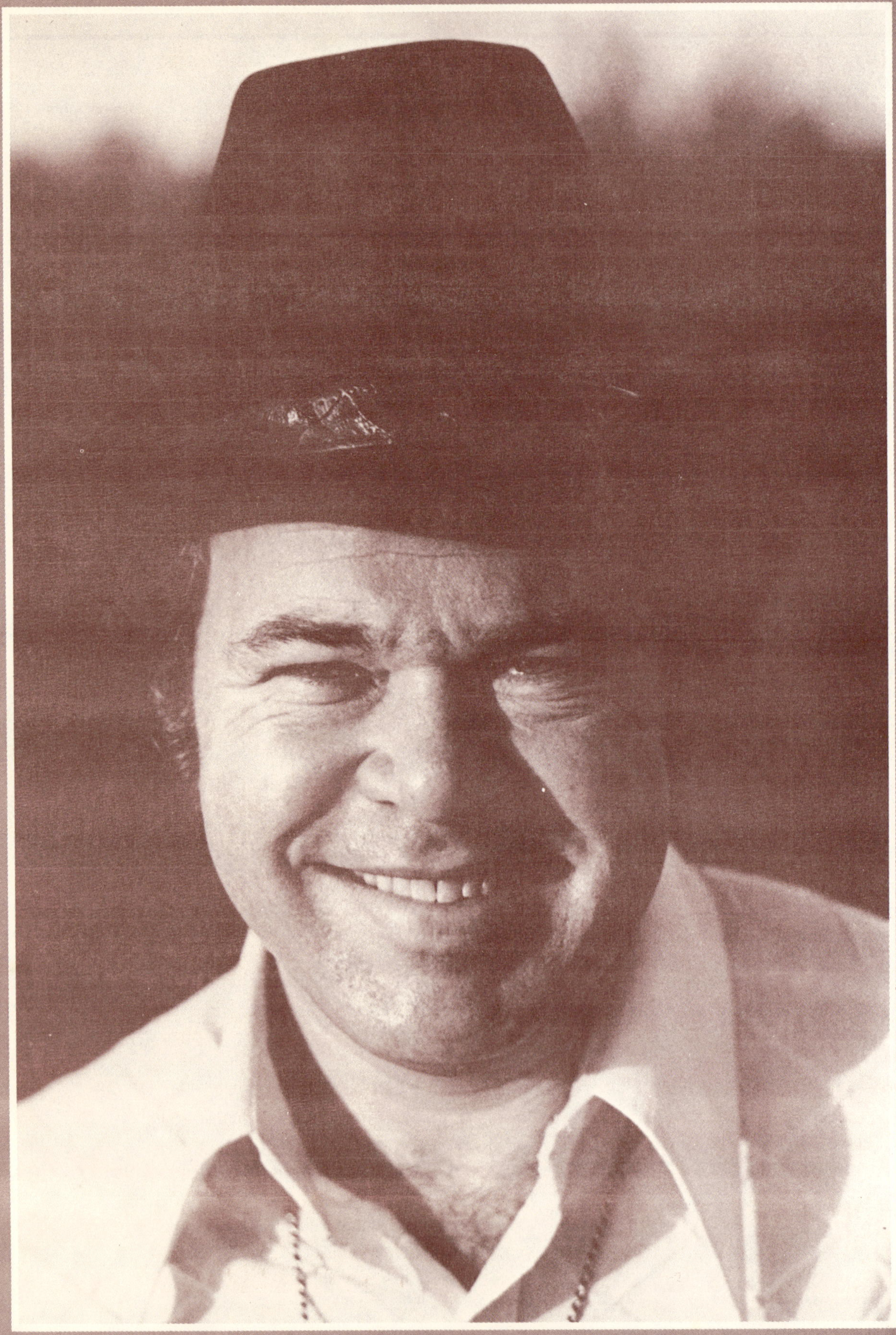

# "...and now, here's Roy..."

Country music superstar, Roy Clark, is a man of so many talents spanning so many mediums that a reviewer once said of him, "The only critical remark I can think of is that Roy's dancing could possibly improve."

The man is a master musician, relying predominately on guitar, 12-string acoustic, banjo and fiddle although he can "get by" on five others. "Boy, can he play," noted guitar designer Leo Fender has been quoted as saying. "If you listen to him play anything, then you have some concept of what the guitar can do."

Roy is a noted comedian who writes all his own material and he has been honored by his peers as Comedian of the Year. He records his songs for the ABC-Dot label; he composes string instrumentals; he is a much sought after guest on major network and syndicated television shows and specials, far more visible on TV than his contemporaries in the field. And yes, he dances, once in white tie and tails down a staircase on The Donny & Marie Show, and then with Mitzi throughout the 1977 Mitzi Gaynor Special for CBS.

Roy Clark is also a pilot, operating from the left front seat of his Mitsubishi prop jet that whisks him from one concert to the next, 250 annually, including the recent May date at Carnegie Hall. That prestigious outing was broadcast worldwide on the largest ad hoc radio network ever assembled for a country music performance. He's a radio broadcaster, a photographer, a boat captain, a gentleman rancher, an outdoorsman, a horse racing enthusiast (particularly when it involves a winner from his own stables), a businessman and even a President, of Roy Clark's Dieter's Choice, the new line of weight control foods.

Roy hosts the "Tonight Show" with Ed McMahon, Glen Campbell and Bob Hope.

Roy Clark is also a pioneer. He was one of the very first to establish country music as a popular and highly successful attraction along the Las Vegas hotel strip, and now he plays the main showroom of the Frontier 12 weeks each year. He is the first country music performer ever to be enshrined in the world famous Movieland Wax Museum in Buena Park, California. And he is also the first country music artist ever to headline his own show in the Soviet Union during an unprecedented three week concert tour there in early 1976. Performances in Riga, Moscow and Leningrad were SRO weeks before his arrival. Roy left the USSR with an invitation by their government for a return engagement in February of '78 because of the unique appeal he brought to the people.

Things weren't always first class for Roy Clark, at least not careerwise. Like everyone else he paid his dues working small, smoky clubs, an opening act for more established artists, sideman for others. Growing up in the Washington area of Meherrin, Va., where his father worked for the federal government, Roy may well have surprised the teachers who didn't predict greatness from the youngster they said could never take things seriously, the very basis of Roy's ineffable humor.

The family was musically inclined with his father, uncles and cousins picking and playing at local events. Roy's mother is a pianist. "I was just a kid of about three when I discovered Dad's banjo and I naturally assumed it was a drum, something to pound on, which is exactly what I did," says Roy. "Well, I got straightened out pretty quick."

That he did, and with Hester Clark's guidance Roy learned to pick well enough to take the nation's Country Music Banjo Championship at the age of 16, coming back the following year to win it again. A special guest appearance at Nashville's Grand Ole Opry was part of the prize and the experience whetted Roy's appetite for a music career.

Performing with Mac Davis.

His aspirations proved a winner, as awards for his achievements have been lavish. Voted Entertainer of the Year in the same year by the Country Music Association and the Academy of Country Music (twice in succession from the latter), he has also held the title of Country Music Star of the Year from the American Guild of Variety Artists. In 1975 Roy joined other special personalities when a "star" was set on his behalf in Hollywood Boulevard's famous Walk of Fame. (He is honored there in the Television category). In 1976 Roy was chosen as the CMA International Friendship Ambassador; he was also given the title of Oklahoma's Ambassador of Goodwill last year.

The Tulsa, Okla., Board of Education honored Roy by naming their newest building The Roy Clark Elementary School. And Fascination, Ltd. of Chicago has introduced the world's first micro-process cocktail unit pinball machine titled "The Entertainer". It carries Roy's image and is being marketed worldwide. He was presented The Jim Reeves Memorial Award by the Board of Directors of the Academy of Country Music

during their televised 12th Anniversary Awards Show in 1977. And, he was recently given the Spirit of Life Award from the City of Hope where the Roy Clark Research Foundation has been enacted, all because of his various humanitarian endeavors including support of the Children's Medical Center of Tulsa which receives proceeds from the annual Roy Clark Celebrity Golf Classic.

Television appearances are multiple: The Mitzi Gaynor Special, The Bell Telephone Jubilee Special, The 1976 CMA Awards Show (co-host), various Bob Hope specials, The Captain & Tennille, Mac Davis, Merv Griffin, Mike Douglas, Dinah, Sammy & Company, The Odd Couple, Flip Wilson, Hollywood Squares, Donny & Marie Osmond, as well as numerous guest and hosting roles for The Tonight Show. Roy also made a rare PBS appearance with Arthur Fiedler and the 90-piece Boston Pops Orchestra. His co-hosting of Hee Haw alone is seen by over 34 million viewers weekly in 221 markets.

Roy and wife, Barbara, live in Tulsa, Oklahoma.

8258

Roy, guesting on the "Dinah Show".

# TUNING THE GUITAR

To tune the strings of your guitar, twist the tuning pegs to raise or lower the pitch.
The six strings of your guitar should match the pitch of the six keys shown on the piano.

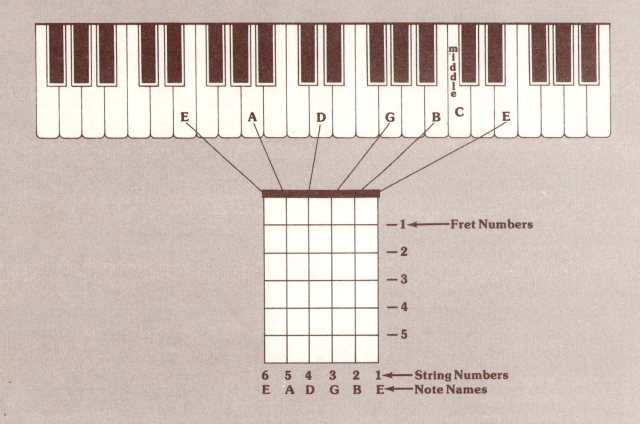

A special set of pitch pipes, available in music stores, may also be used to tune the guitar.

## TUNING BY STRINGS

If you have the correct pitch for the 6th string (E), then you may tune the rest of the strings this way:

Place a finger on the fifth fret of the 6th string and match pitch with the 5th string open.

The 4th string open should give the same pitch as the 5th string, fifth fret.

The 3rd string open should give the same pitch as the 4th string, fifth fret.

The 2nd string open should give the same pitch as the 3rd string, fourth fret.

The 1st string open should give the same pitch as the 2nd string, fifth fret.

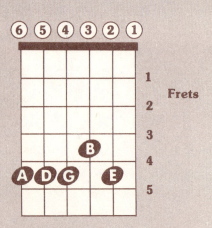

8174

# CHORD FRAMES

A chord diagram is used to indicate the position of the fingers of the LEFT hand.

NOTATION

THE FINGERS OF THE LEFT HAND
ARE INDICATED AS FOLLOWS:

1 = index finger
2 = middle finger
3 = ring finger
4 = little finger
0 = open string

REMEMBER: Strings with no finger
markings are not to be played. Strings
with open circles above the nut are to
be played.

C Major Chord
Frame

nut
1st fret
2nd fret
strings

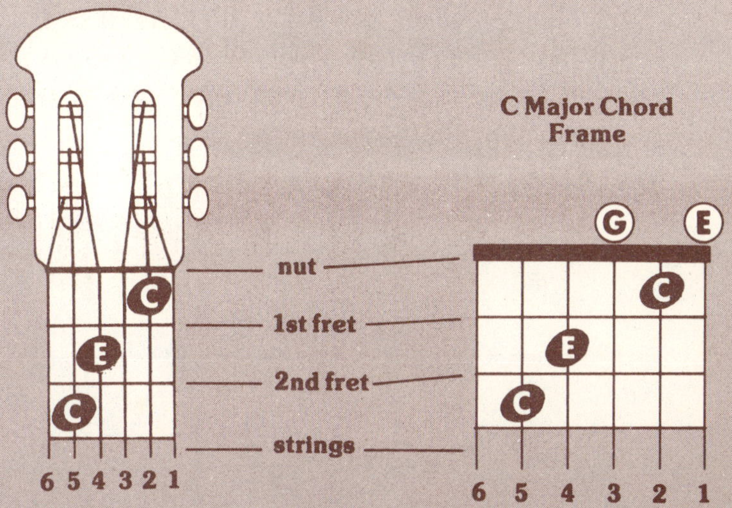

Note that the 6th string
is not played.

---

# BARS And MEASURES

The STAFF is divided into MEASURES by BAR LINES.
The last MEASURE of a piece of music always has a DOUBLE BAR.

| MEASURE | MEASURE | MEASURE | MEASURE |

BAR LINES  DOUBLE BAR

---

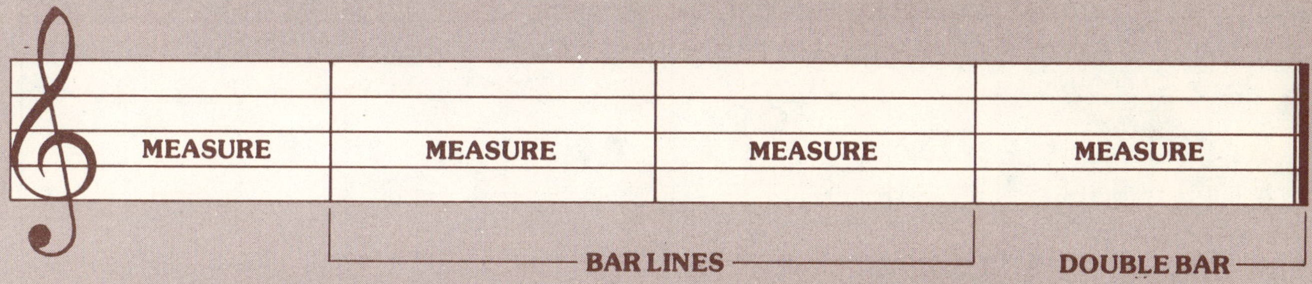

## Notes and Rests
### AND THE TIME VALUE FOR EACH

| Name | Notes | Rests | Counts |
|------|-------|-------|--------|
| WHOLE | 𝅝 | ▬ | 4 |
| HALF | 𝅗𝅥 | ▬ | 2 |
| QUARTER | ♩ | 𝄽 | 1 |
| EIGHTH | ♪ | 𝄾 | 1/2 |
| SIXTEENTH | 𝅘𝅥𝅯 | 𝄿 | 1/4 |

## Time Signatures

The TIME SIGNATURE is placed on the
STAFF at the beginning of a piece of music
to indicate how many counts (beats) are in
each measure, and what type of note
receives one beat.

**2** = 2 counts per measure
**4** = quarter note receives one count.

**3** = 3 counts per measure.
**4** = quarter note receives one count.

**4** = 4 counts per measure.
**4** = quarter note receives one count.

# TRI-CHORDS

Many songs can be harmonized by using the three basic chords of the key. In Music Theory, these chords are called the Principal Chords of the key. In Popular Music, they are called the TRI-CHORDS. Here are the Tri-Chords for the four most common keys for guitar: C, G, D and A minor.

8258

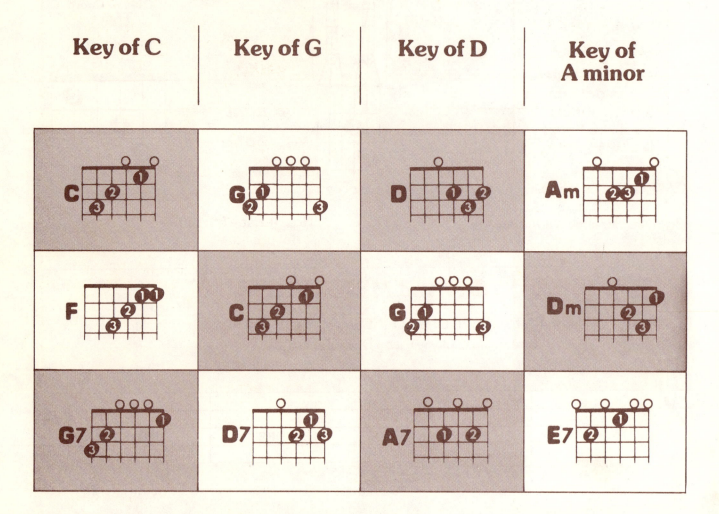

| Key of C | Key of G | Key of D | Key of A minor |

## Sharps and Flats

This symbol ♯ is called a Sharp. When a Sharp is placed in front of a note it means to play the note one fret *higher* than you normally would. For example: This note would normally be played on the second string at the 3rd fret (refer to the chart). If a Sharp appears in front of the note, like this, you would play the note on the second string at the *4th* fret.

This symbol ♭ is called a Flat. When a Flat is placed in front of a note it means to play the note one fret *lower* than normal. The note would then be played on the second string at the *2nd* fret.

Here is a more concise chart to show the fingering of not only the main Tri-Chords but the remainder of the chords in this entire book.

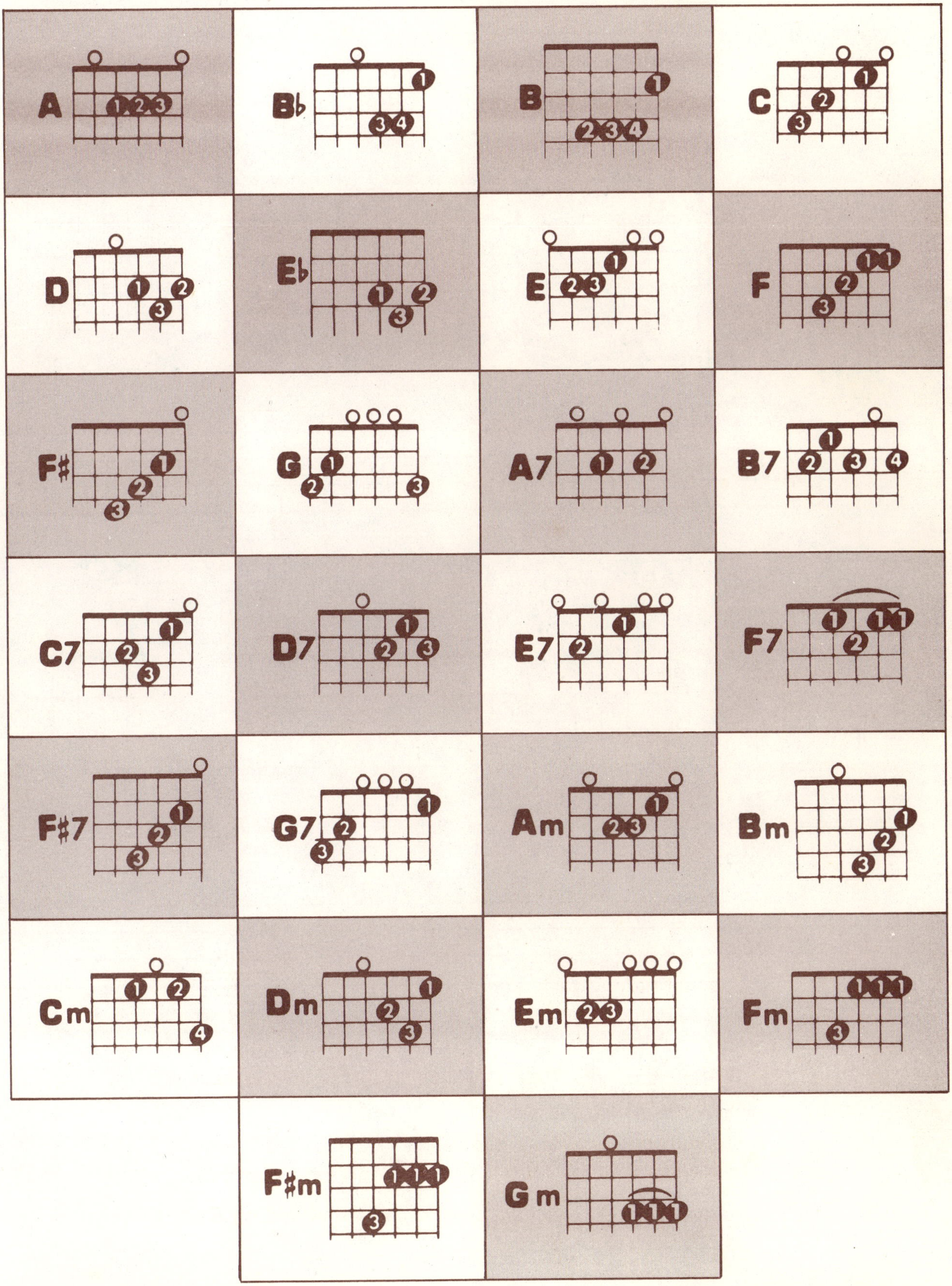

# FINGERBOARD CHART

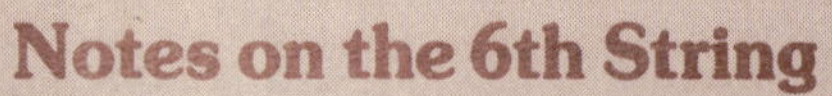

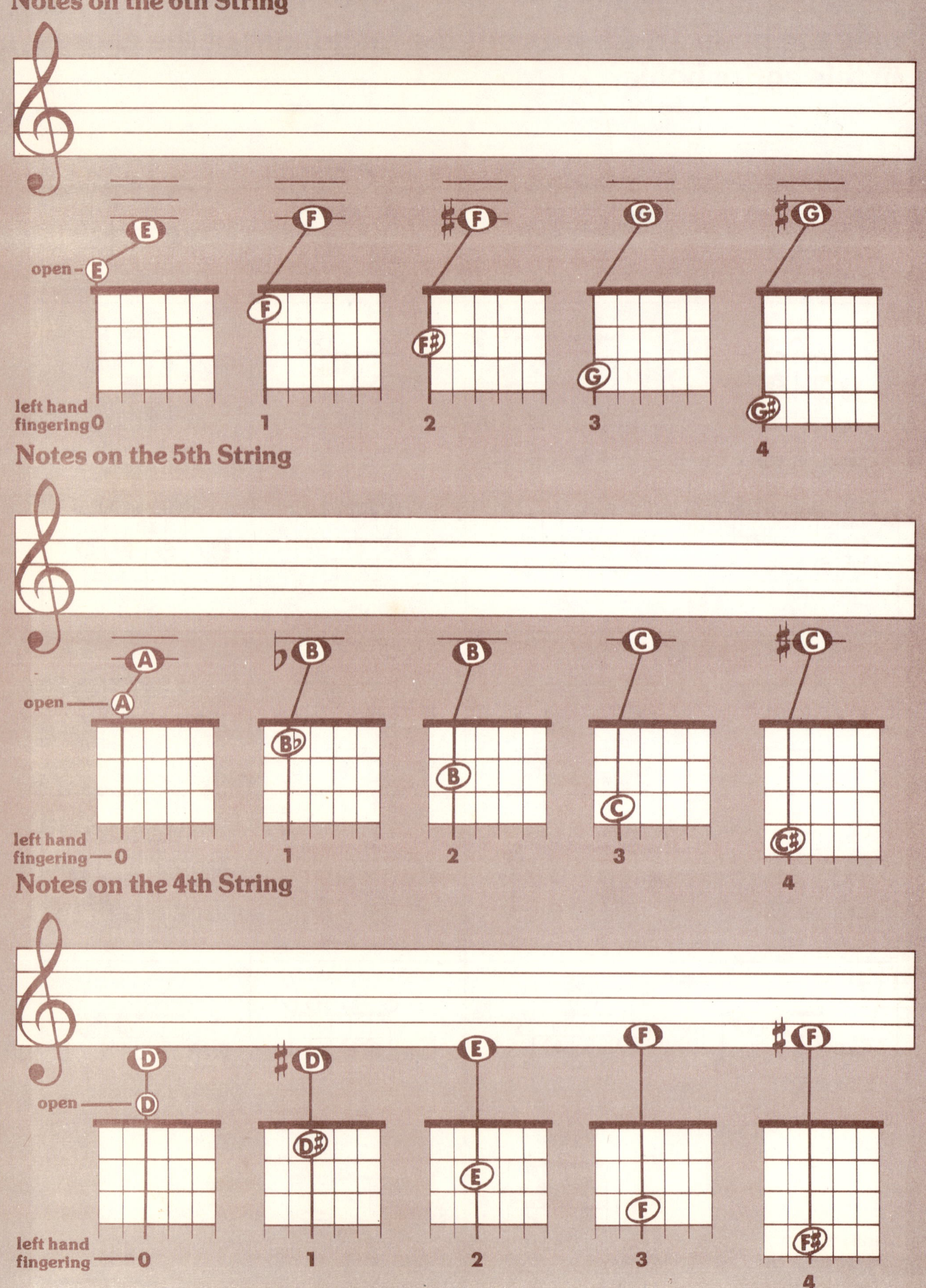

## Notes on the 3rd String

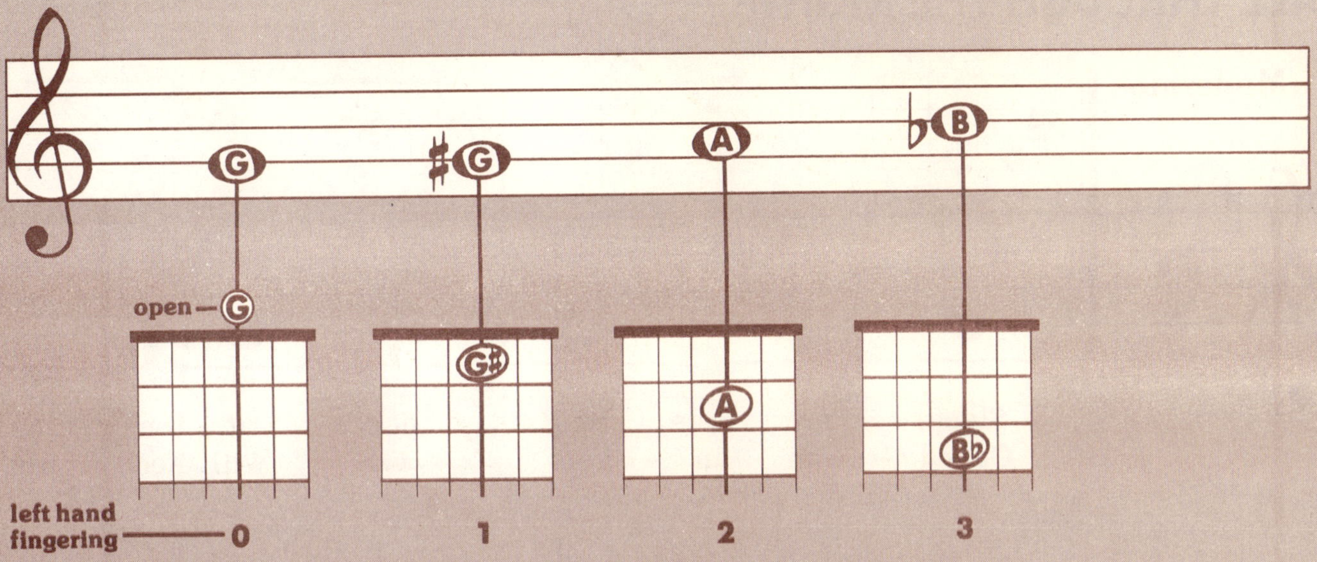

## Notes on the 2nd String

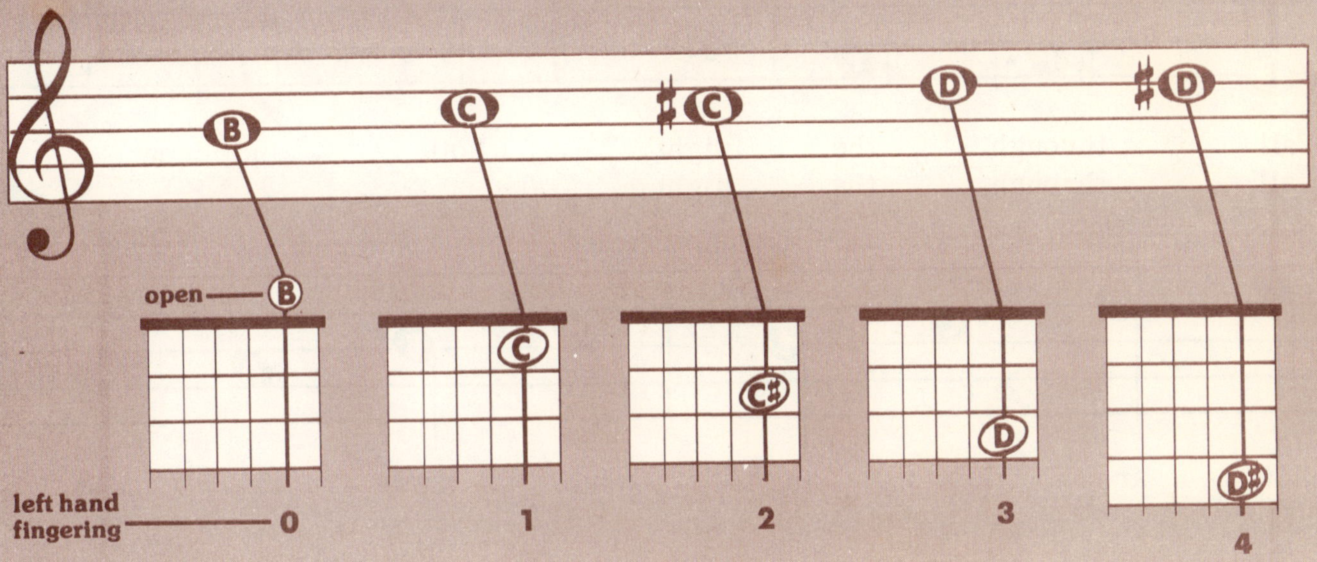

## Notes on the 1st String

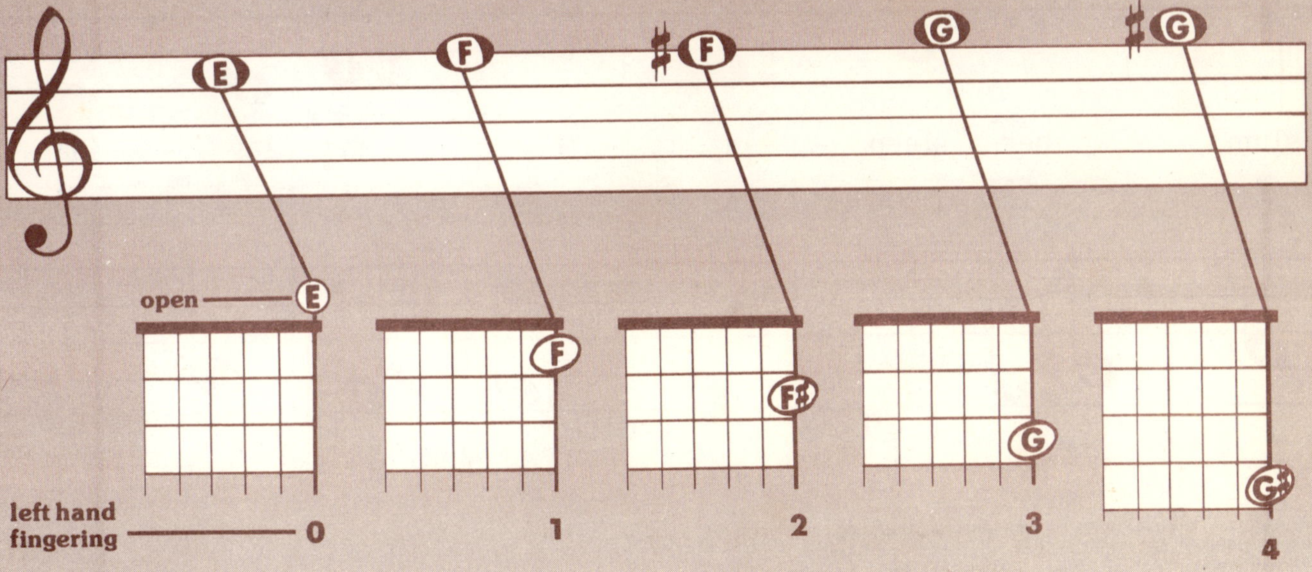

# ALL THROUGH THE NIGHT

OLD WELSH SONG

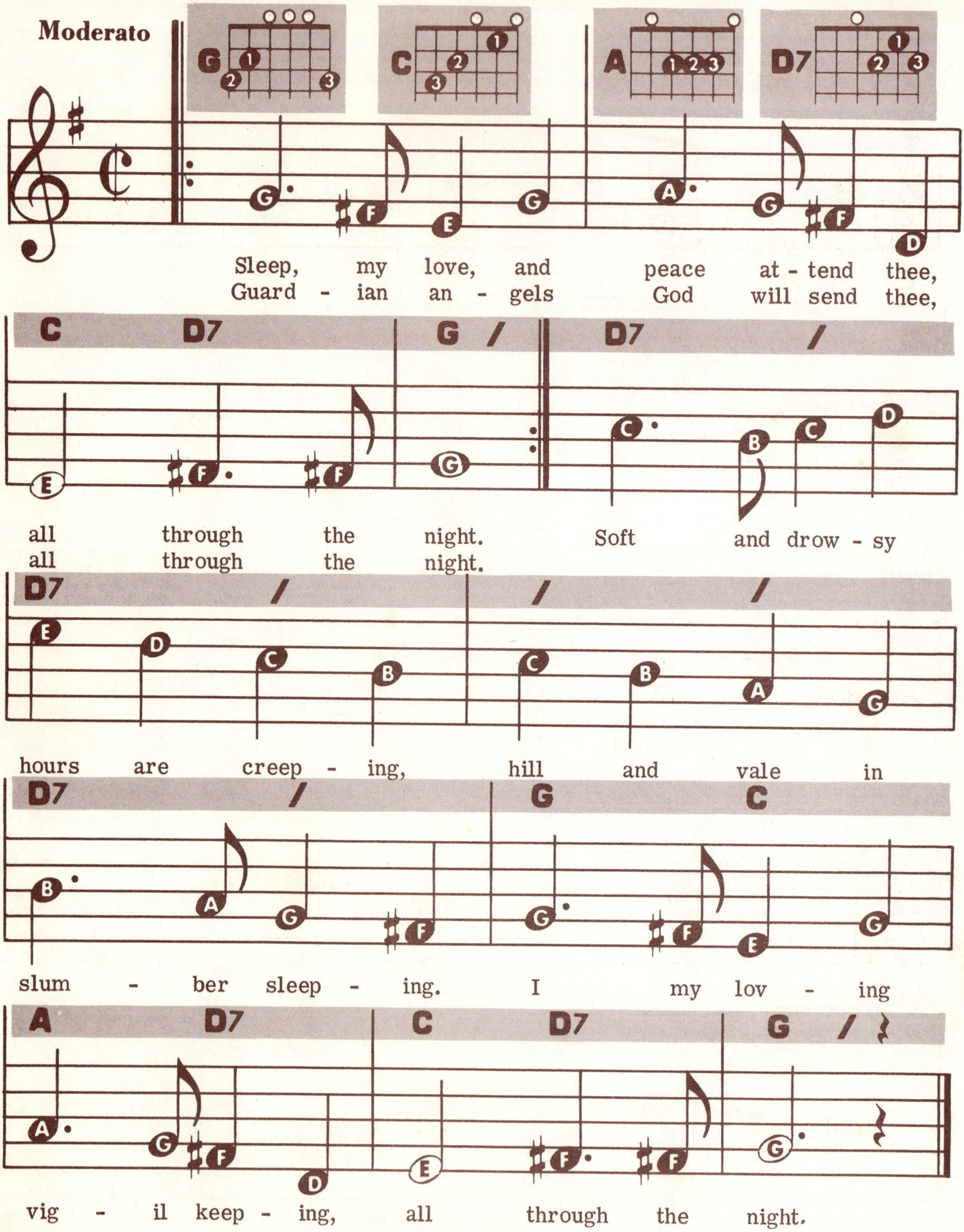

Sleep, my love, and peace at-tend thee,
Guard-ian an-gels God will send thee,

all through the night. Soft and drow-sy
all through the night.

hours are creep-ing, hill and vale in

slum-ber sleep-ing. I my lov-ing

vig-il keep-ing, all through the night.

# ALLEY CAT

By FRANK BJORN

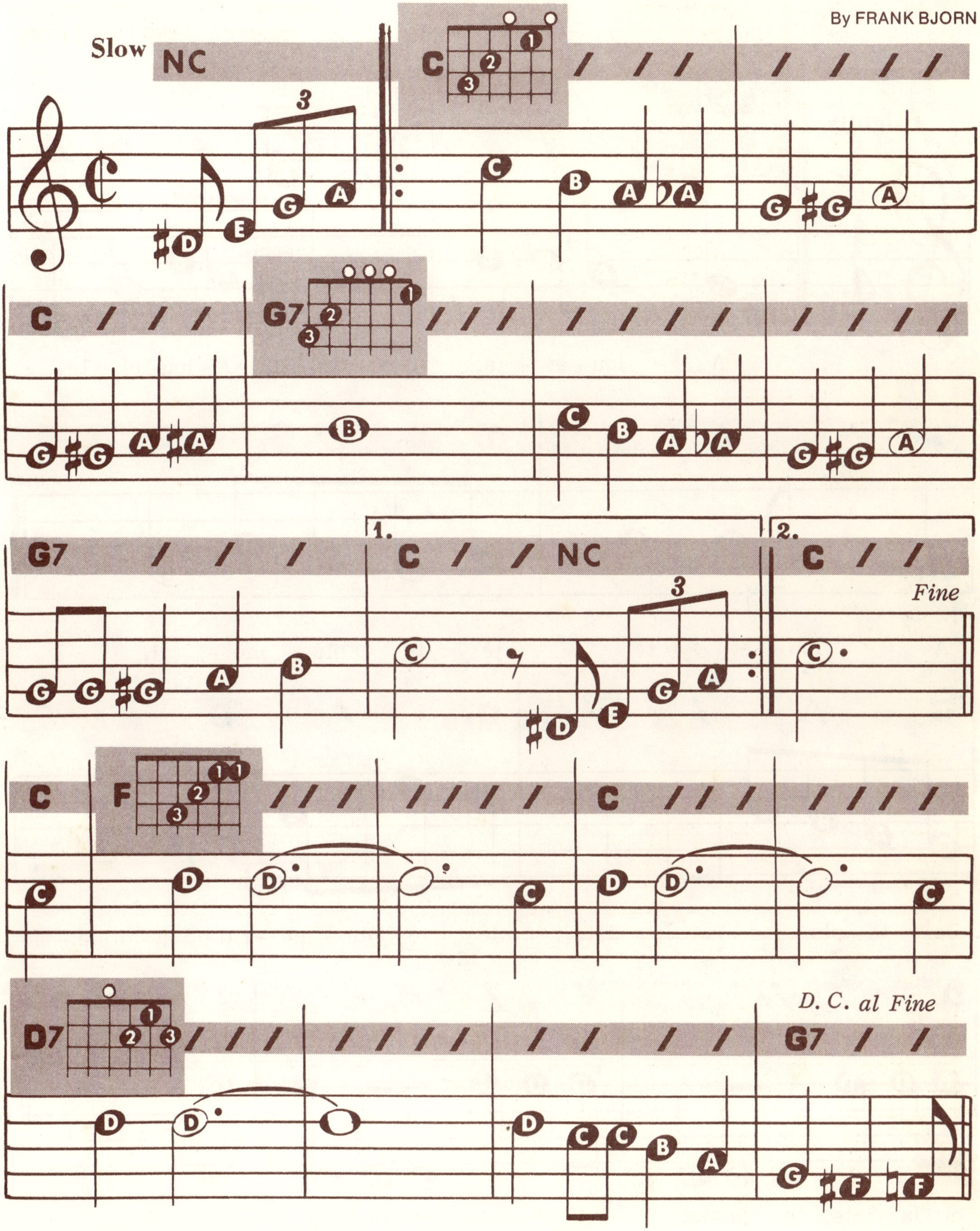

# ALOUETTE

FRENCH TRADITIONAL

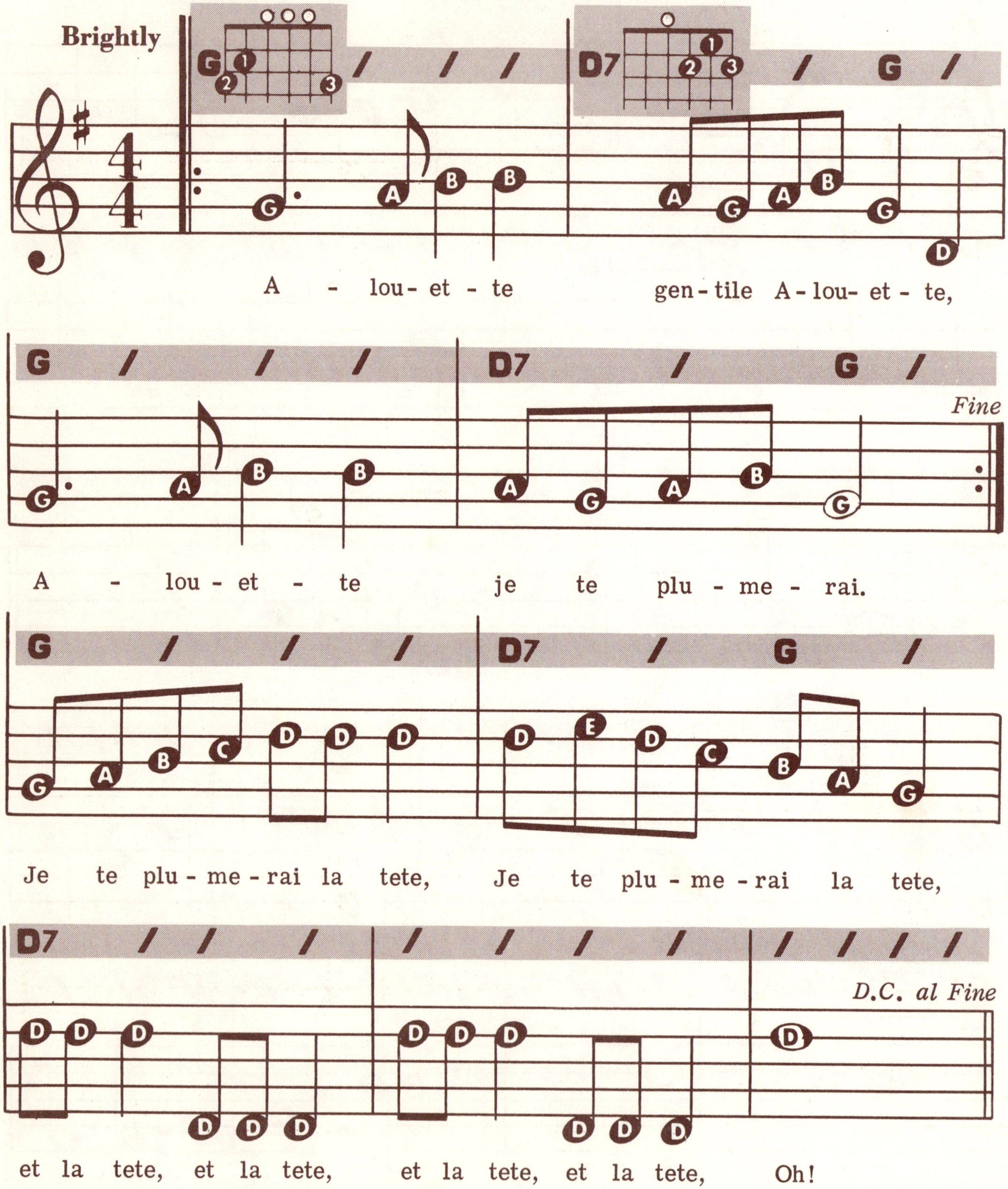

# AMAZING GRACE

TRADITIONAL

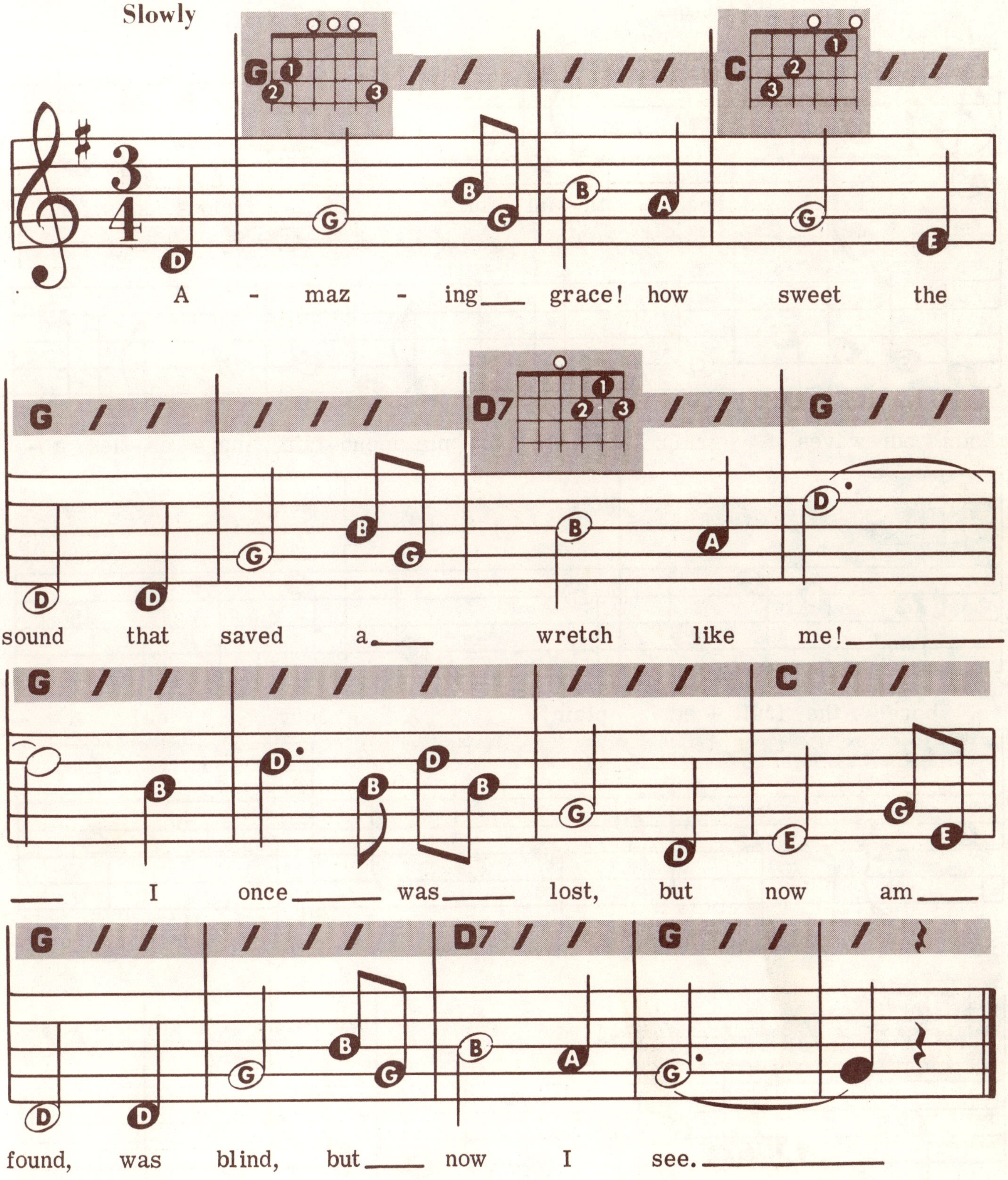

A - maz - ing___ grace! how sweet the sound that saved a___ wretch like me!___

___ I once___ was___ lost, but now am___ found, was blind, but___ now I see.___

# AMERICA, THE BEAUTIFUL

Words by KATHARINE LEE BATES
Music by SAMUEL A. WARD

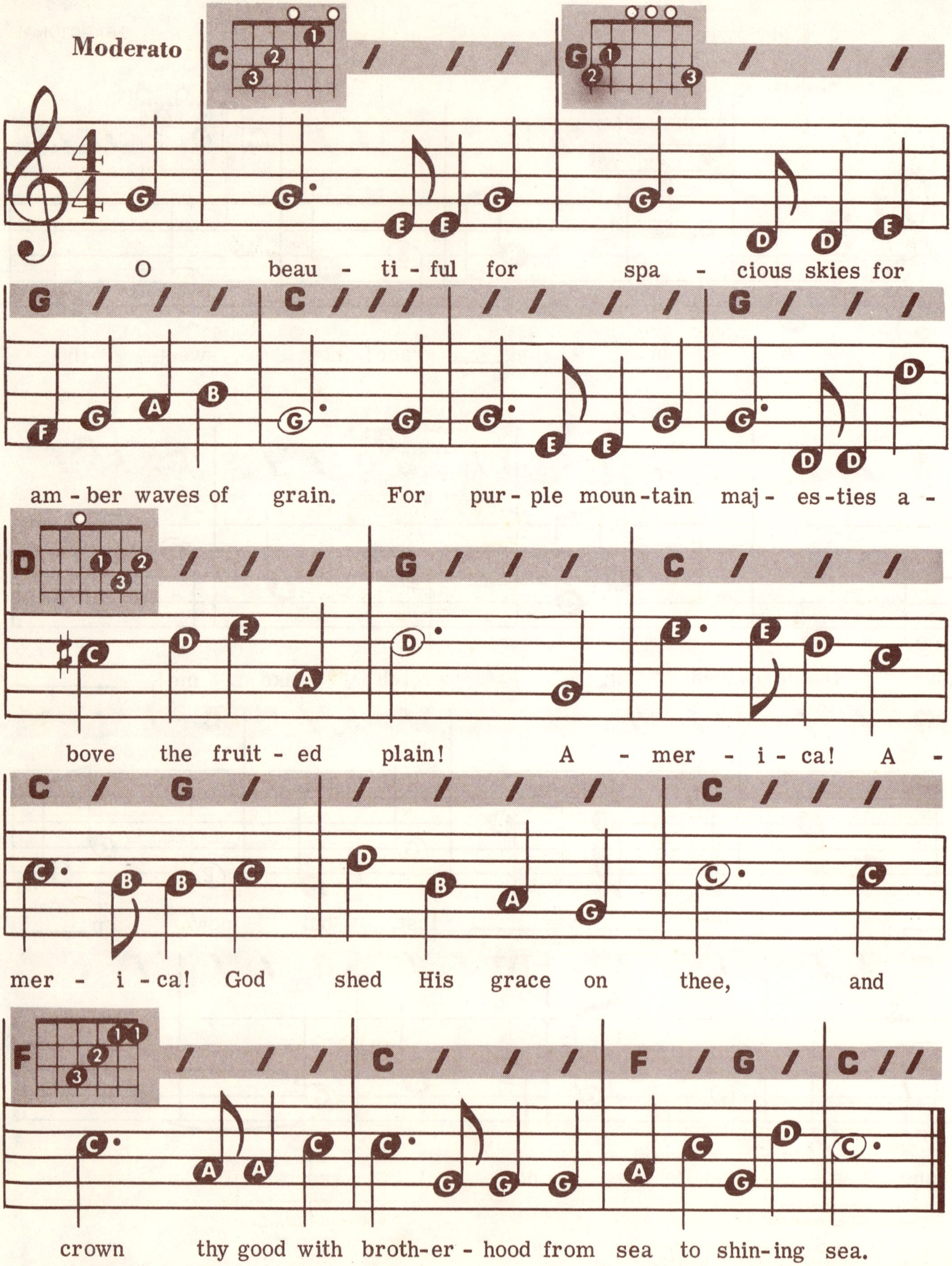

O beau - ti - ful for spa - cious skies for am - ber waves of grain. For pur - ple moun - tain maj - es - ties a - bove the fruit - ed plain! A - mer - i - ca! A - mer - i - ca! God shed His grace on thee, and crown thy good with broth - er - hood from sea to shin - ing sea.

# BEAUTIFUL DREAMER
**Moderato**

By STEPHEN FOSTER

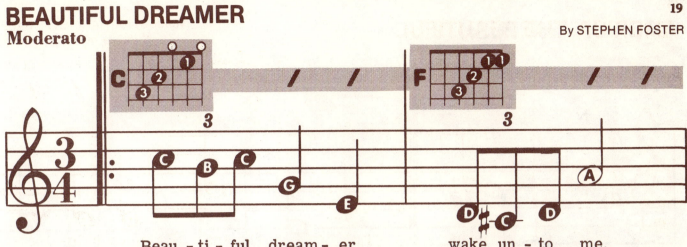

Beau - ti - ful dream - er wake un - to me,
Sounds of the rude world, heard in a day,
Gone are the cares of life's bus - y throng,

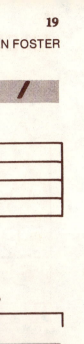

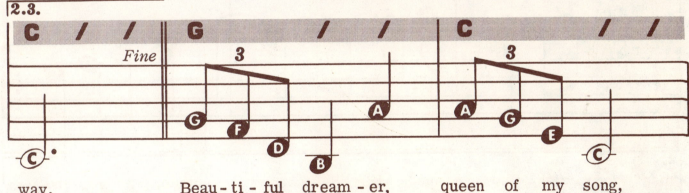

star - lights and dew - drops are wait - ing for thee;
lulled by the moon - light have all passed a -
beau - ti - ful dream - er a - wake un - to

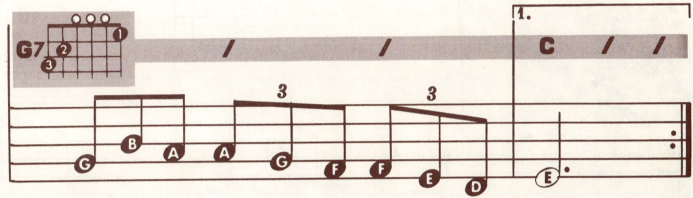

way.
me.
Beau - ti - ful dream - er, queen of my song,

*D.C. al Fine*

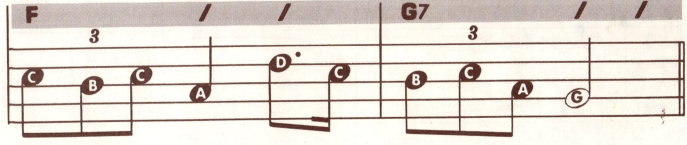

list while I woo thee with soft mel - o - dy.

# BACK UP AND PUSH

By ROY CLARK

**Moderately Bright**

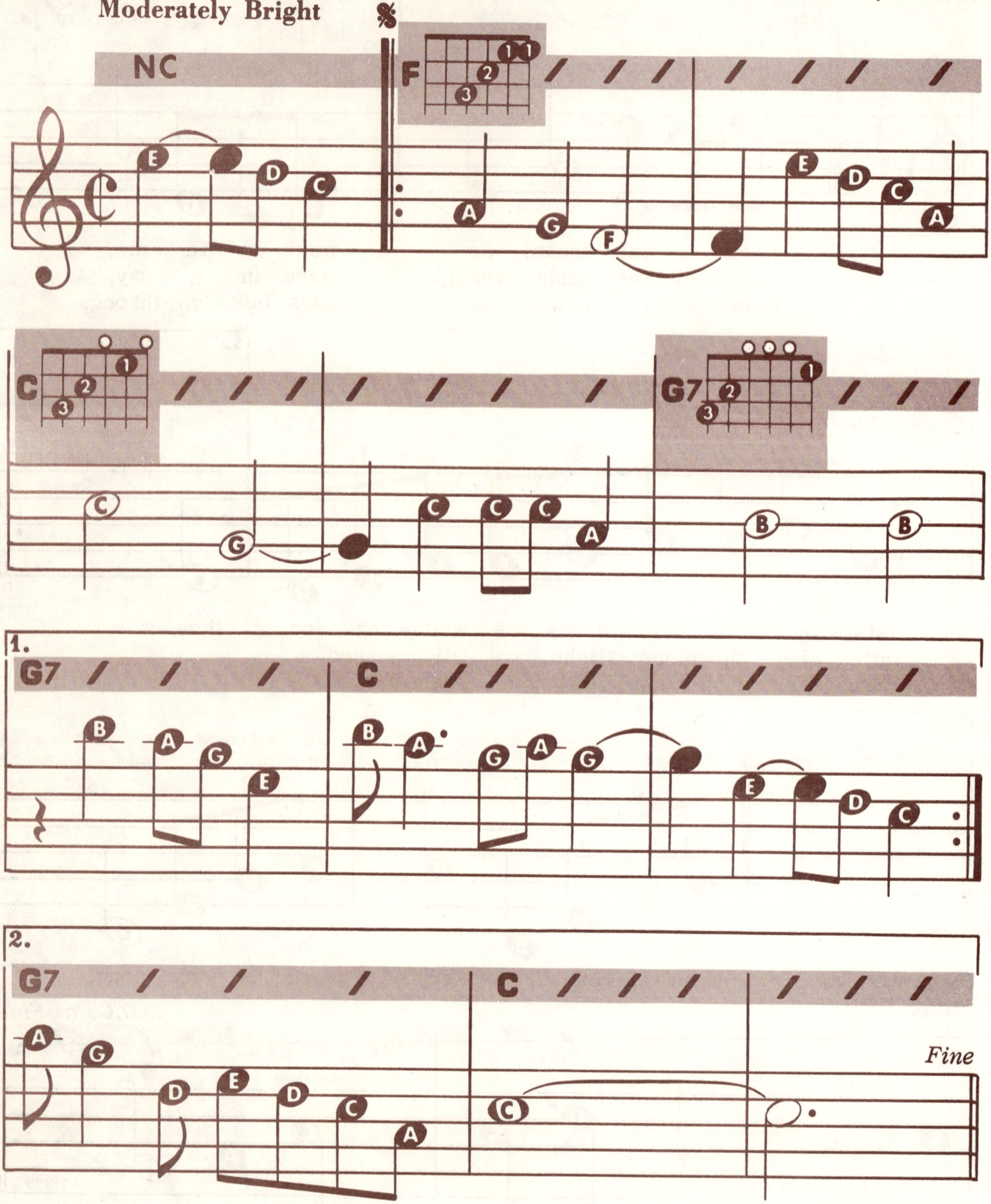

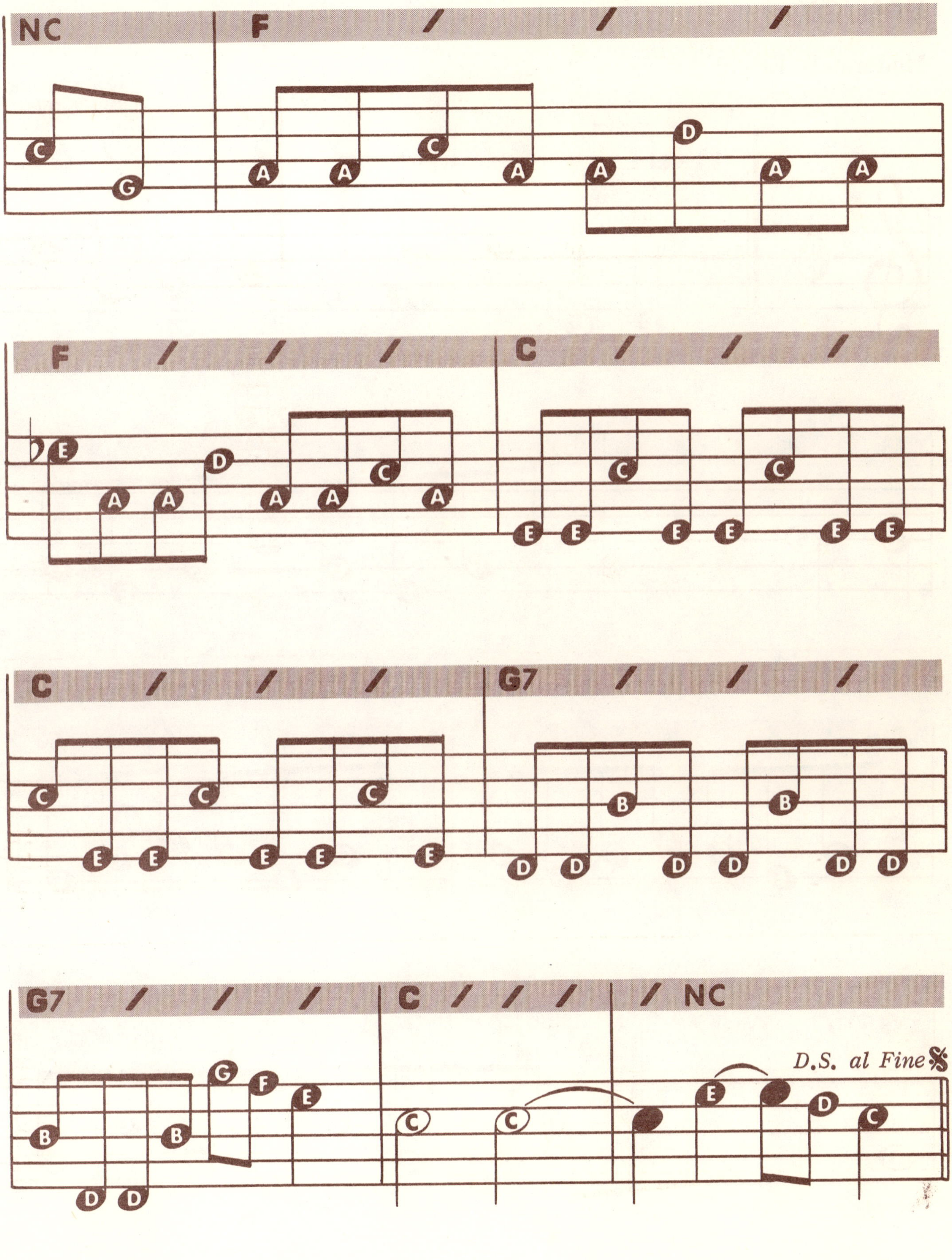

Back Up And Push-2-2

# BANJOY

**Moderately Bright**

By ROY CLARK
and BUCK TRENT

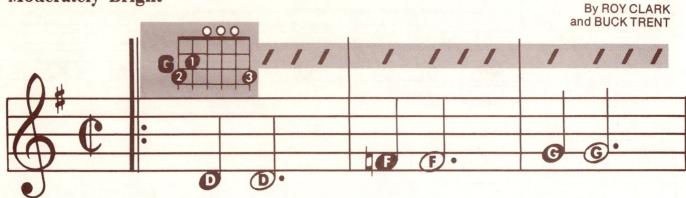

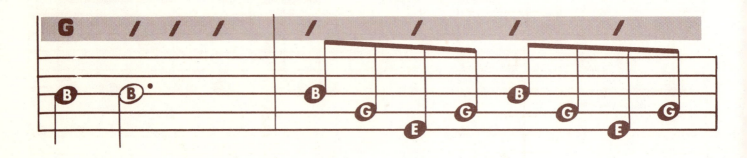

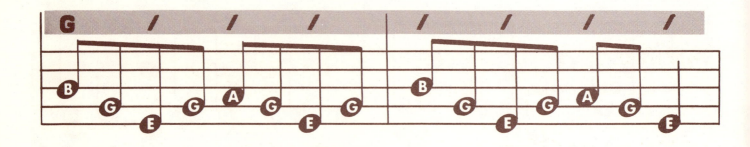

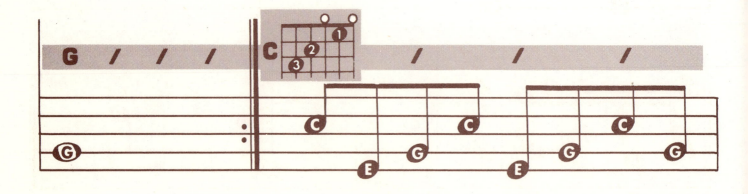

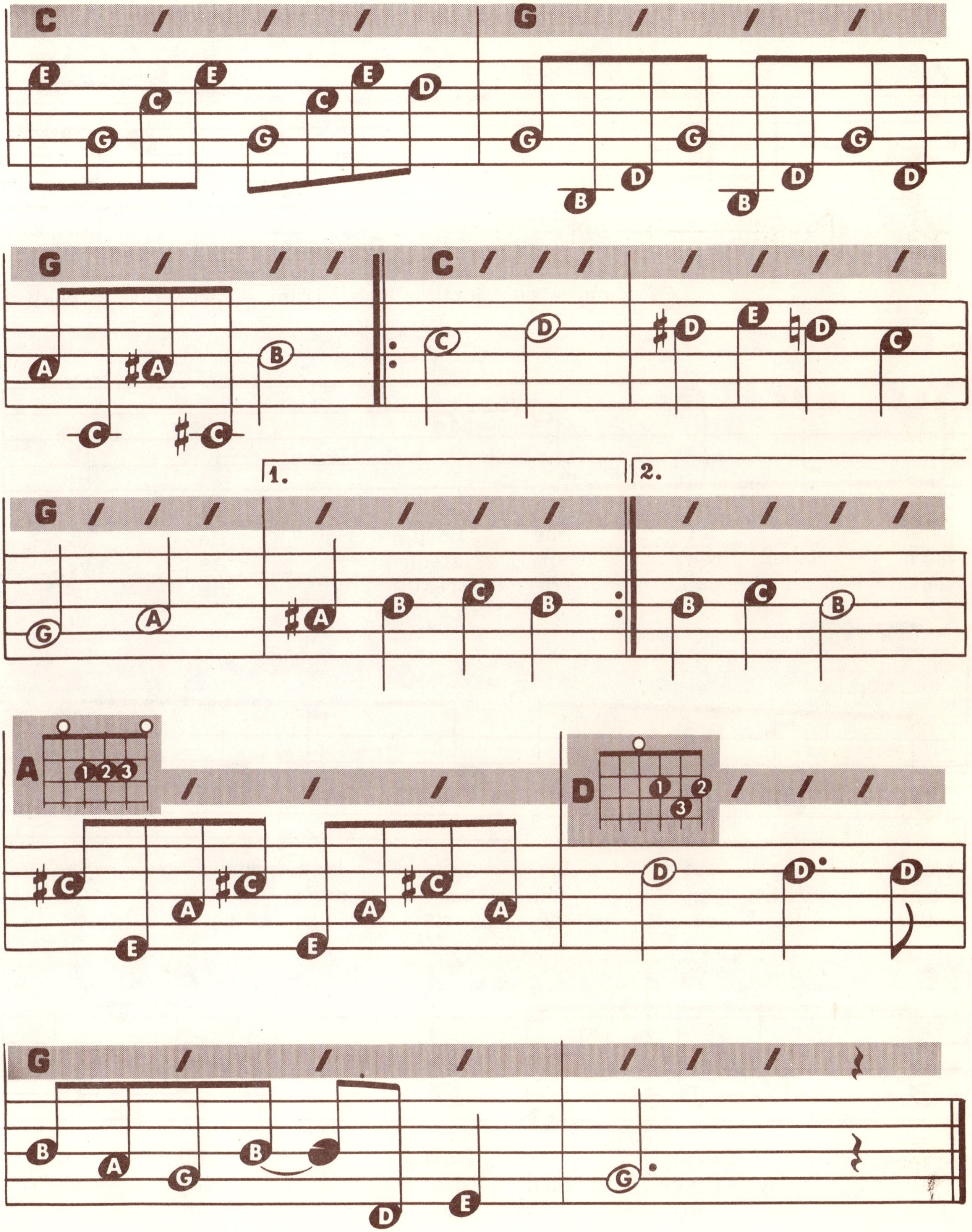
C
E G C E G C E D
G
G B D G B D G D
G
A C ♯A ♯C B
C
C D ♯D E ♮D C
1.
2.
G
G A ♯A B C B B C B
A
1 2 3
♯C E A ♯C E A ♯C A
D
1 2 3
D D D
G
B A G B D E G

# BATTLE HYMN OF THE REPUBLIC

By JULIA WARD HOWE
and WILLIAM STEFFE

Alla Marcia

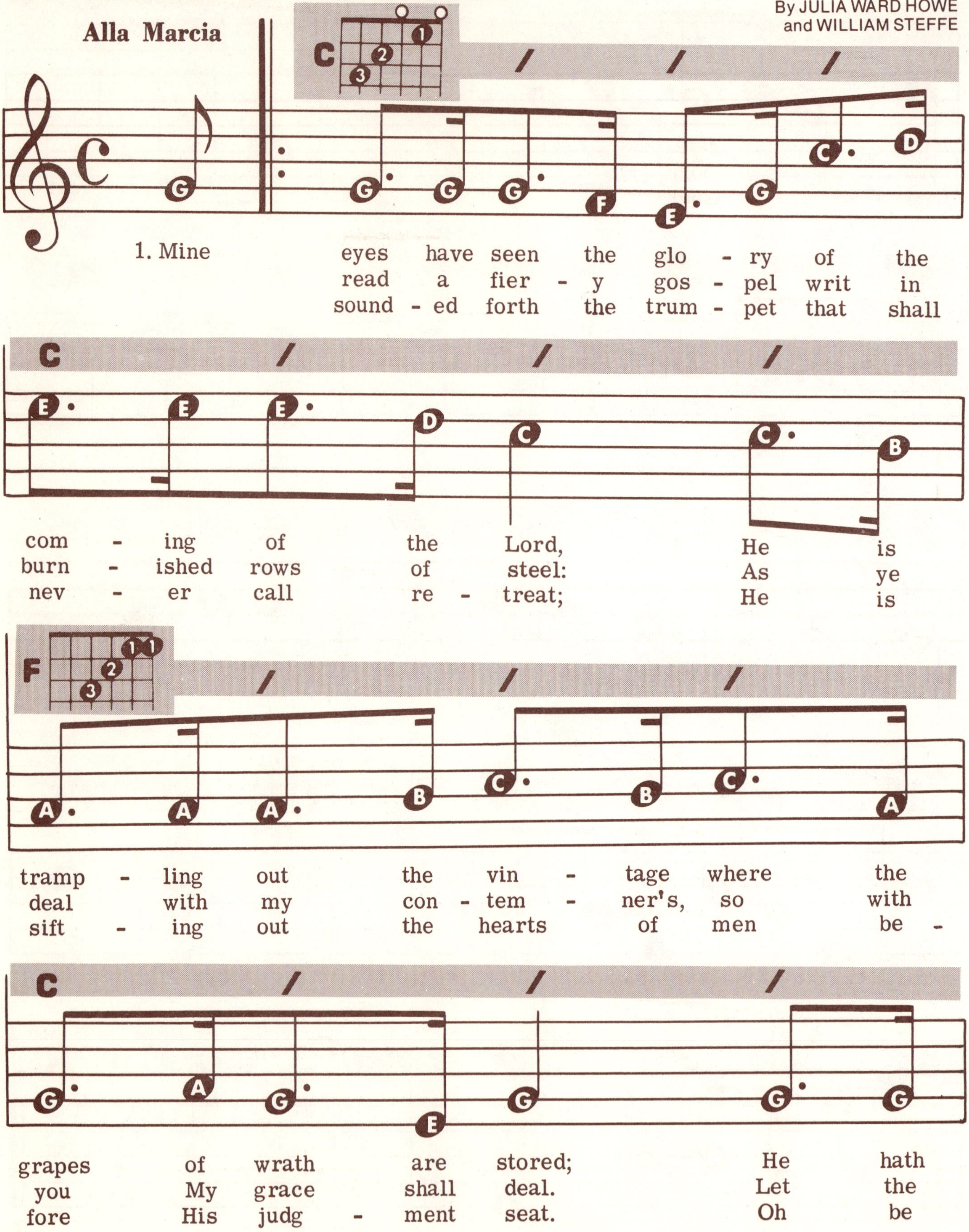

1. Mine eyes have seen the glo - ry of the
read a fier - y gos - pel writ in
sound - ed forth the trum - pet that shall

com - ing of the Lord, He is
burn - ished rows of steel: As ye
nev - er call re - treat; He is

tramp - ling out the vin - tage where the
deal with my con - tem - ner's, so with
sift - ing out the hearts of men be -

grapes of wrath are stored; He hath
you My grace shall deal. Let the
fore His judg - ment seat. Oh be

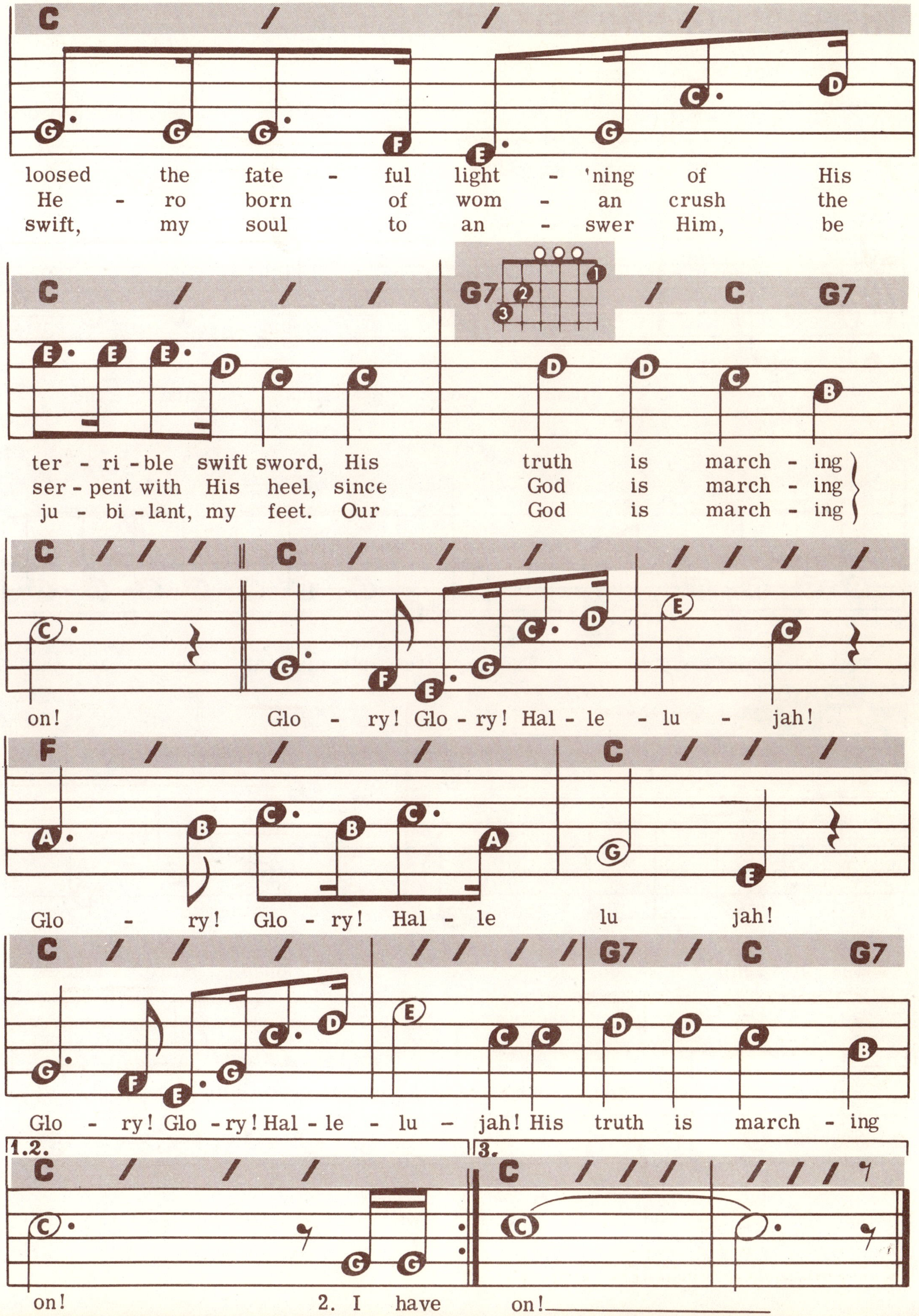

loosed the fate - ful light - 'ning of His
He - ro born of wom - an crush His the
swift, my soul to an - swer Him, be

ter - ri - ble swift sword, His truth is march - ing
ser - pent with His heel, since God is march - ing
ju - bi - lant, my feet. Our God is march - ing

on! Glo - ry! Glo - ry! Hal - le - lu - jah!

Glo - ry! Glo - ry! Hal - le lu jah!

Glo - ry! Glo - ry! Hal - le - lu - jah! His truth is march - ing

on! 2. I have on!

# THE BATTLE OF NEW ORLEANS

By JIMMY DRIFTWOOD

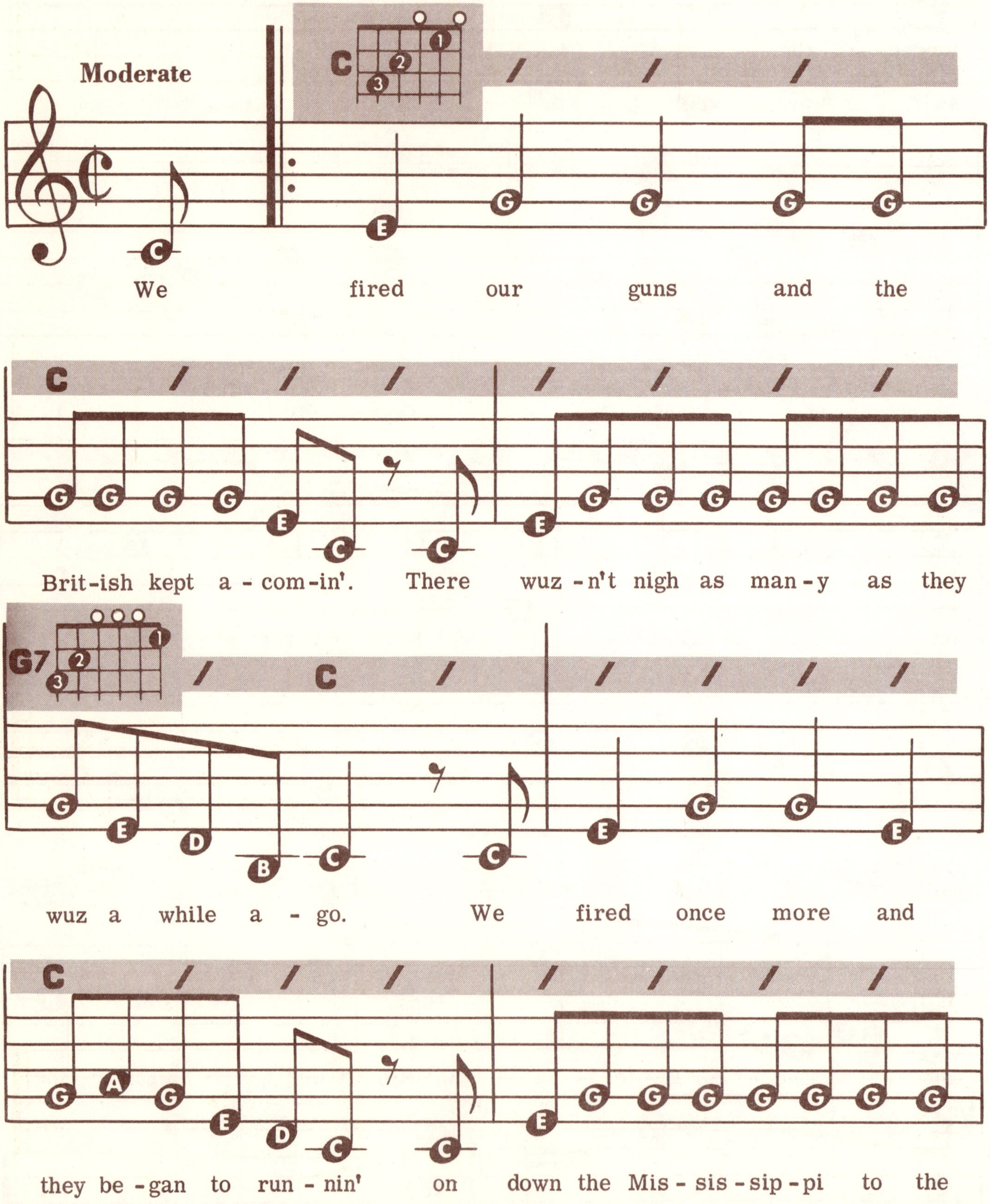

We fired our guns and the Brit-ish kept a-com-in'. There wuz-n't nigh as man-y as they wuz a while a-go. We fired once more and they be-gan to run-nin' on down the Mis-sis-sip-pi to the

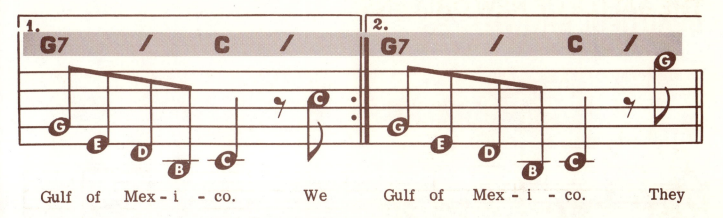

**1.** **2.**

Gulf of Mex - i - co.        We        Gulf of Mex - i - co.        They

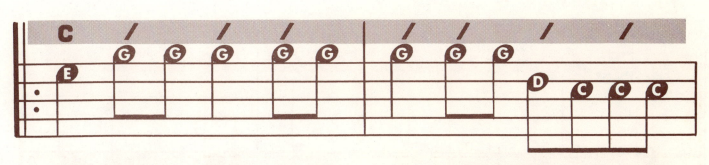

ran    through  the   briars   and  they        ran  through the bram - bles and they
ran    so_____    fast    that the        hounds could - n't catch 'em ___ on

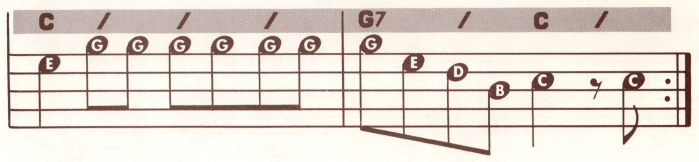

ran through the bush - es where  a        rab - bit could - n't   go.        They
down the Mis - sis - sip - pi    to    the        Gulf  of  Mex - i - co.        On

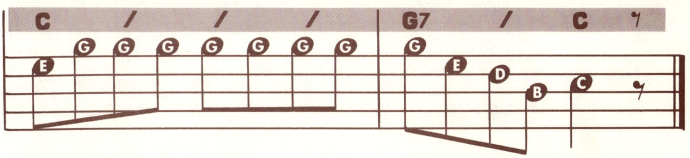

down the Mis - sis - sip - pi   to    the        Gulf  of  Mex  i - co.

The Battle Of New Orleans -2-2

# BEAUTIFUL BROWN EYES

TRADITIONAL

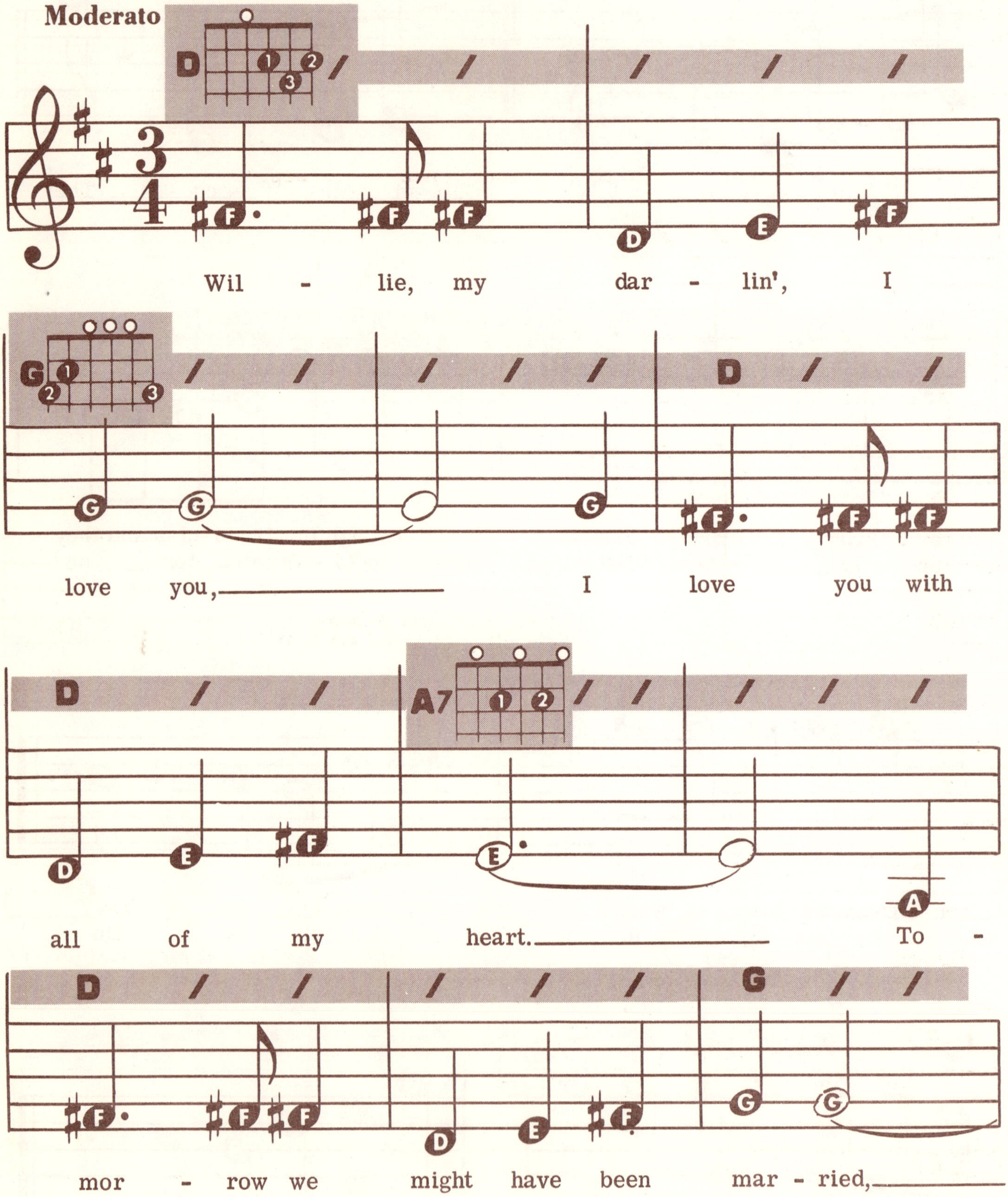

Moderato

Wil - lie, my dar - lin', I love you,_____ I love you with all of my heart._____ To - mor - row we might have been mar - ried,_____

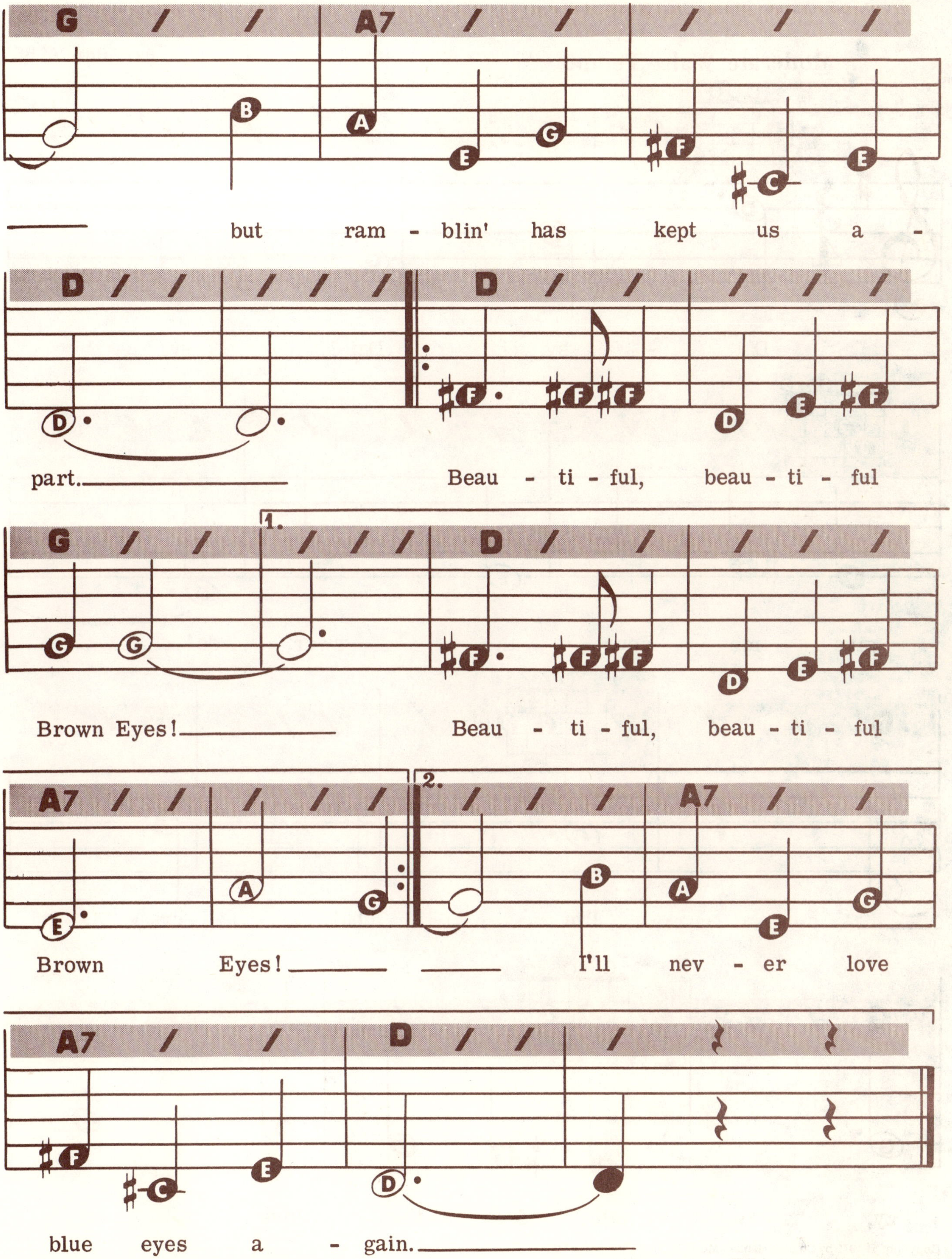
G A7 D G A7 D
but ram - blin' has kept us a - part.
Beau - ti - ful, beau - ti - ful Brown Eyes!
Beau - ti - ful, beau - ti - ful Brown Eyes!
1. 2.
I'll nev - er love blue eyes a - gain.

# A BICYCLE BUILT FOR TWO

By HARRY DACRE

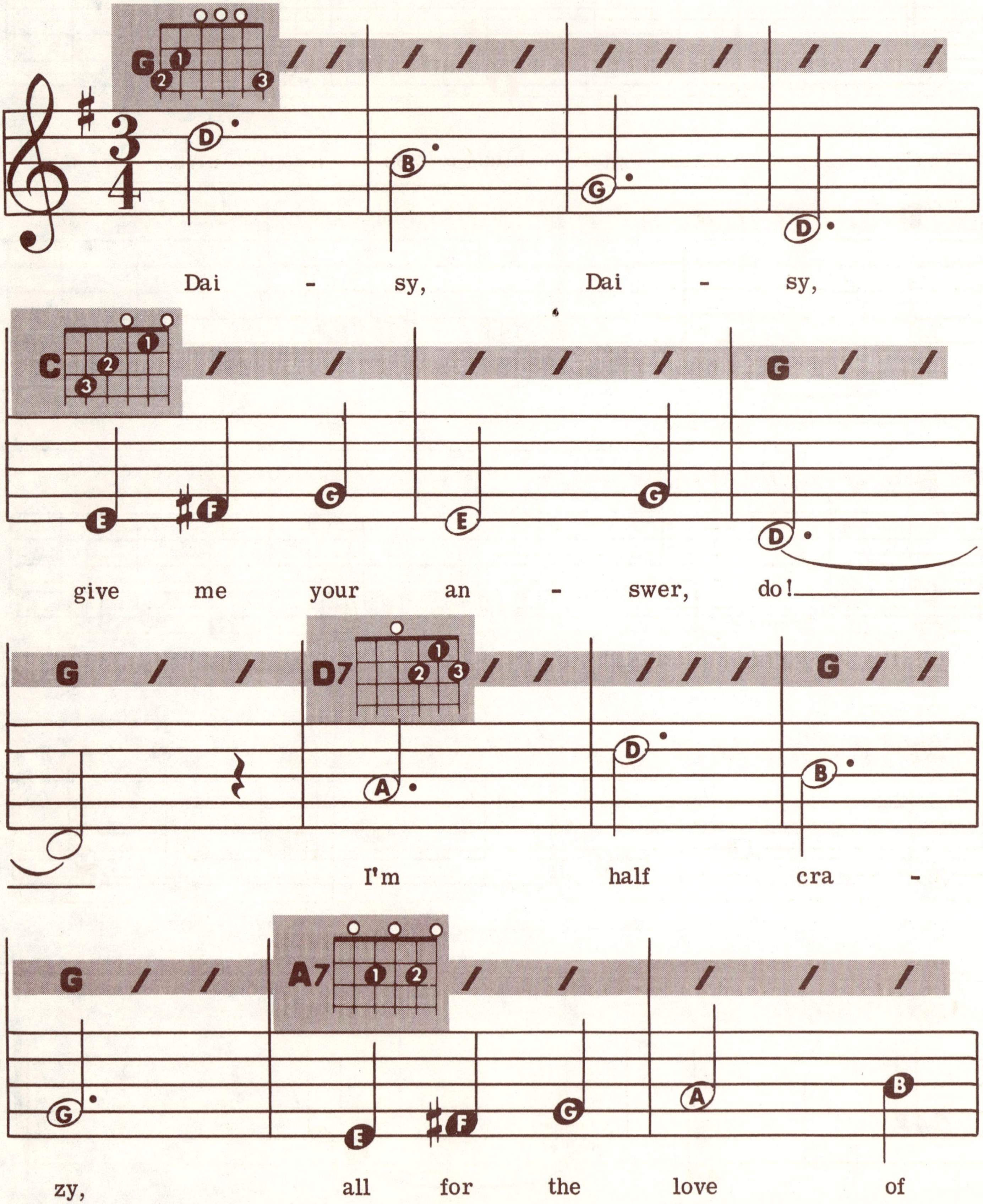

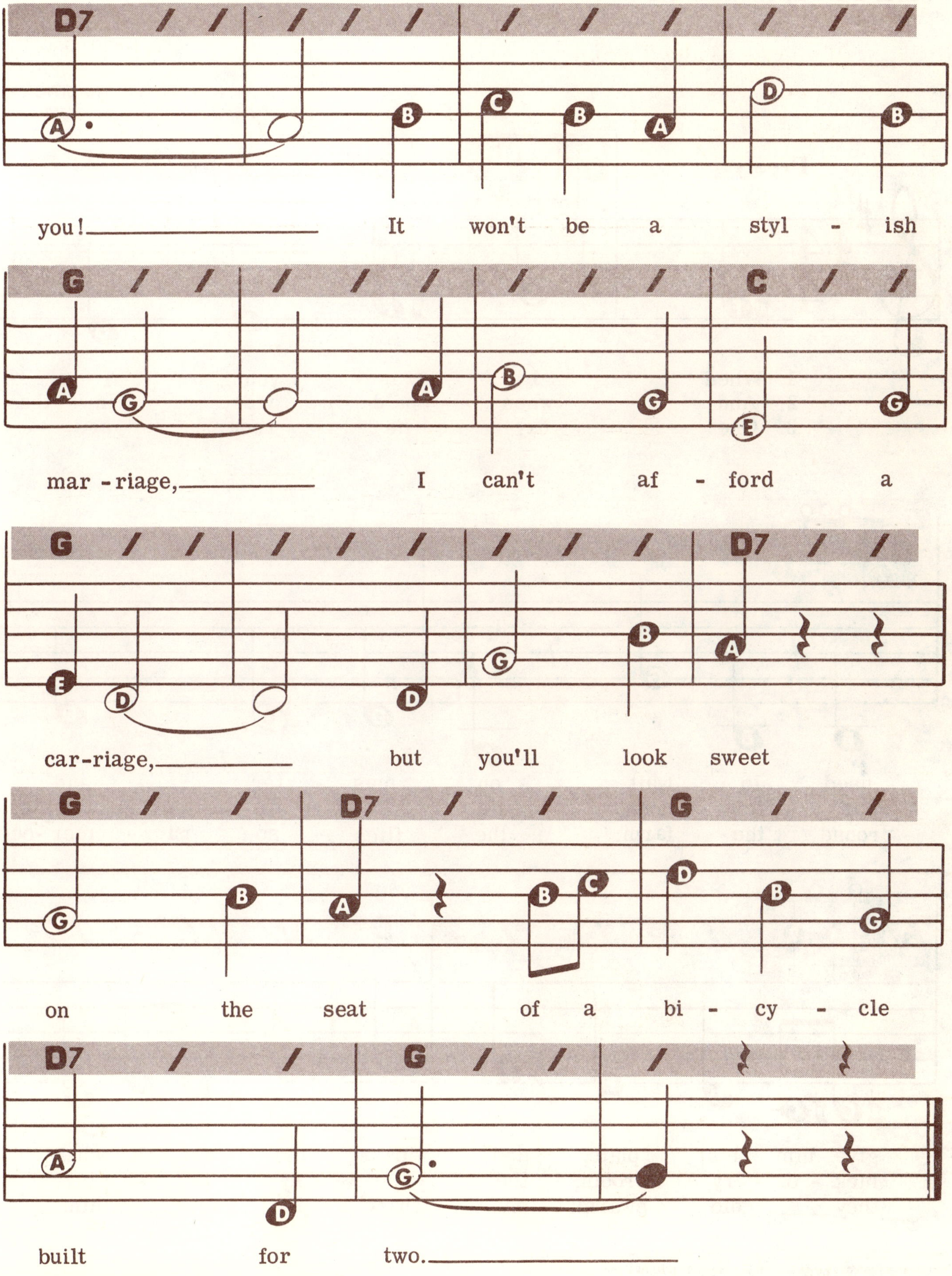
D7
A B C B A D B
you! It won't be a styl - ish
G C
A G A B G E G
mar - riage, I can't af - ford a
G D7
E D D G B A
car-riage, but you'll look sweet
G D7 G
G B A B C D B G
on the seat of a bi - cy - cle
D7 G
A D G
built for two.

# THE BLUE TAIL FLY

TRADITIONAL

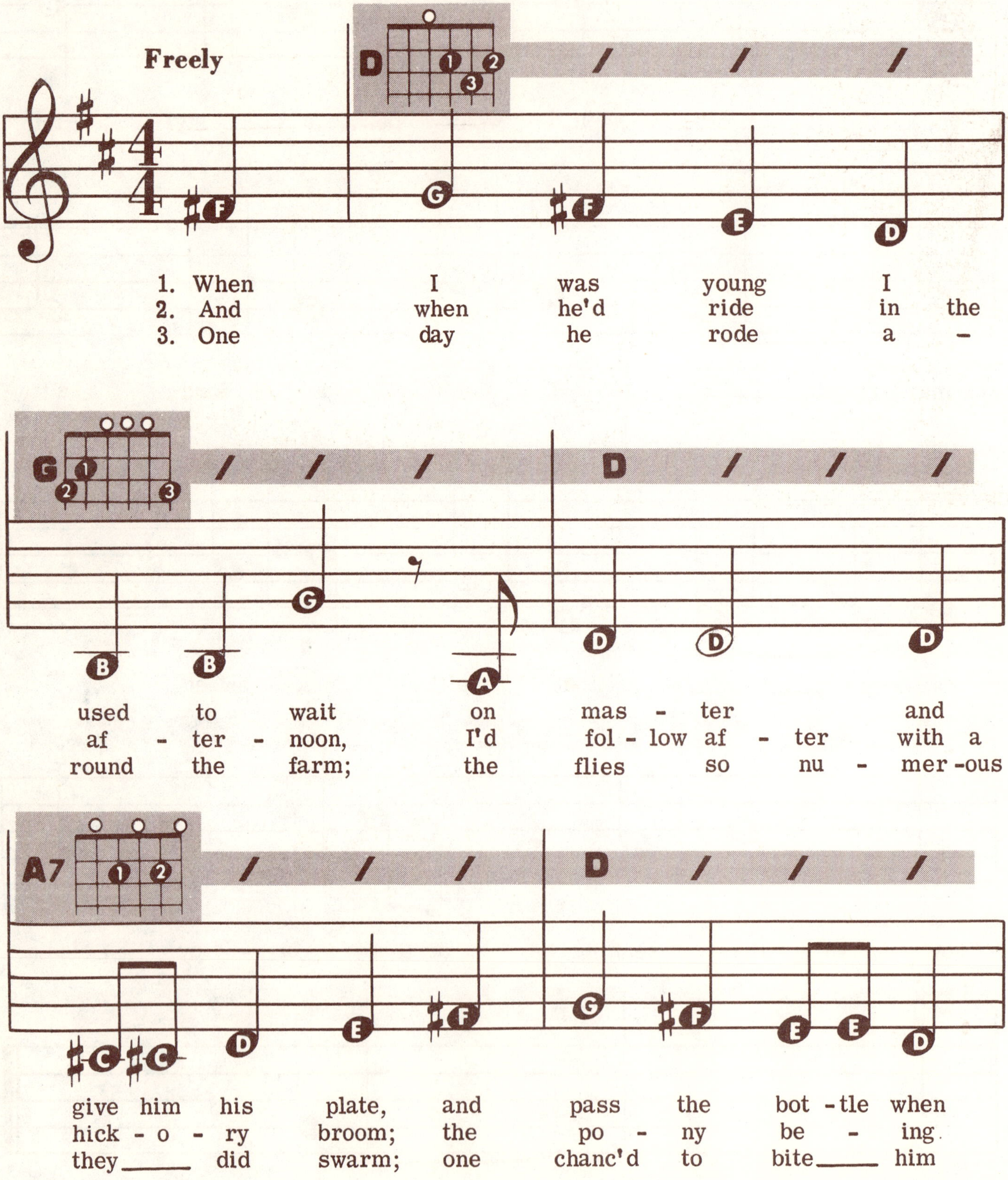

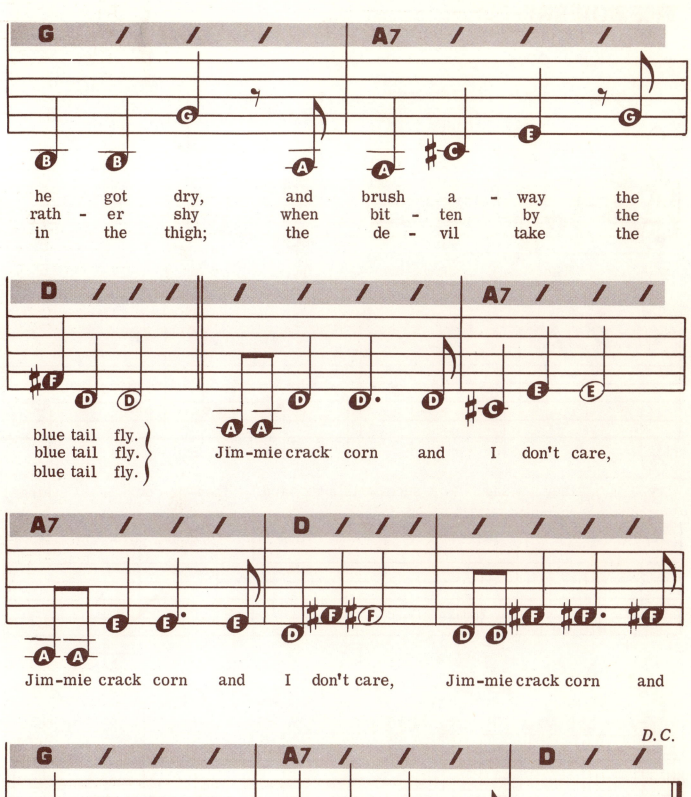

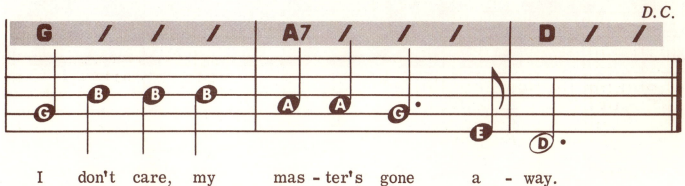

The Blue Tail Fly-2-2

45853

G A7
he got dry, and brush a - way the
rath - er shy when bit - ten by the
in the thigh; the de - vil take the
D A7
Jim-mie crack corn and I don't care,
A7 D
Jim-mie crack corn and I don't care, Jim-mie crack corn and
D.C.
G A7 D
I don't care, my mas - ter's gone a - way.

# THE BOWERY

Words by CHAS. H. HOYT
Music by PERCY GAUNT

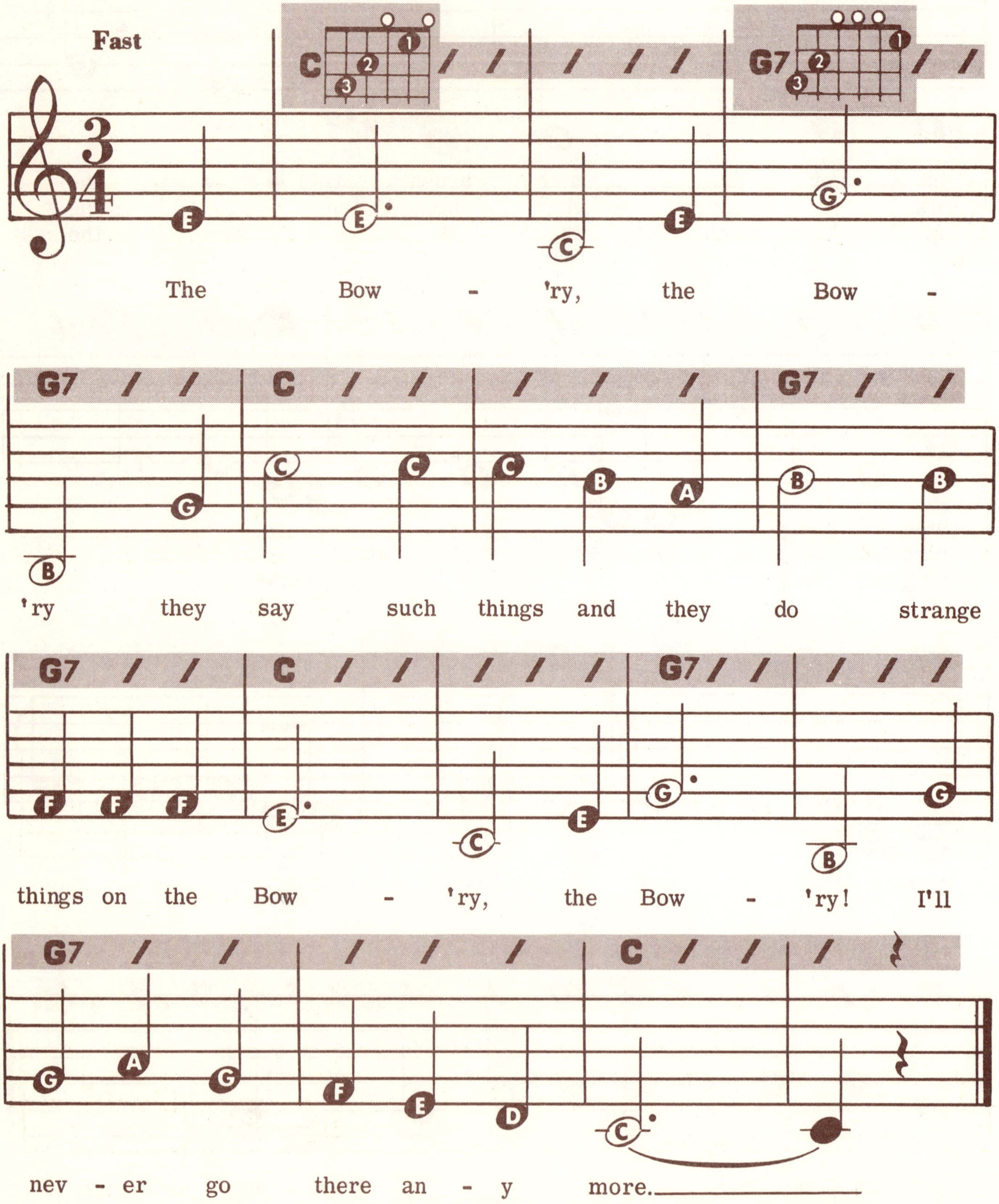

The Bow - 'ry, the Bow - 'ry they say such things and they do strange things on the Bow - 'ry, the Bow - 'ry! I'll nev - er go there an - y more.____

# BLUE BAYOU

By ROY ORBISON and JOE MELSON

I feel so bad, I've got a wor-ried mind,

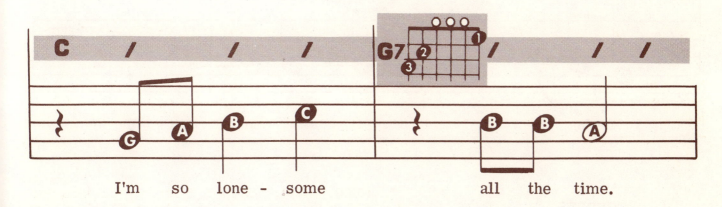

I'm so lone-some all the time.

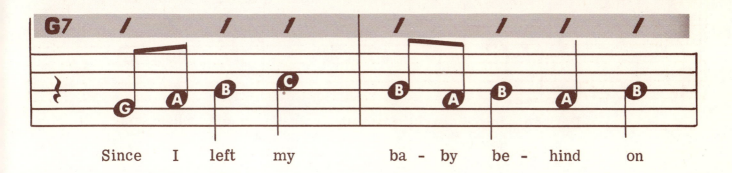

Since I left my ba-by be-hind on

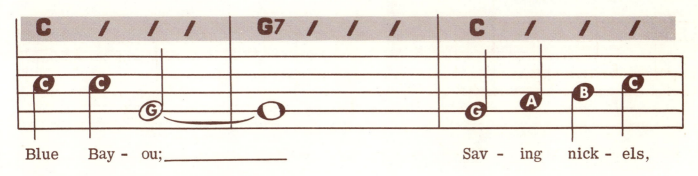

Blue Bay-ou;_____ Sav-ing nick-els,

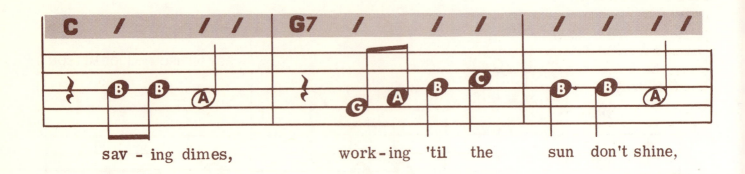

sav - ing dimes, work-ing 'til the sun don't shine,

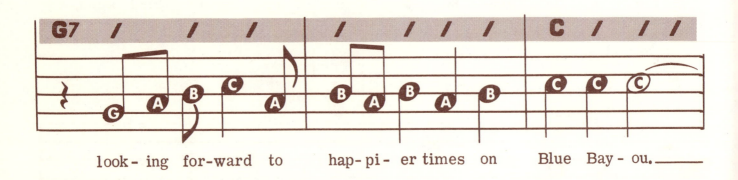

look-ing for-ward to hap-pi- er times on Blue Bay- ou.____

CHORUS

____ I'm go - ing back some day, come what may to

Blue Bay - ou_____ where you sleep all day and the

Blue Bayou-3-2

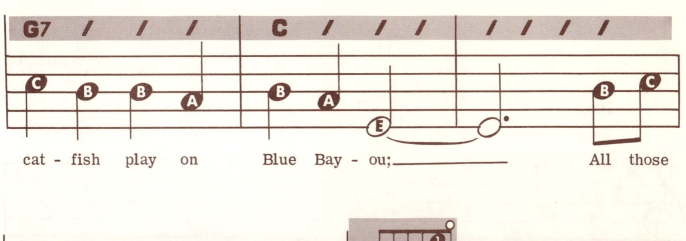

cat - fish    play    on        Blue  Bay - ou;_____        All   those

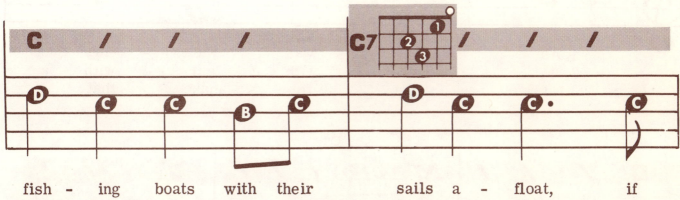

fish - ing   boats   with   their        sails  a - float,          if

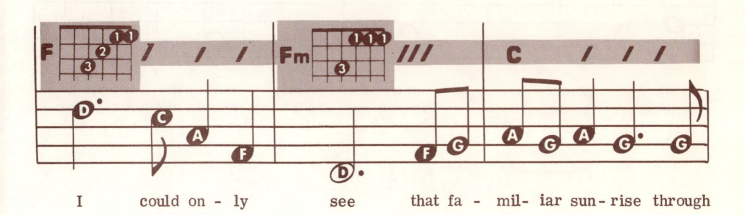

I      could  on - ly        see        that fa - mil - iar sun - rise through

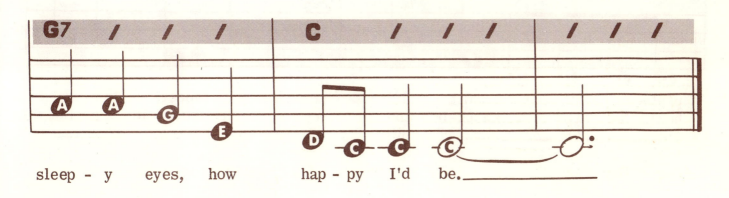

sleep - y    eyes,   how       hap - py  I'd   be._____

Blue Bayou-3-3

# BUFFALO GALS

AMERICAN SONG

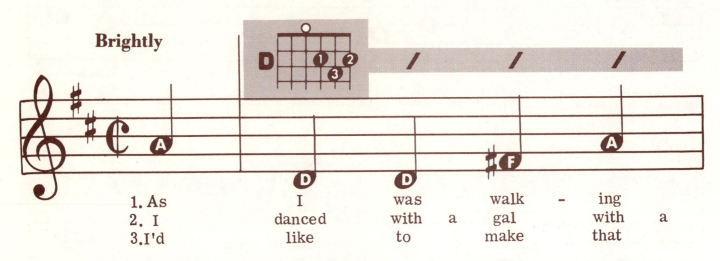

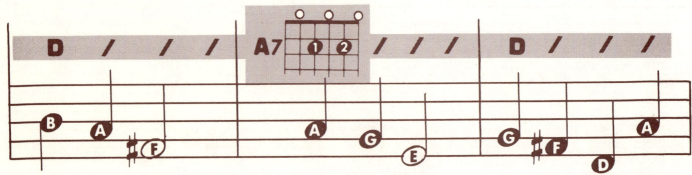

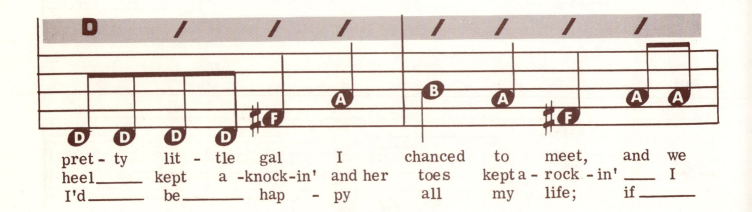

A7 / / / D / / /
danced by the light of the moon.
danced by the light of the moon.
I had her by me.
D / A7 / D / / /
Buf - fa - lo gals, won't you come out to - night, won't you
A7 / / / D / / /
come out to - night, won't you come out to - night?
D / A7 / D / / /
Buf - fa - lo gals, won't you come out to - night, and
A7 / / / D / /
D. C.
dance by the light of the moon.

# BRINGING IT BACK

Words and Music by
GREG GORDON

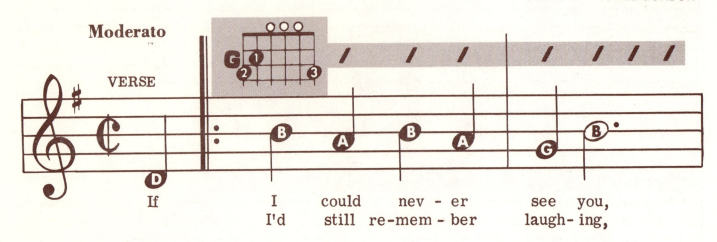

If I could nev - er see you,
I'd still re-mem-ber laugh-ing,

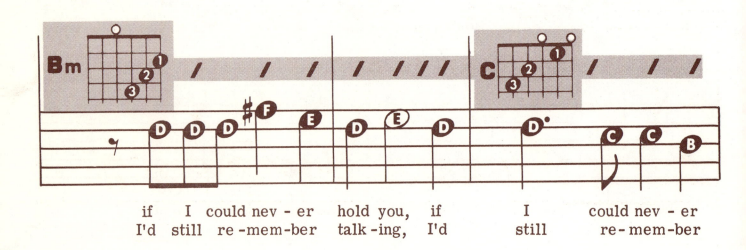

if I could nev - er hold you, if I could nev - er
I'd still re -mem-ber talk -ing, I'd still re-mem-ber

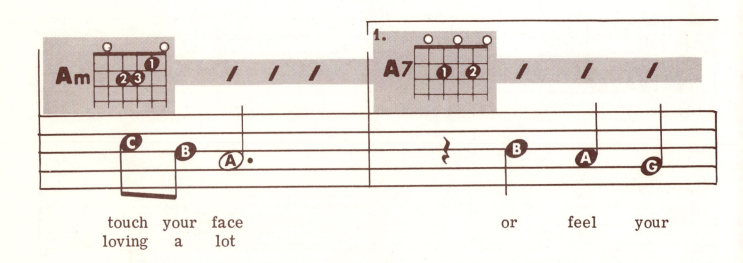

touch your face or feel your
loving a lot

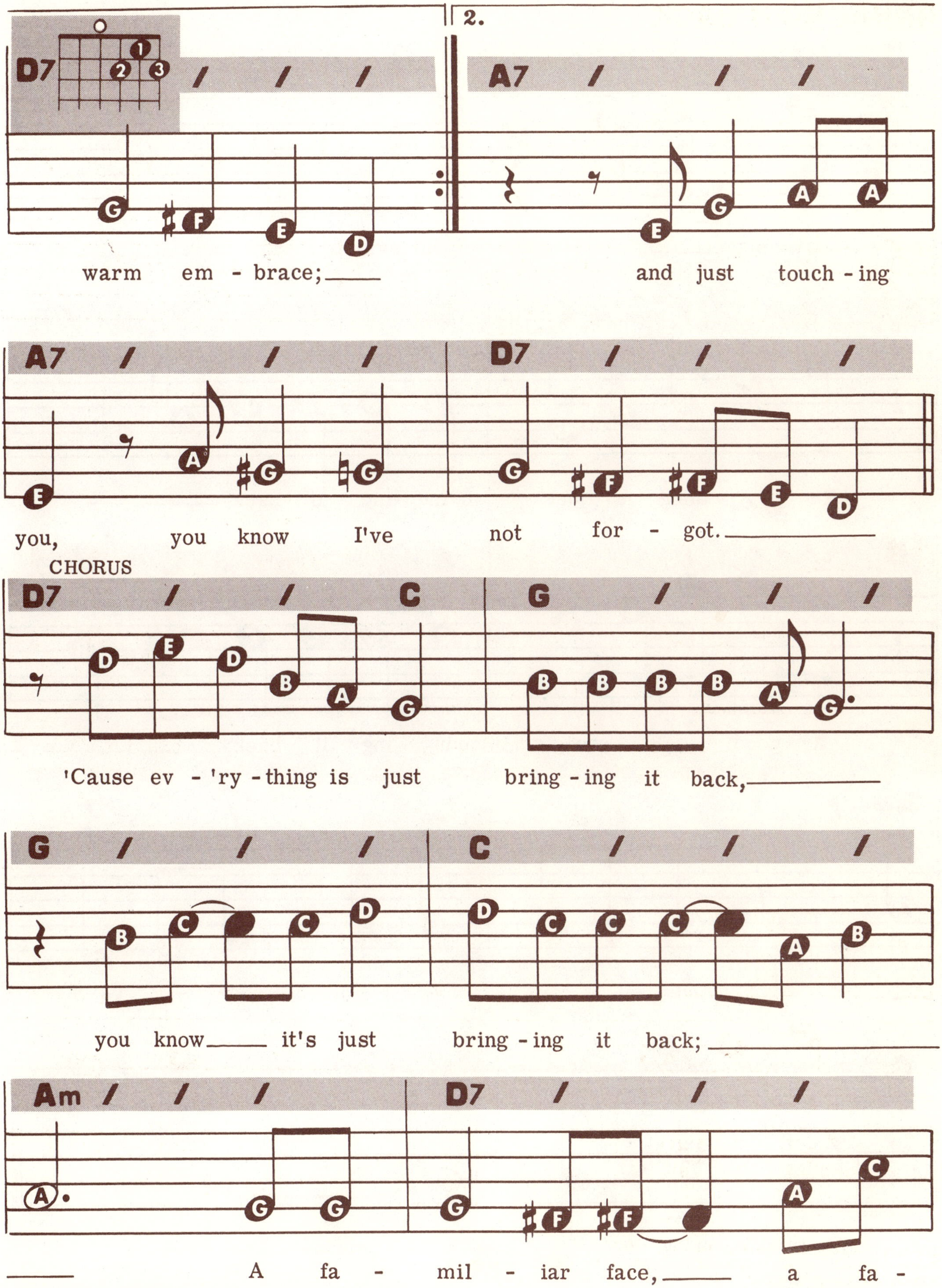

warm em - brace;____ and just touch - ing

you, you know I've not for - got.____

CHORUS

'Cause ev - 'ry - thing is just bring - ing it back,____

you know____ it's just bring - ing it back;____

____ A fa - mil - iar face,____ a fa -

Bringing It Back-3-2

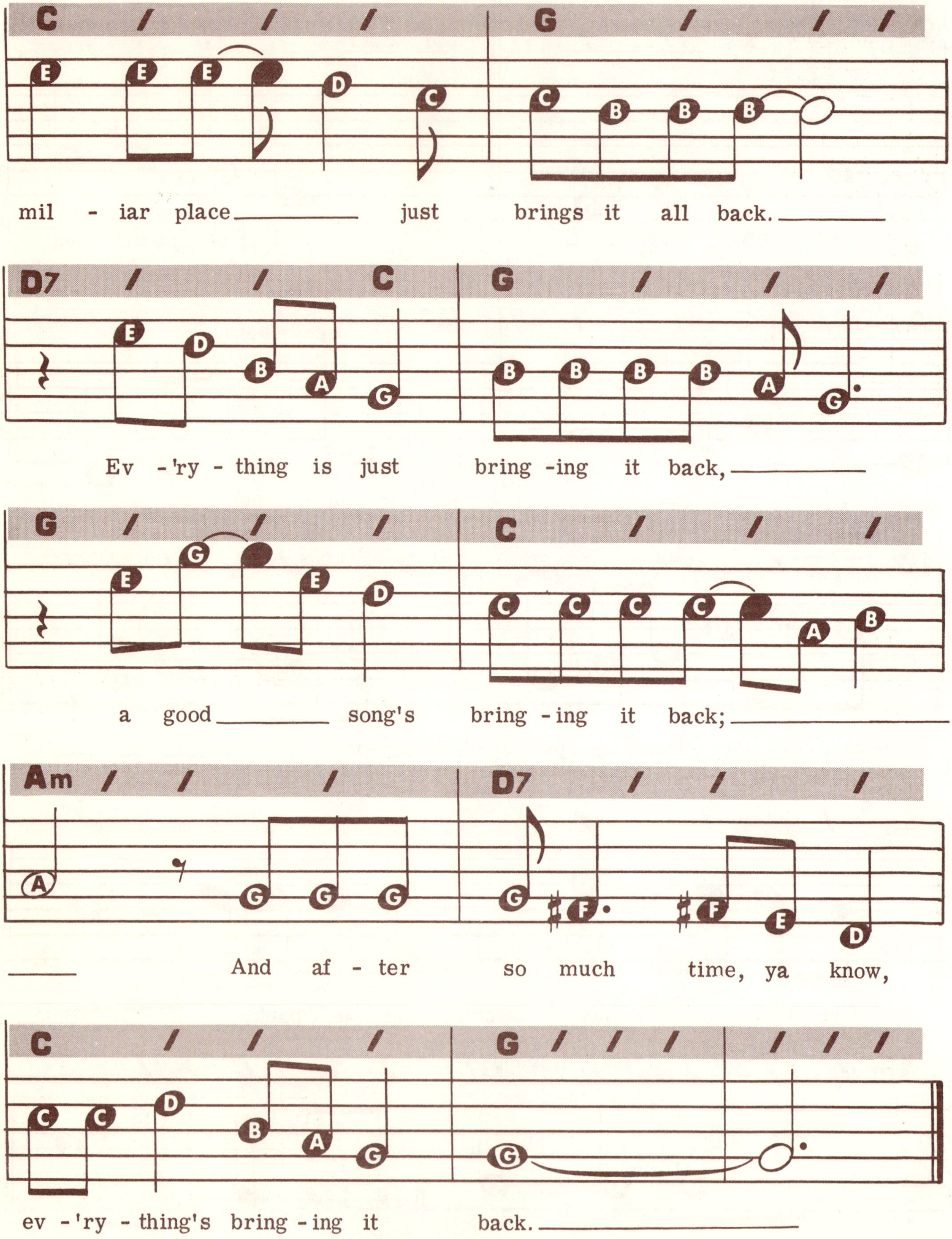
C G
mil - iar place just brings it all back.
D7 C G
Ev - 'ry - thing is just bring - ing it back,
G C
a good song's bring - ing it back;
Am D7
And af - ter so much time, ya know,
C G
ev - 'ry - thing's bring - ing it back.

# C.C. RIDER

**Moderately**

TRADITIONAL

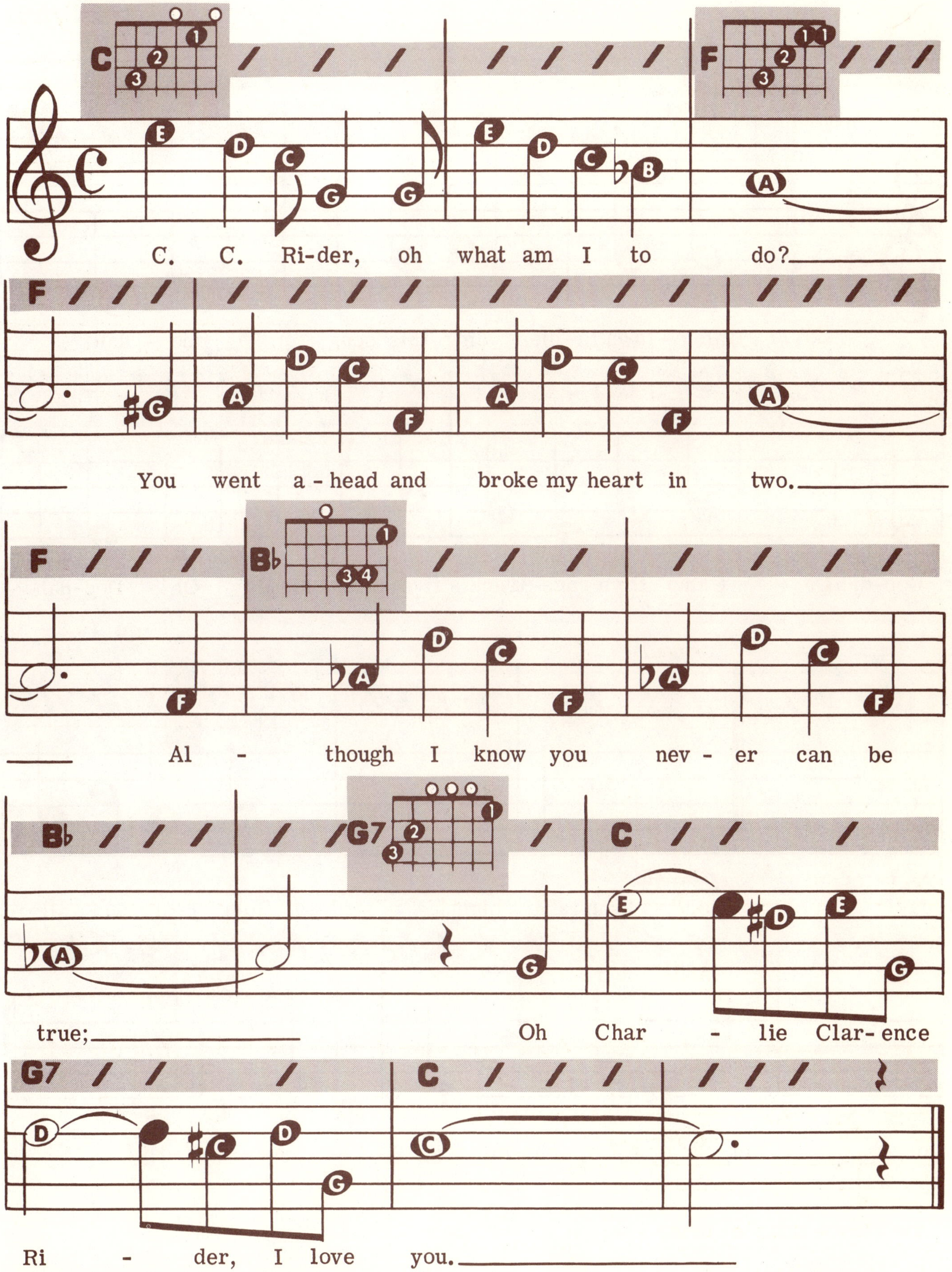

C. C. Ri-der, oh what am I to do?

You went a-head and broke my heart in two.

Al - though I know you nev - er can be

true;_____ Oh Char - lie Clar-ence

Ri - der, I love you._____

# CAMPTOWN RACES

STEPHEN FOSTER

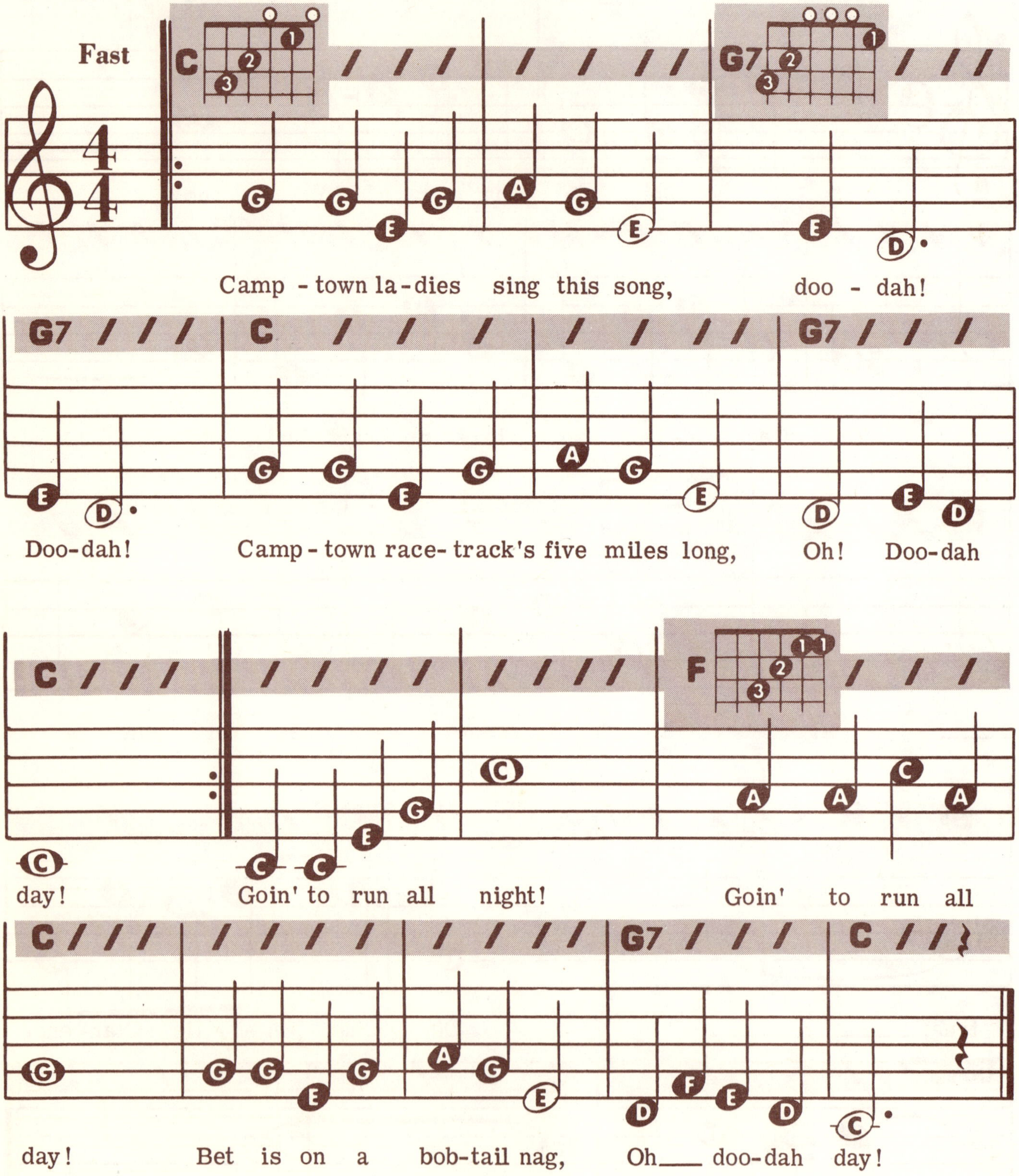

# CARELESS LOVE

**Moderato**

TRADITIONAL

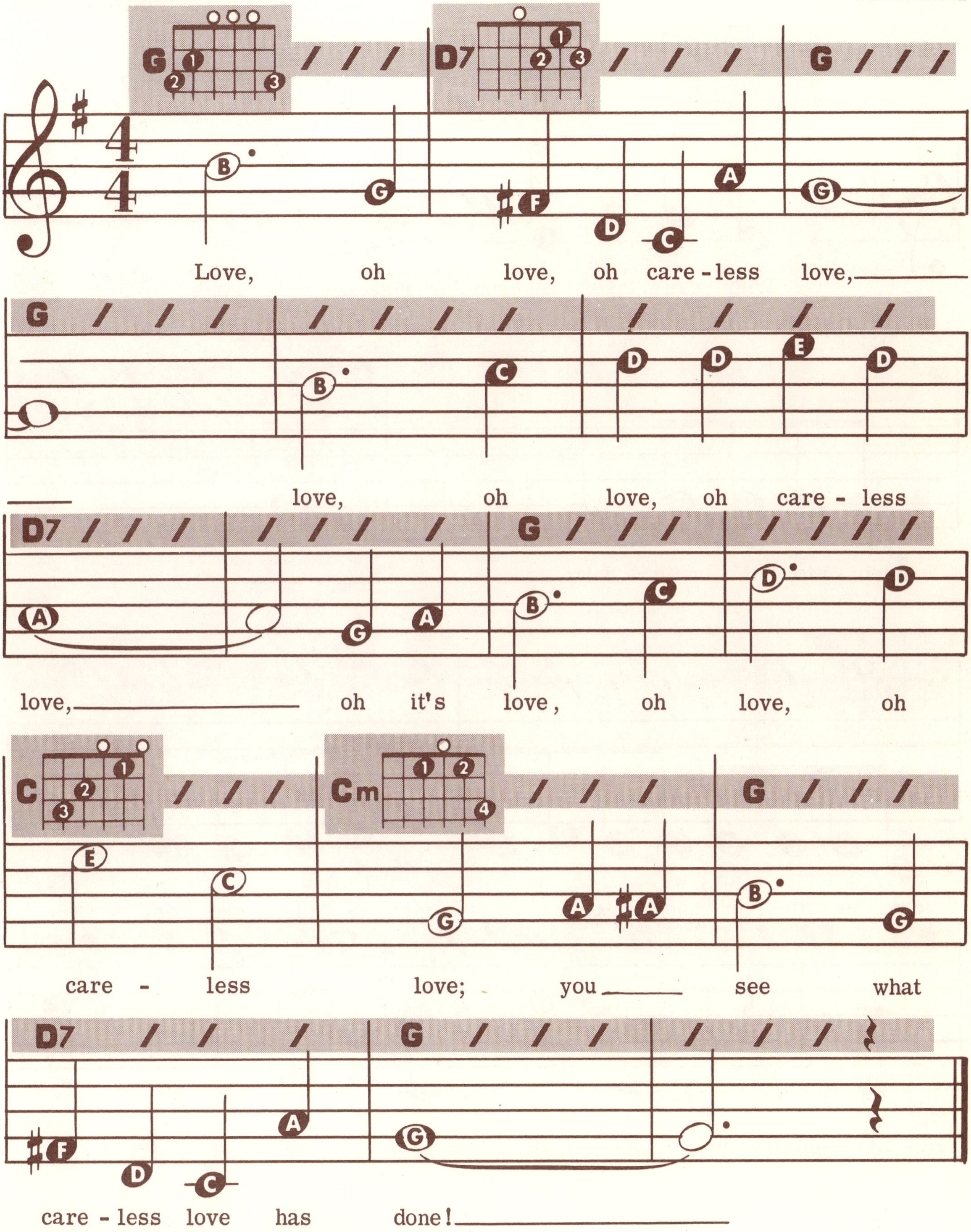

Love, oh love, oh care-less love,____ love, oh love, oh care-less love,____ oh it's love, oh love, oh care-less love; you____ see what care-less love has done!____

*From the Film "WILLY WONKA AND THE CHOCOLATE FACTORY"*

# THE CANDY MAN

Words and Music by
LESLIE BRICUSSE and
ANTHONY NEWLEY

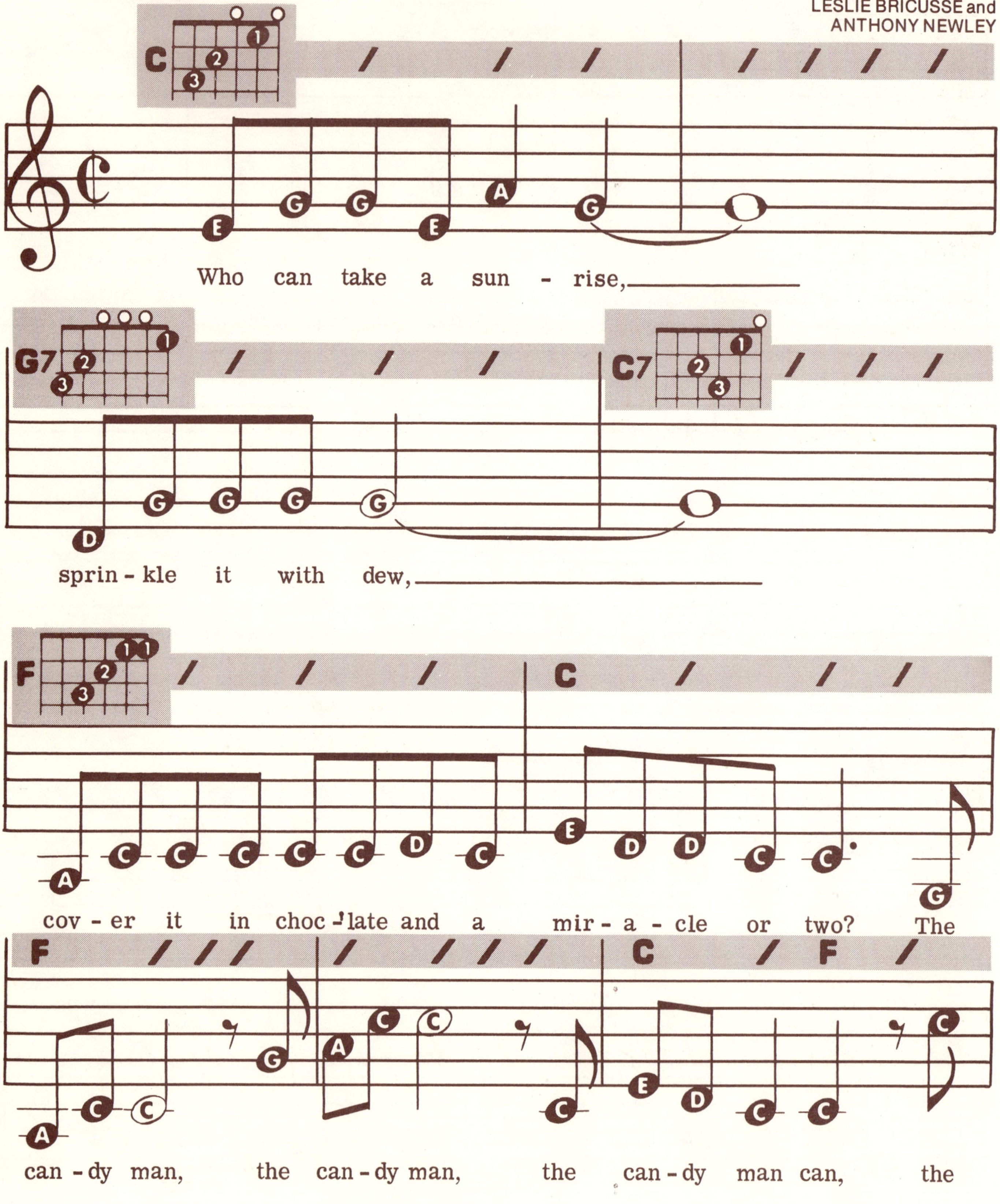

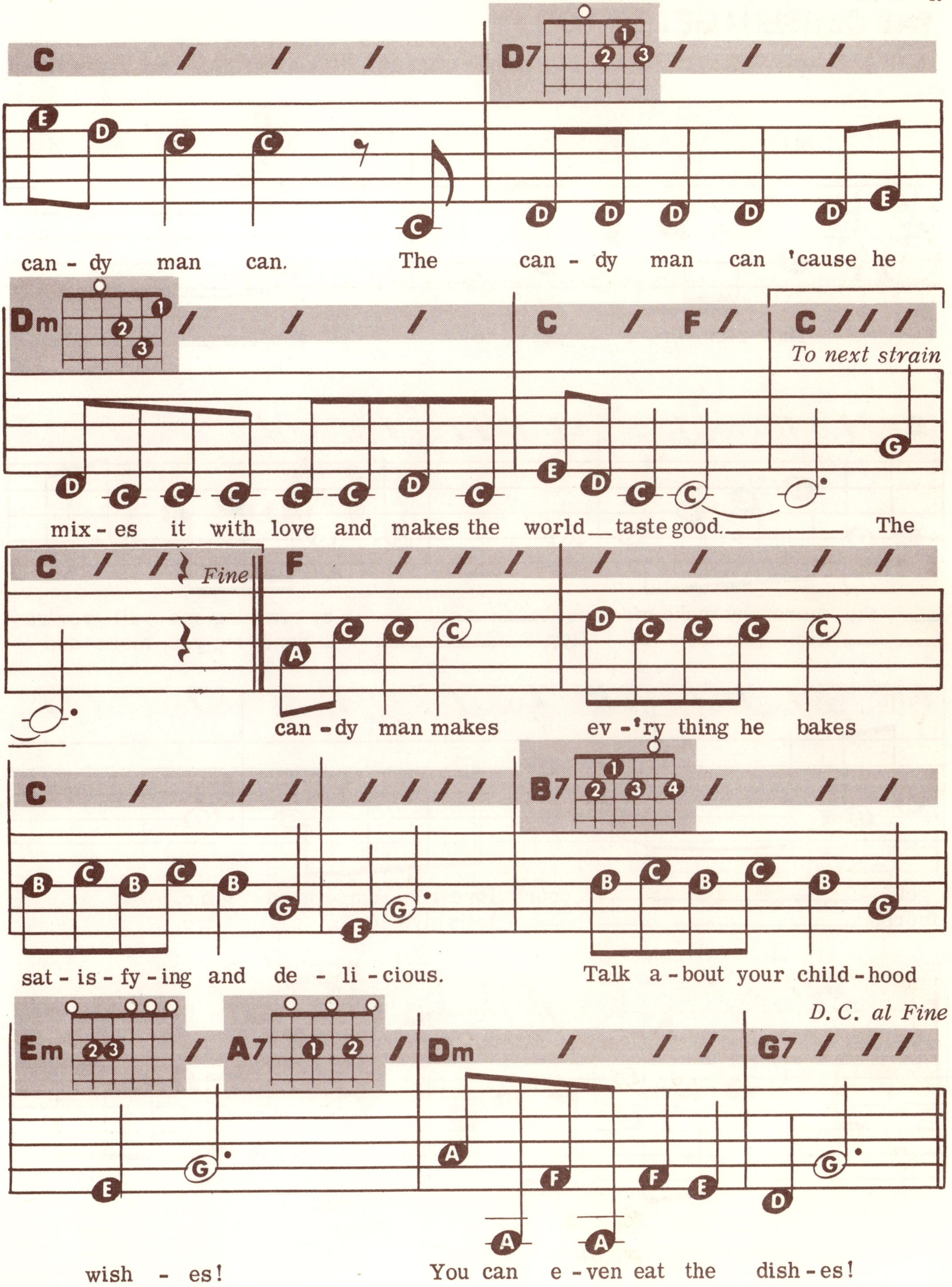

can - dy man can. The can - dy man can 'cause he mix - es it with love and makes the world taste good. The can - dy man makes ev - 'ry thing he bakes sat - is - fy - ing and de - li - cious. Talk a - bout your child - hood wish - es!

You can e - ven eat the dish - es!

To next strain

Fine

D.C. al Fine

The Candy Man-2-2

# THE CLOSER I GET TO YOU

By J. MTUME
and R. LUCAS

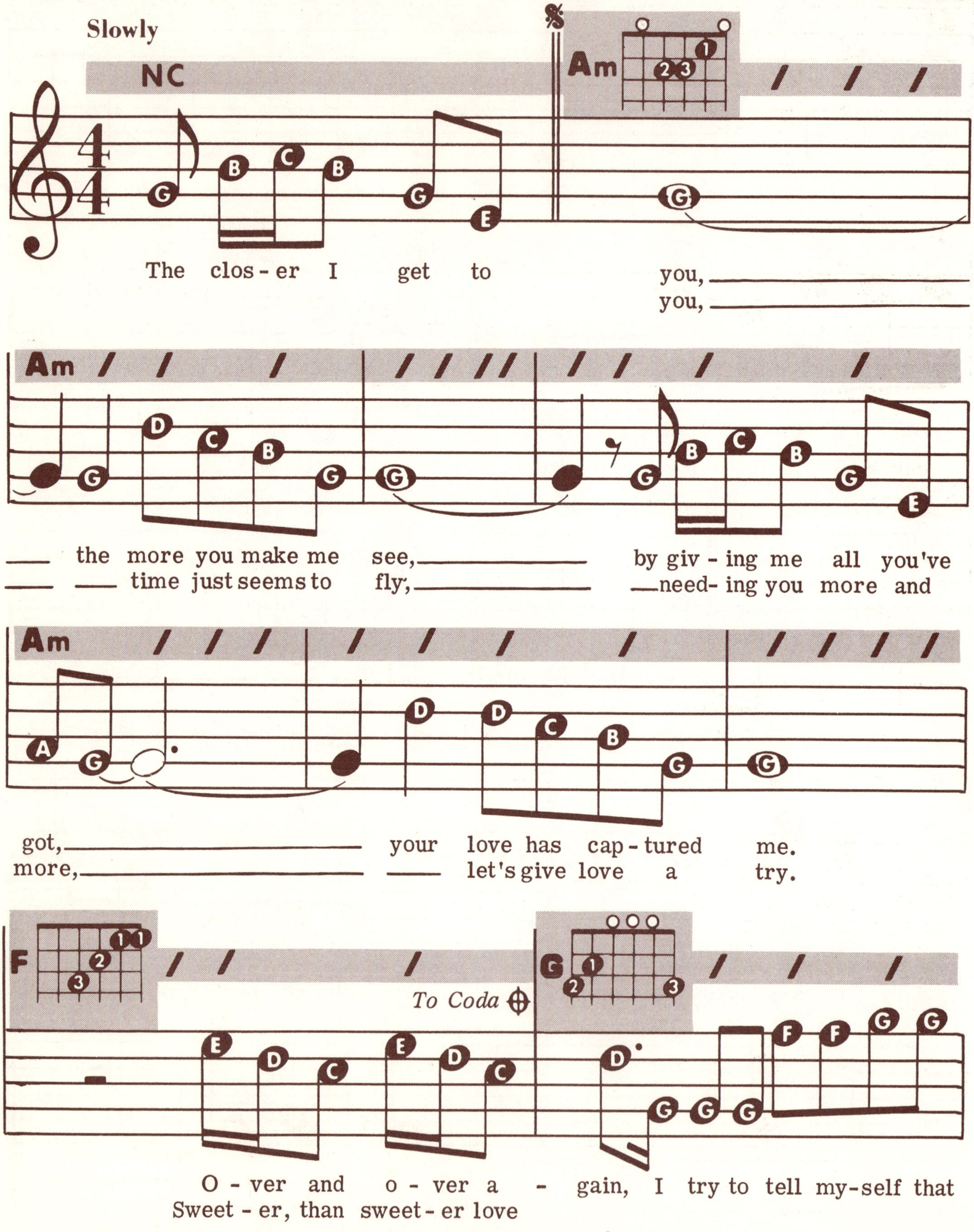

49

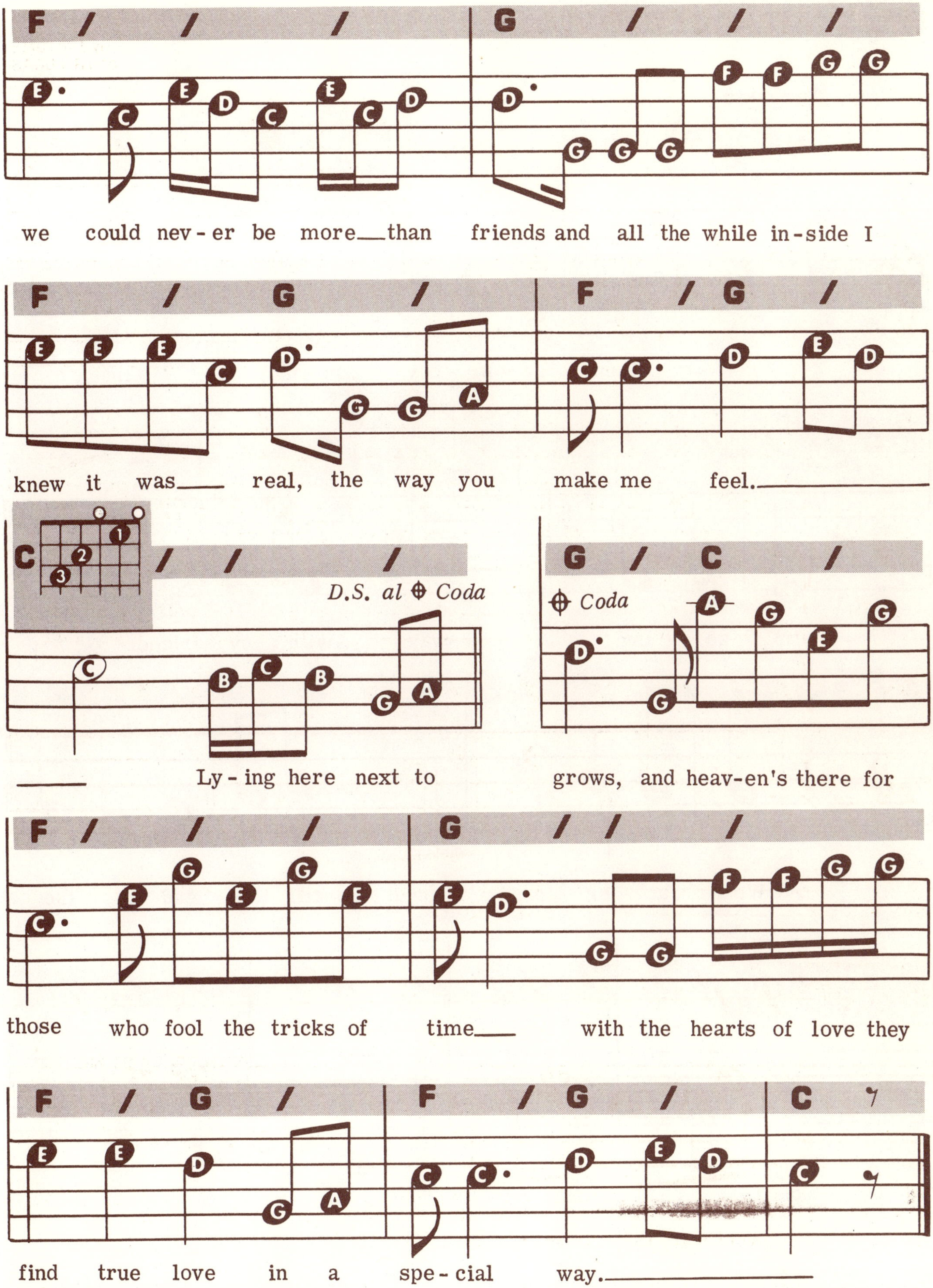

The Closer I Get To You-2-2

we could nev-er be more— than friends and all the while in-side I
knew it was— real, the way you make me feel.—
— Ly-ing here next to
D.S. al ⊕ Coda
⊕ Coda
grows, and heav-en's there for
those who fool the tricks of time— with the hearts of love they
find true love in a spe-cial way.—

From the Paramount Picture "THE STERILE CUCKOO"

# COME SATURDAY MORNING

By DORY PREVIN
and FRED KARLIN

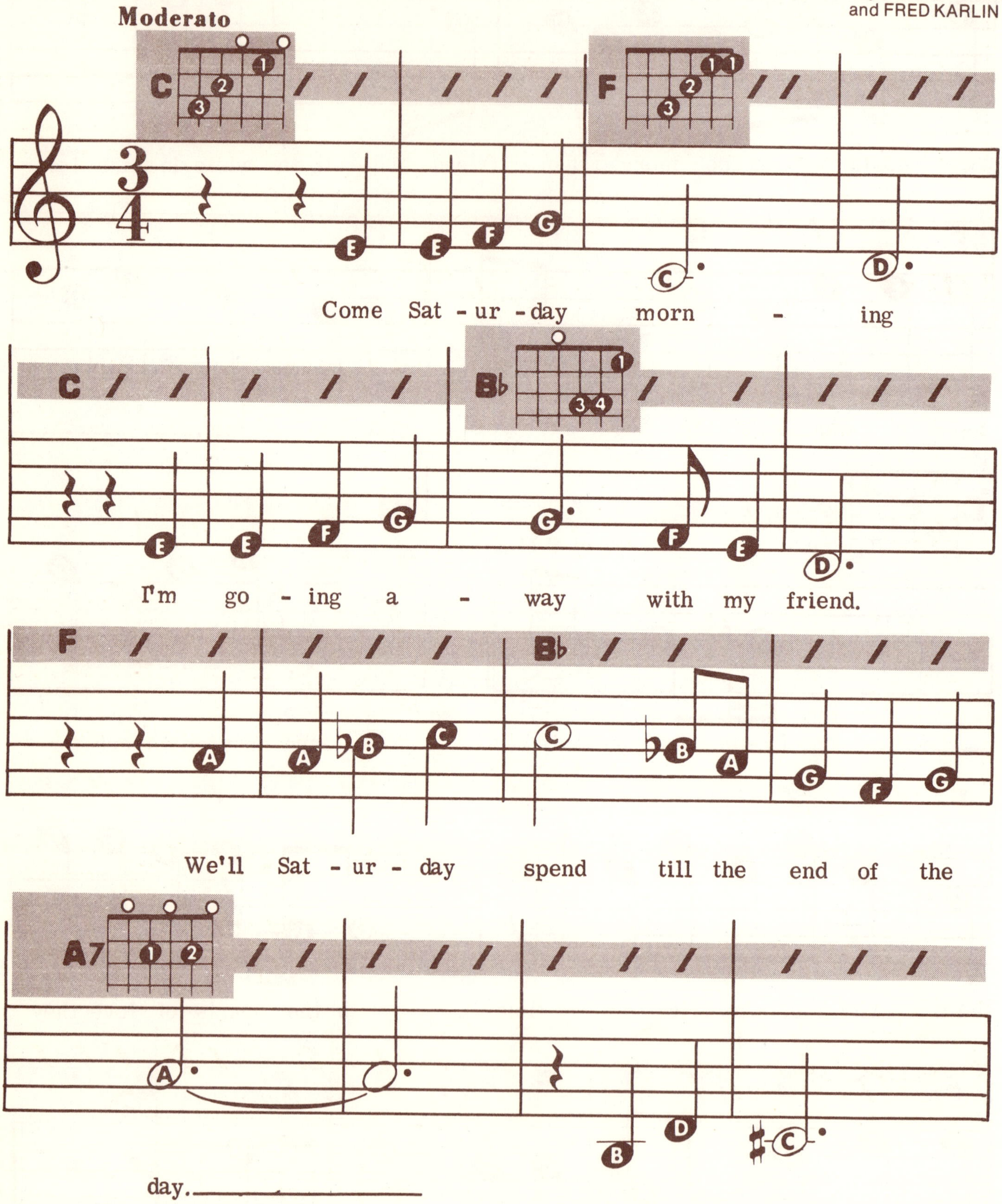

Come Sat - ur - day morn - ing

I'm go - ing a - way with my friend.

We'll Sat - ur - day spend till the end of the

day.

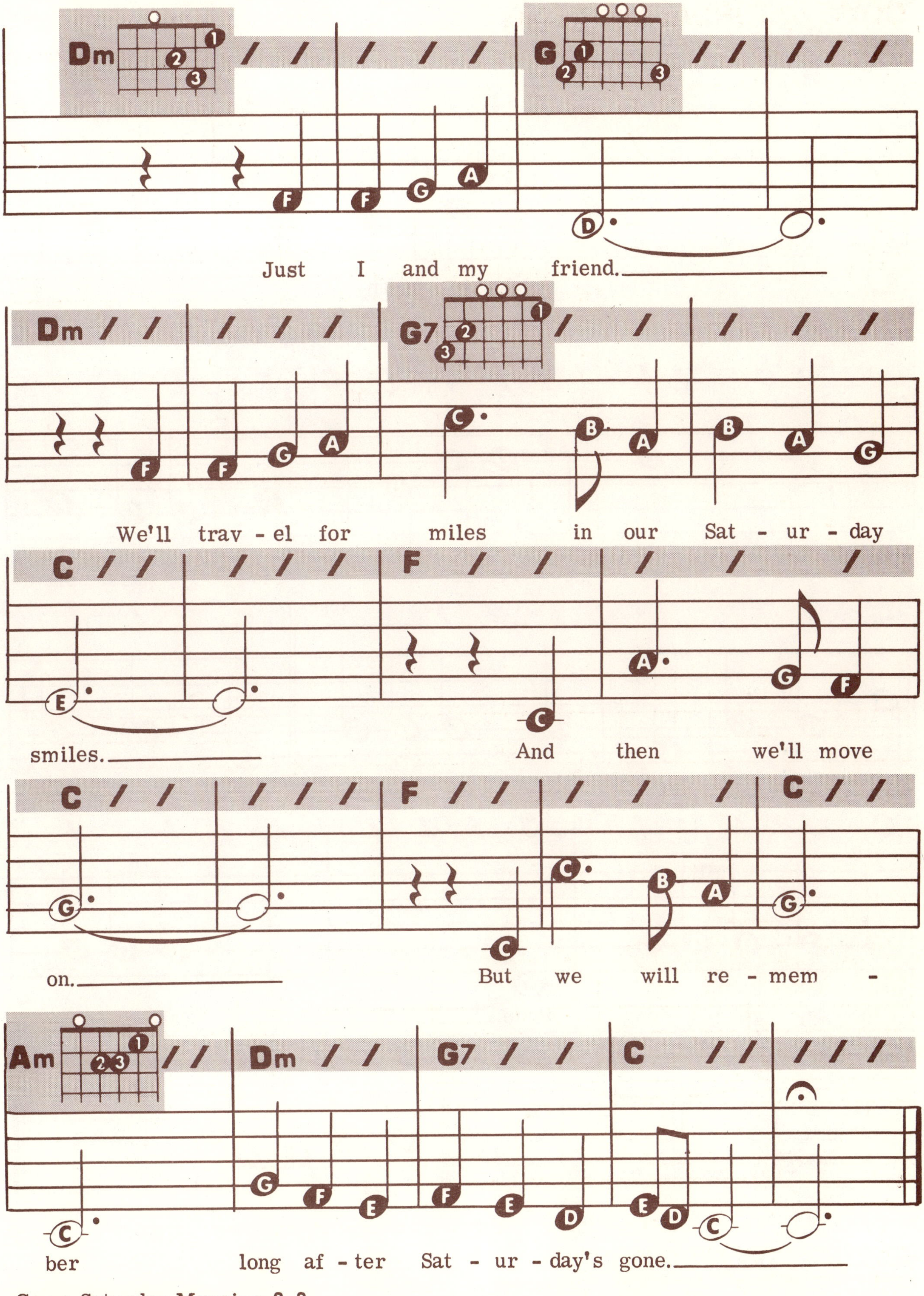

Come Saturday Morning-2-2

Dm
Just I and my friend.
Dm
G7
We'll trav - el for miles in our Sat - ur - day
F
smiles.
And then we'll move
F
on.
But we will re - mem -
Am
Dm
G7
ber long af - ter Sat - ur - day's gone.

## CINDY

AMERICAN FOLK SONG

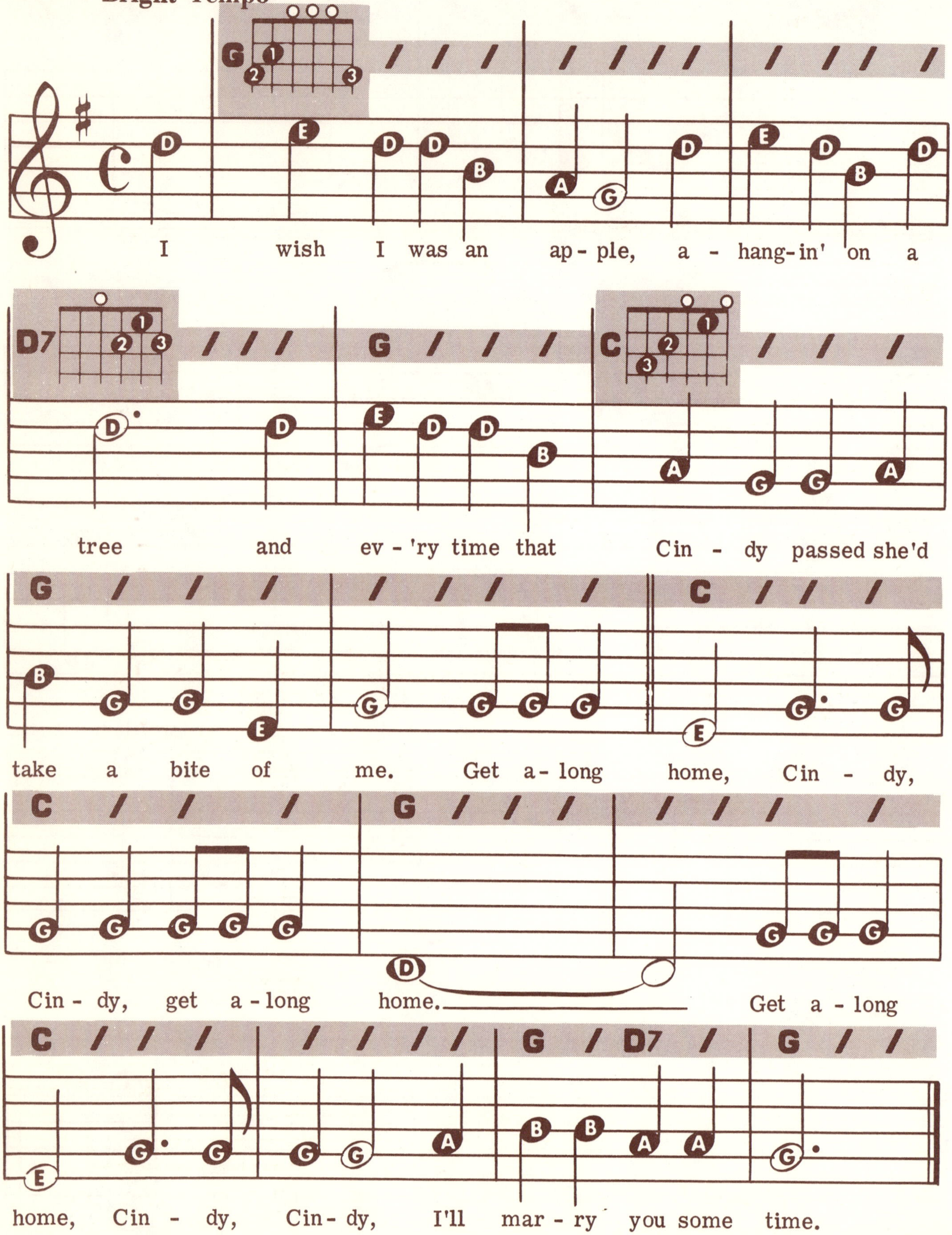

I wish I was an ap-ple, a-hang-in' on a tree and ev-'ry time that Cin-dy passed she'd take a bite of me. Get a-long home, Cin-dy, Cin-dy, get a-long home._____ Get a-long home, Cin-dy, Cin-dy, I'll mar-ry you some time.

# FEELINGS

Words and Music by
MORRIS ALBERT

**Moderately Slow**

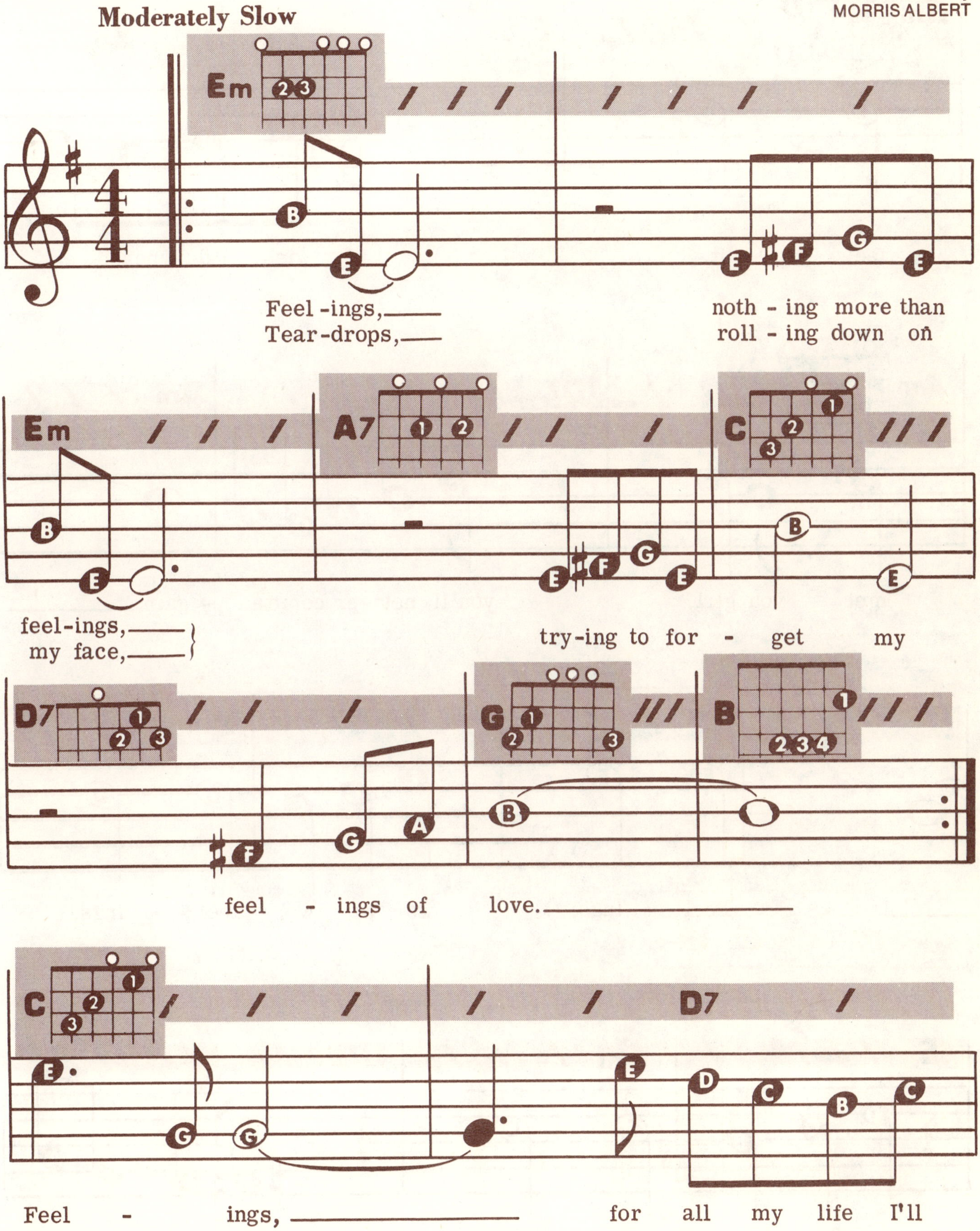

Feel -ings,_____ noth - ing more than
Tear -drops,_____ roll - ing down on

feel-ings,_____
my face,_____ } try-ing to for - get my

feel - ings of love._____

Feel - ings, _____ for all my life I'll

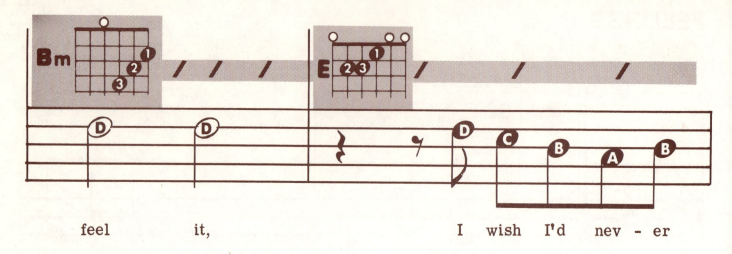

feel       it,                             I  wish  I'd  nev - er

met    you, girl,             you'll  nev - er come a   - gain._____

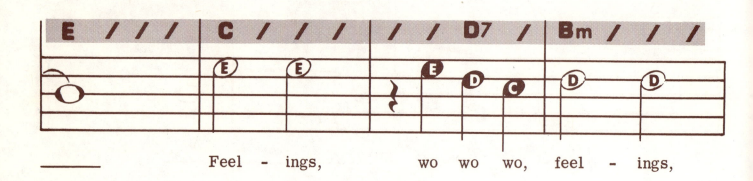

_____         Feel - ings,        wo  wo  wo,  feel - ings,

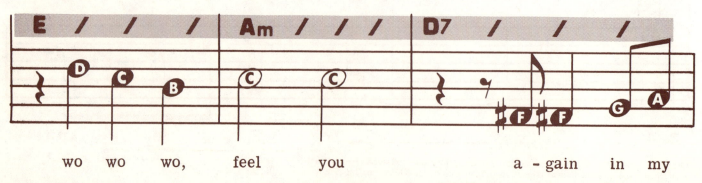

wo  wo  wo,  feel    you           a - gain  in  my

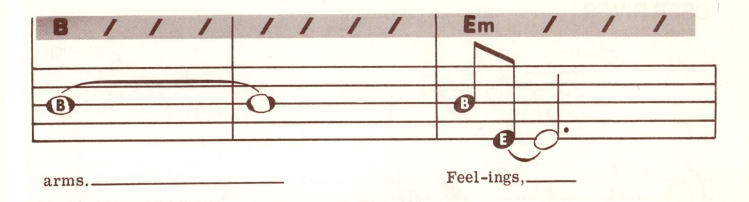

arms. Feel-ings,

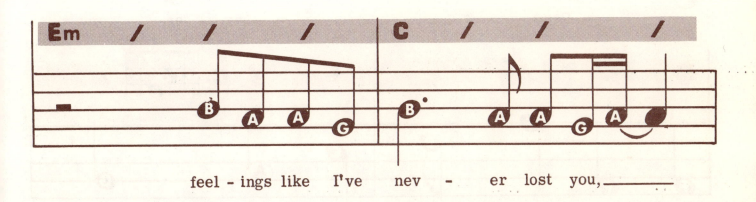

feel-ings like I've nev - er lost you,

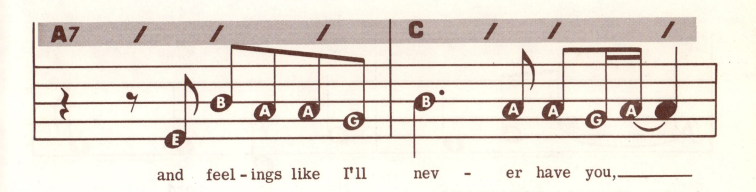

and feel-ings like I'll nev - er have you,

a - gain in my heart.

Feelings-3-3

# DEEP RIVER

Deep_____ riv - er, my home is o - ver Jor - dan, deep_____ riv - er, Lord, I want to go o - ver in - to camp - ground.

Lord,     I    am    a  –  com  –  in',

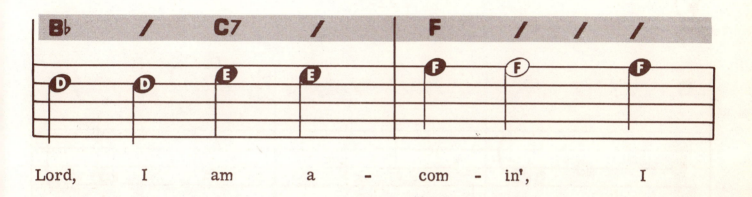

Lord,     I    am    a  –  com  –  in',     I

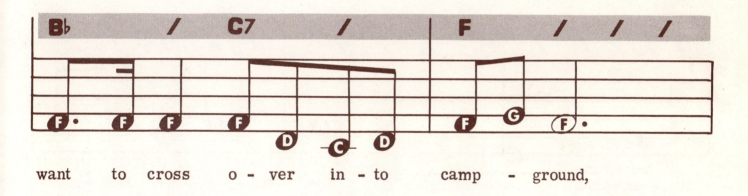

want    to   cross    o – ver   in – to    camp  –  ground,

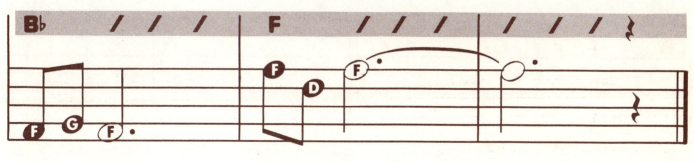

camp – ground,         Lord!_____

Deep River-2-2

# DOWN BY THE RIVERSIDE

TRADITIONAL

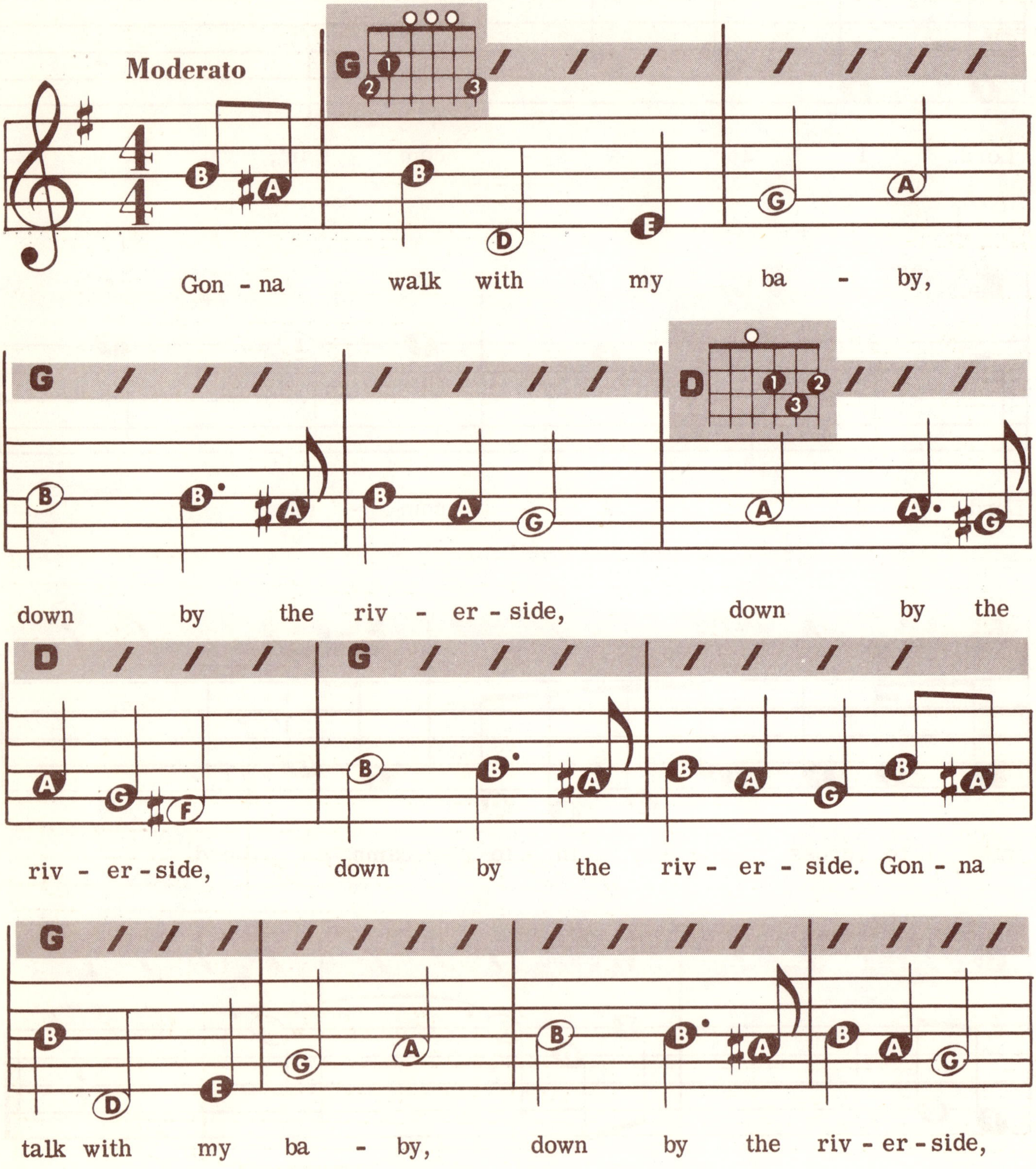

Gon - na walk with my ba - by,

down by the riv - er - side, down by the

riv - er - side, down by the riv - er - side. Gon - na

talk with my ba - by, down by the riv - er - side,

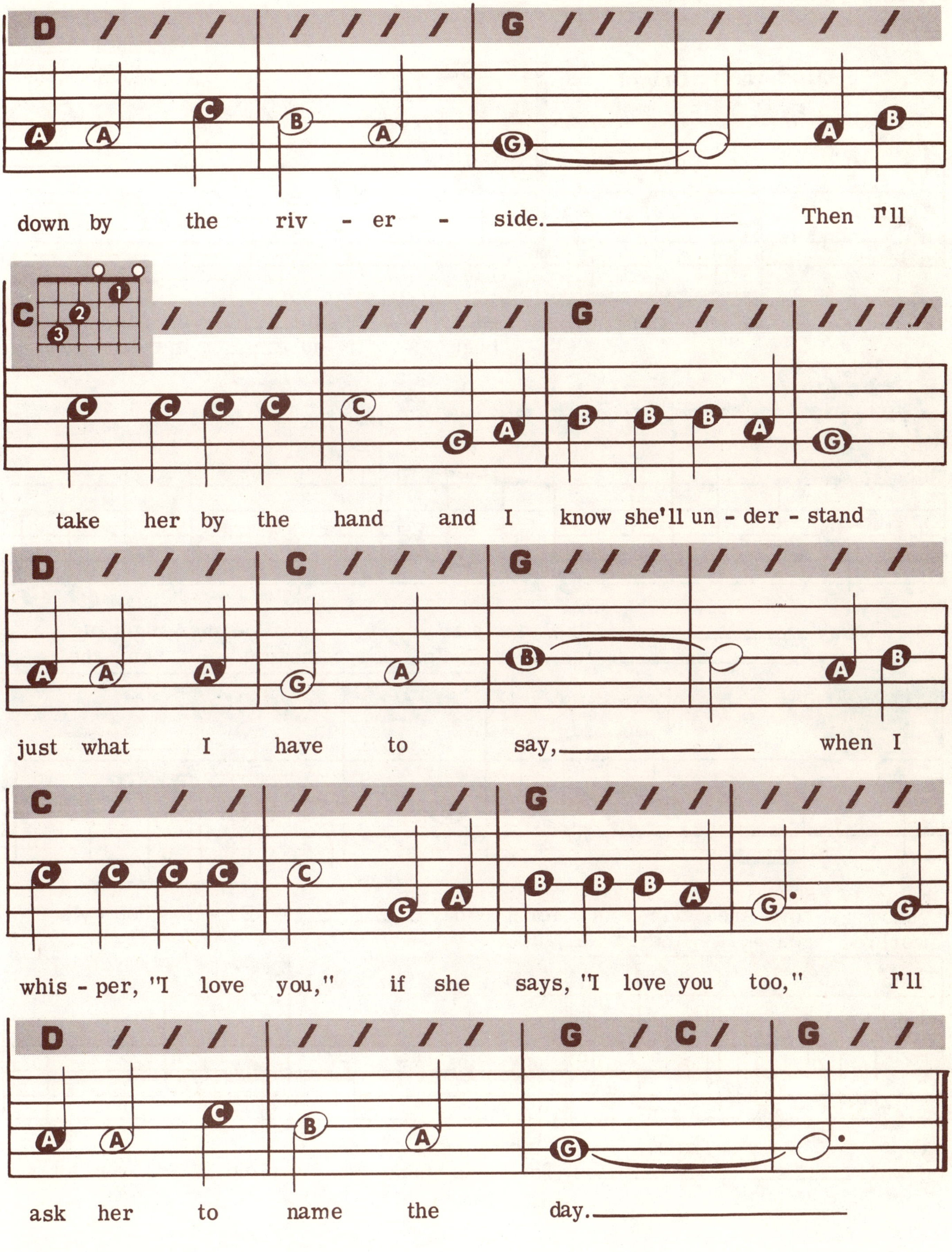

down by   the   riv - er - side._____   Then I'll

take   her by   the   hand   and I   know she'll un - der - stand

just what   I   have   to   say,_____   when I

whis - per, "I   love   you,"   if   she   says, "I   love you   too,"   I'll

ask   her   to   name   the   day._____

Down By The Riverside-2-2

# EVERYTHING IS BEAUTIFUL

Words and Music by
RAY STEVENS

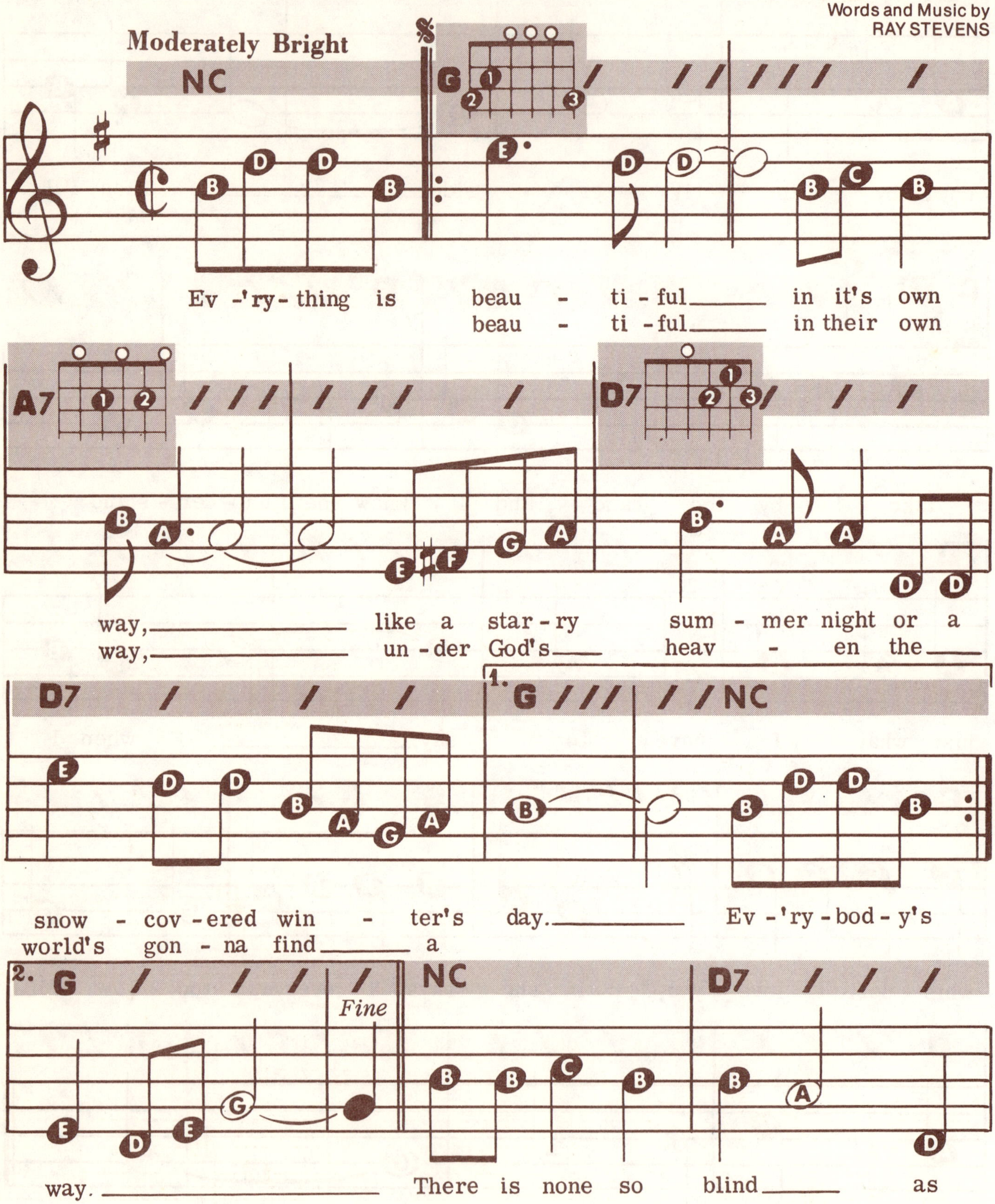

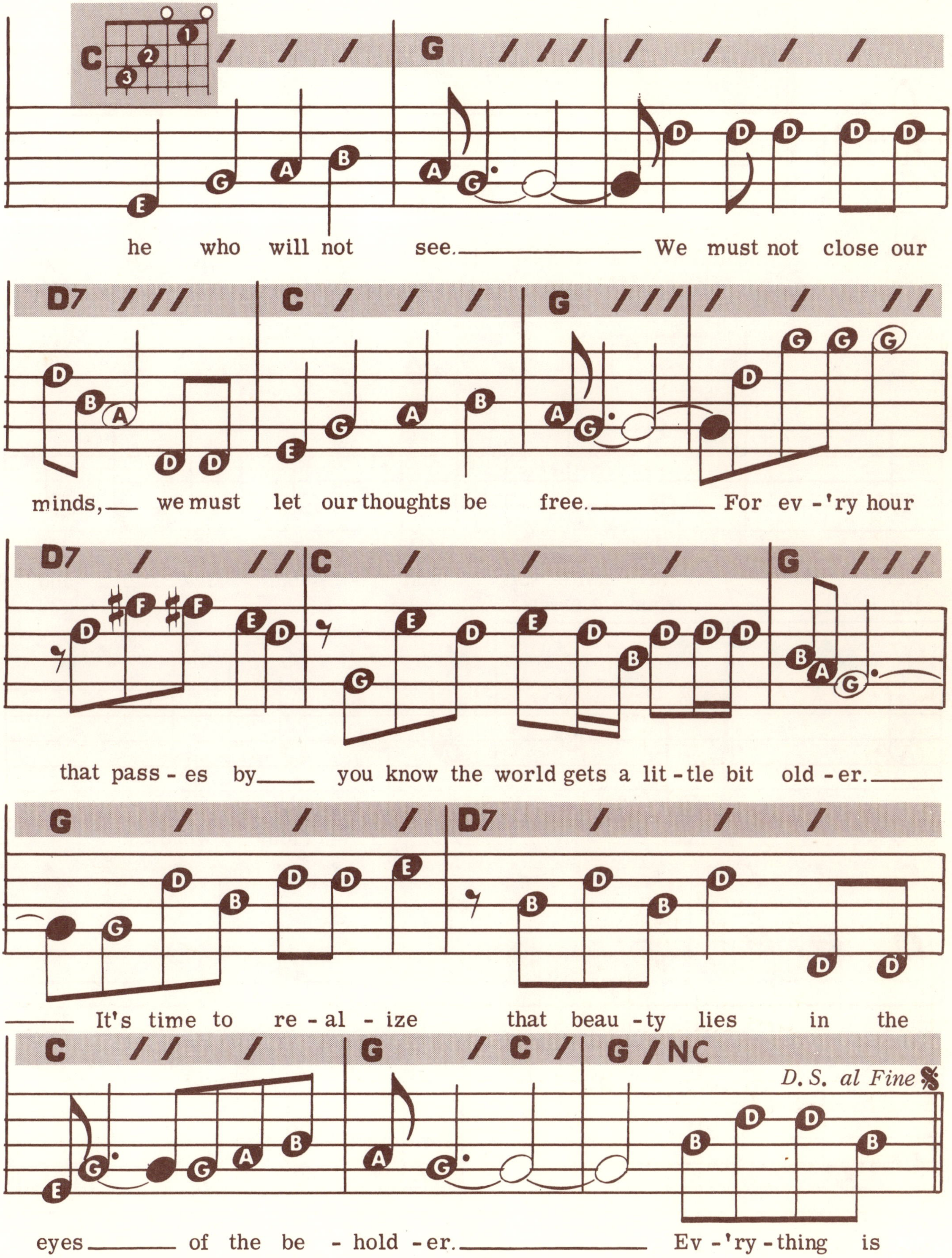

Everything Is Beautiful-2 -2

C G
he who will not see. We must not close our
D7 C G
minds, we must let our thoughts be free. For ev-'ry hour
D7 C G
that pass-es by you know the world gets a lit-tle bit old-er.
G D7
It's time to re-al-ize that beau-ty lies in the
C G C G NC
D. S. al Fine
eyes of the be-hold-er. Ev-'ry-thing is

# FAITH OF OUR FATHERS

By HENRI F. HEMY
FREDERICK W. FABER

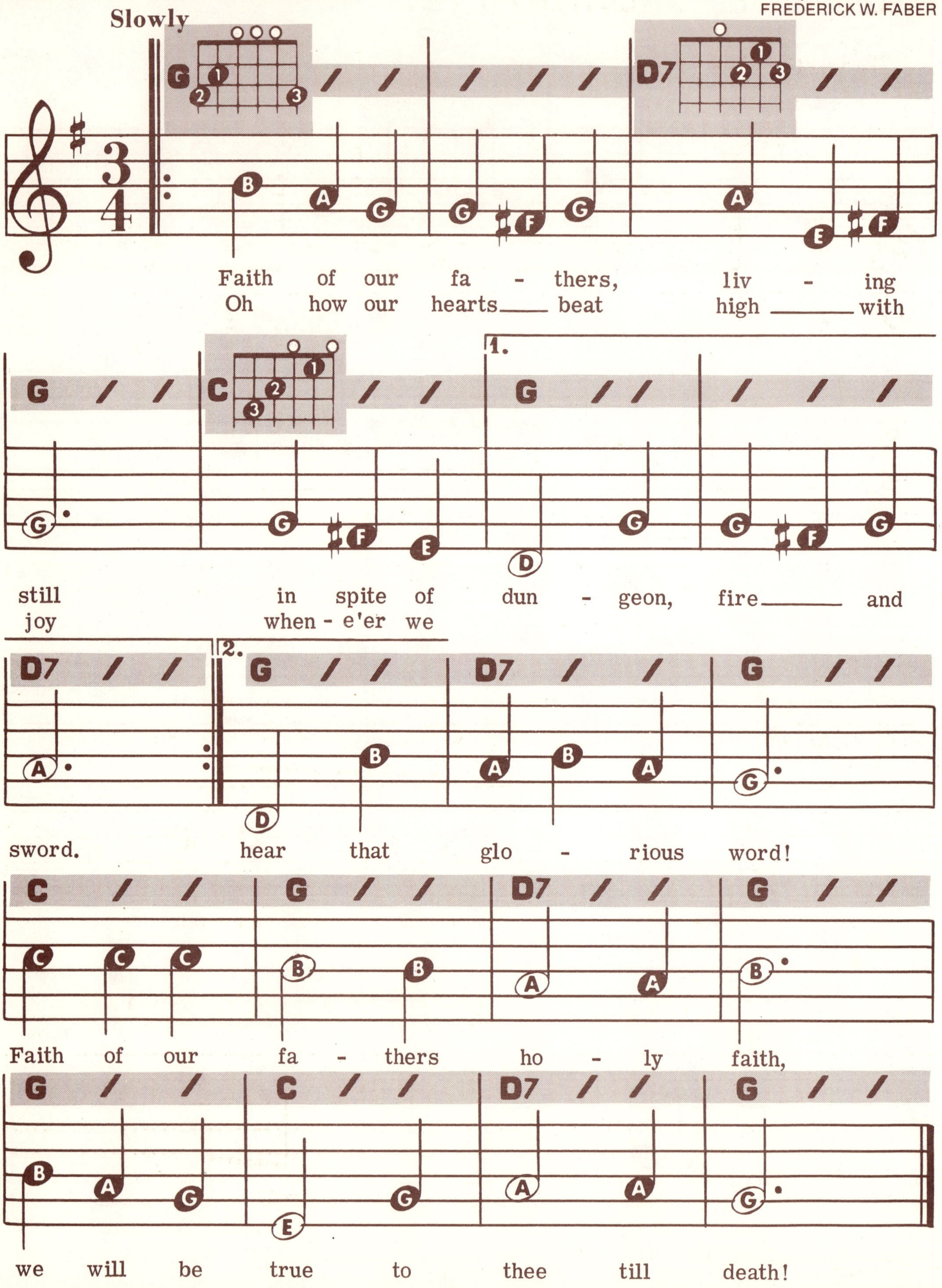

Faith of our fa - thers, liv - ing
Oh how our hearts beat high with

still in spite of dun - geon, fire and
joy when - e'er we

sword. hear that glo - rious word!

Faith of our fa - thers ho - ly faith,

we will be true to thee till death!

# FIND YOURSELF ANOTHER PUPPET

By JIMBEAU HINSON

**Moderately Fast**

CHORUS

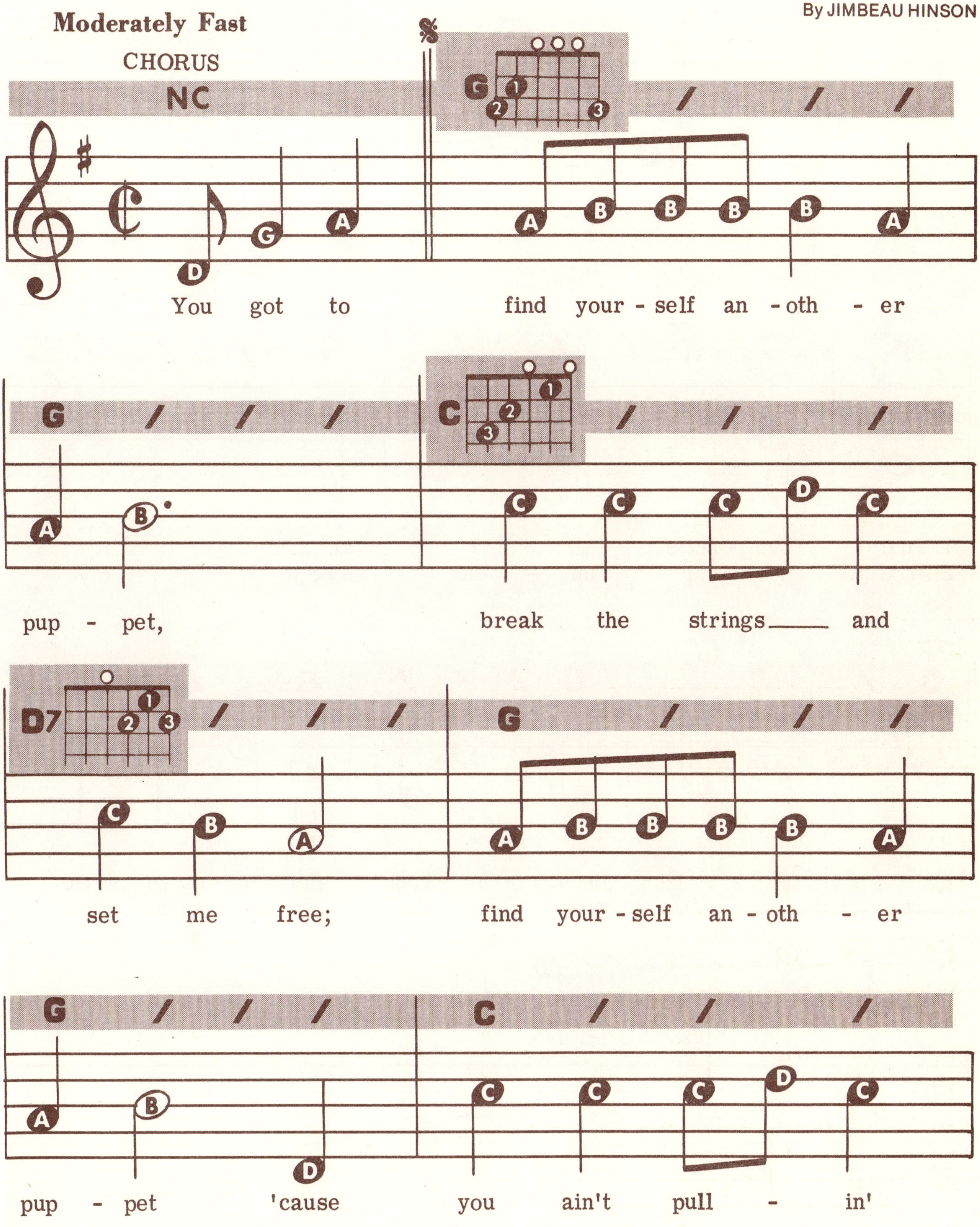

You got to find your-self an -oth - er

pup - pet, break the strings____ and

set me free; find your-self an -oth - er

pup - pet 'cause you ain't pull - in'

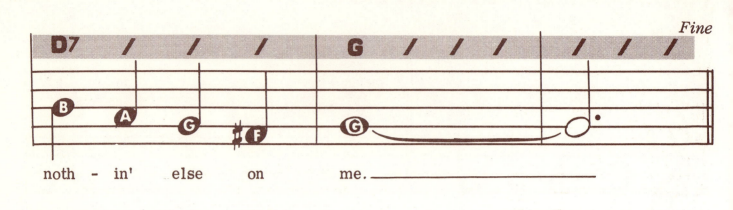

*Fine*

noth - in' else on me.

**VERSE**

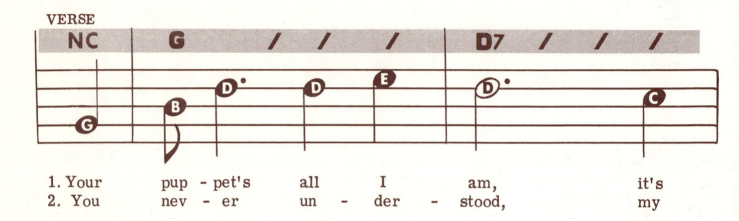

1. Your    pup - pet's    all    I    am,    it's
2. You    nev - er    un - der - stood,    my

all    I've ev - er    been;    Your    fun - ny    lit - tle
heart    ain't made of    wood;    And    I    ain't    gon - na

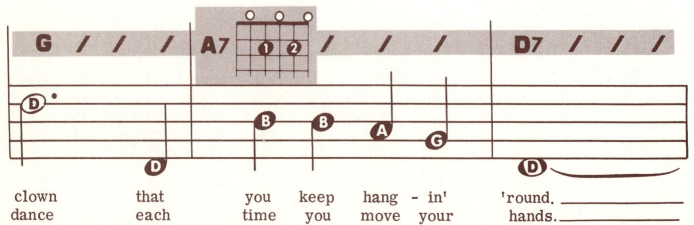

clown    that    you    keep    hang - in'    'round.
dance    each    time    you    move    your    hands.

**Find Yourself Another Puppet-3-2**

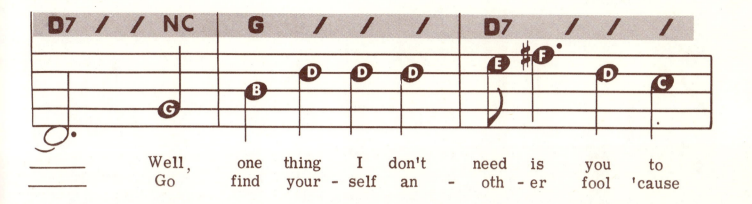

Well,     one   thing   I   don't     need   is     you   to
Go      find   your - self   an   -   oth - er     fool   'cause

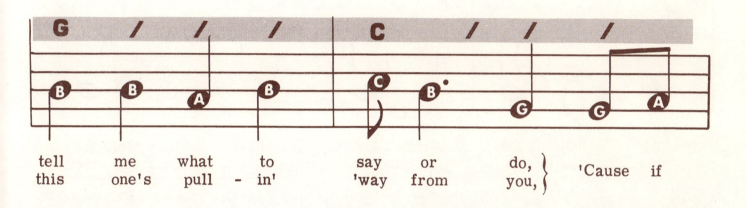

tell     me     what     to       say     or       do,  ⎫   'Cause if
this    one's  pull - in'   'way   from   you, ⎭

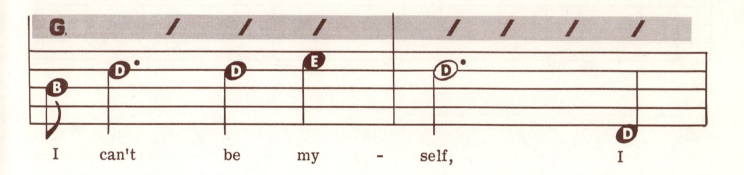

I    can't      be      my   -   self,           I

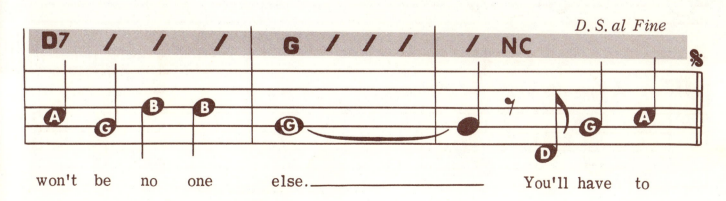

*D. S. al Fine*

won't   be   no   one     else._____     You'll   have   to

Find Yourself Another Puppet-3-3

# FIVE HUNDRED MILES

### Moderately Slow

By HEDY WEST

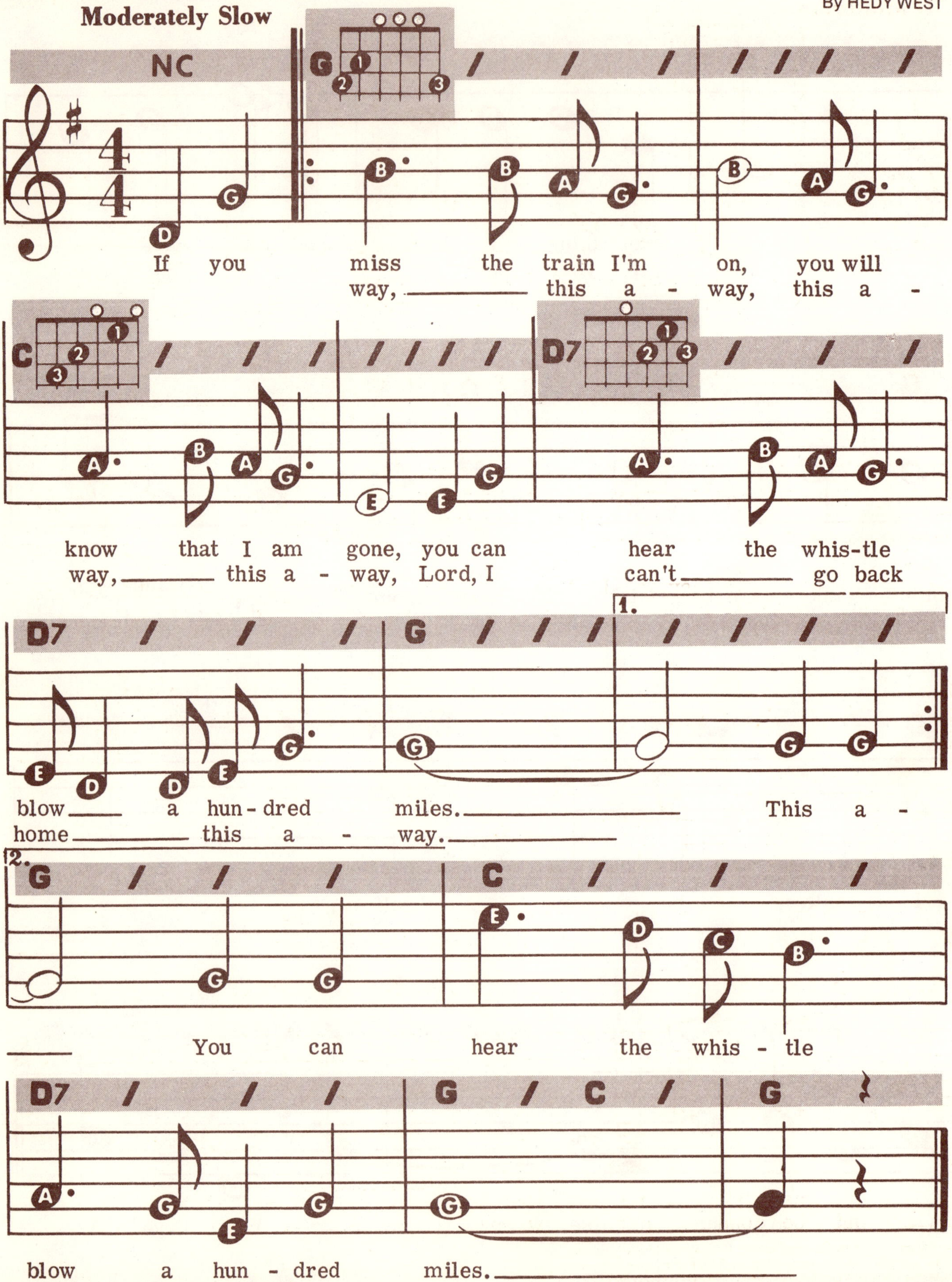

If you miss the train I'm on, you will
way, _____ this a - way, this a -

know that I am gone, you can
way, _____ this a - way, Lord, I

hear the whis-tle
can't _____ go back

blow _____ a hun-dred miles. _____ This a -
home _____ this a - way.

You can hear the whis - tle

blow a hun - dred miles. _____

# FRANKIE AND JOHNNY

**Moderato**

TRADITIONAL

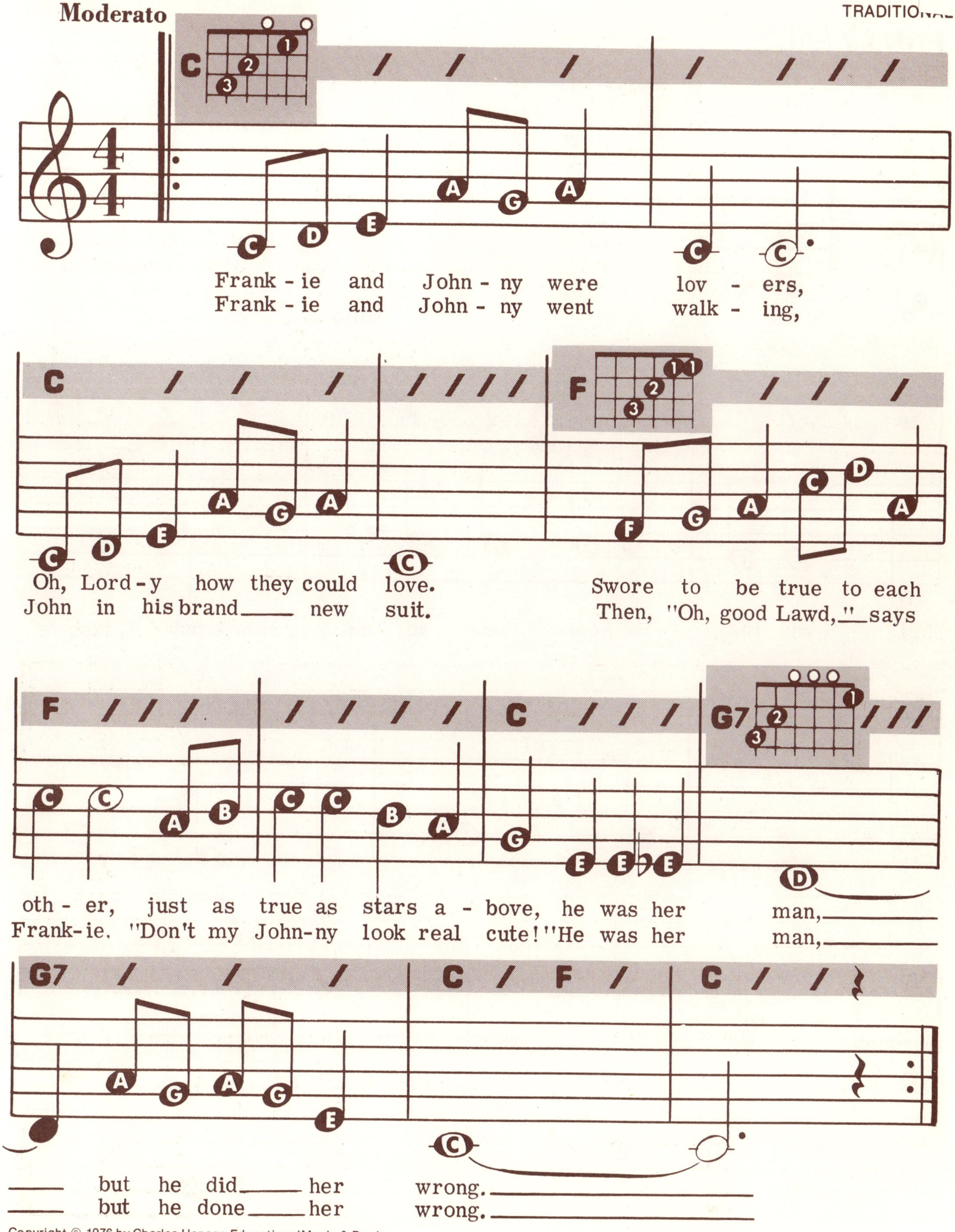

Frank - ie and John - ny were lov - ers,
Frank - ie and John - ny went walk - ing,

Oh, Lord - y how they could love.
John in his brand____ new suit.

Swore to be true to each
Then, "Oh, good Lawd," says

oth - er, just as true as stars a - bove, he was her man,____
Frank - ie. "Don't my John - ny look real cute!" He was her man,____

____ but he did____ her wrong.____
____ but he done____ her wrong.____

# FUNNY FACE

Words and Music by
DONNA FARGO

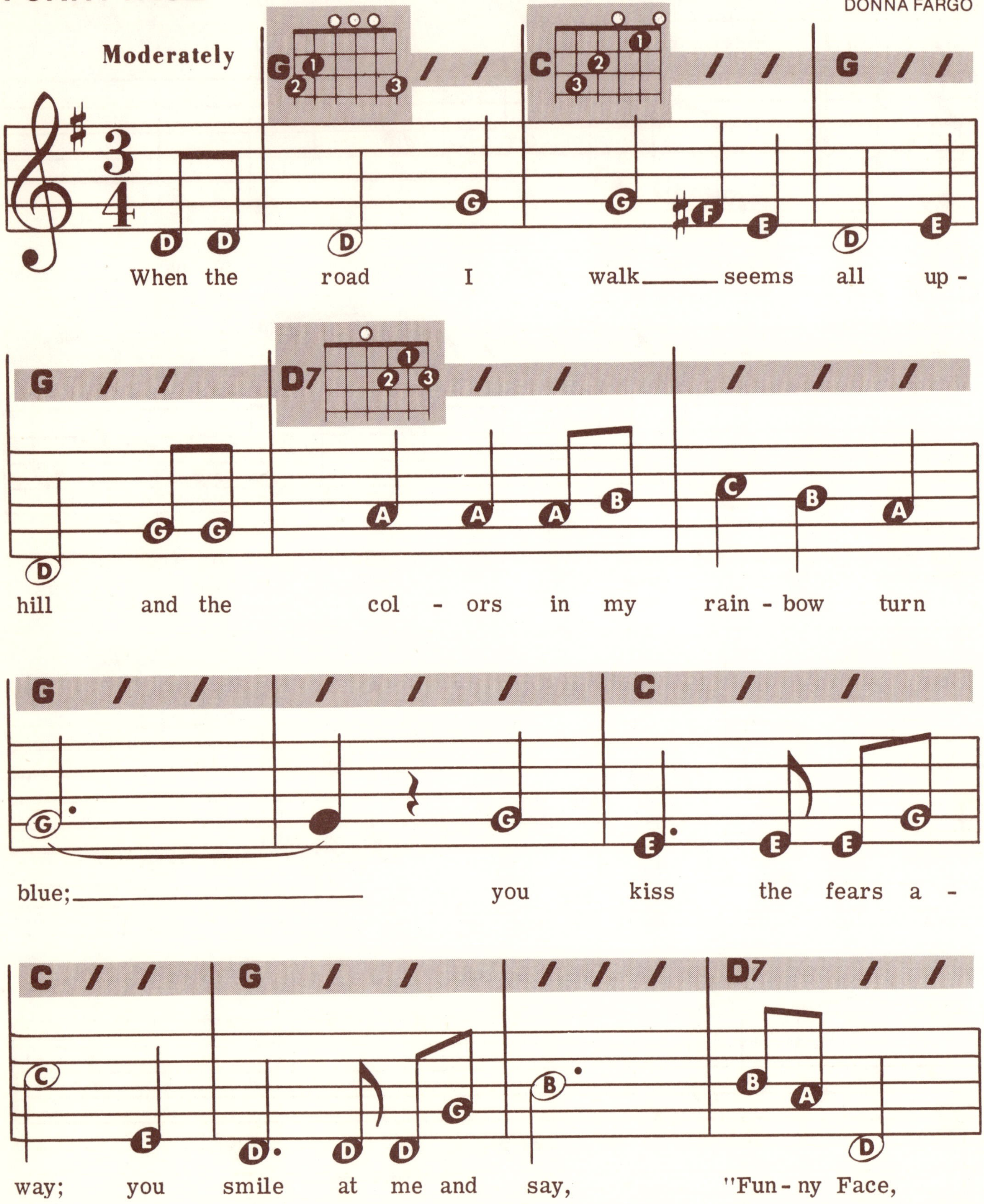

When the road I walk seems all up-hill and the col-ors in my rain-bow turn blue; you kiss the fears a-way; you smile at me and say, "Fun-ny Face,

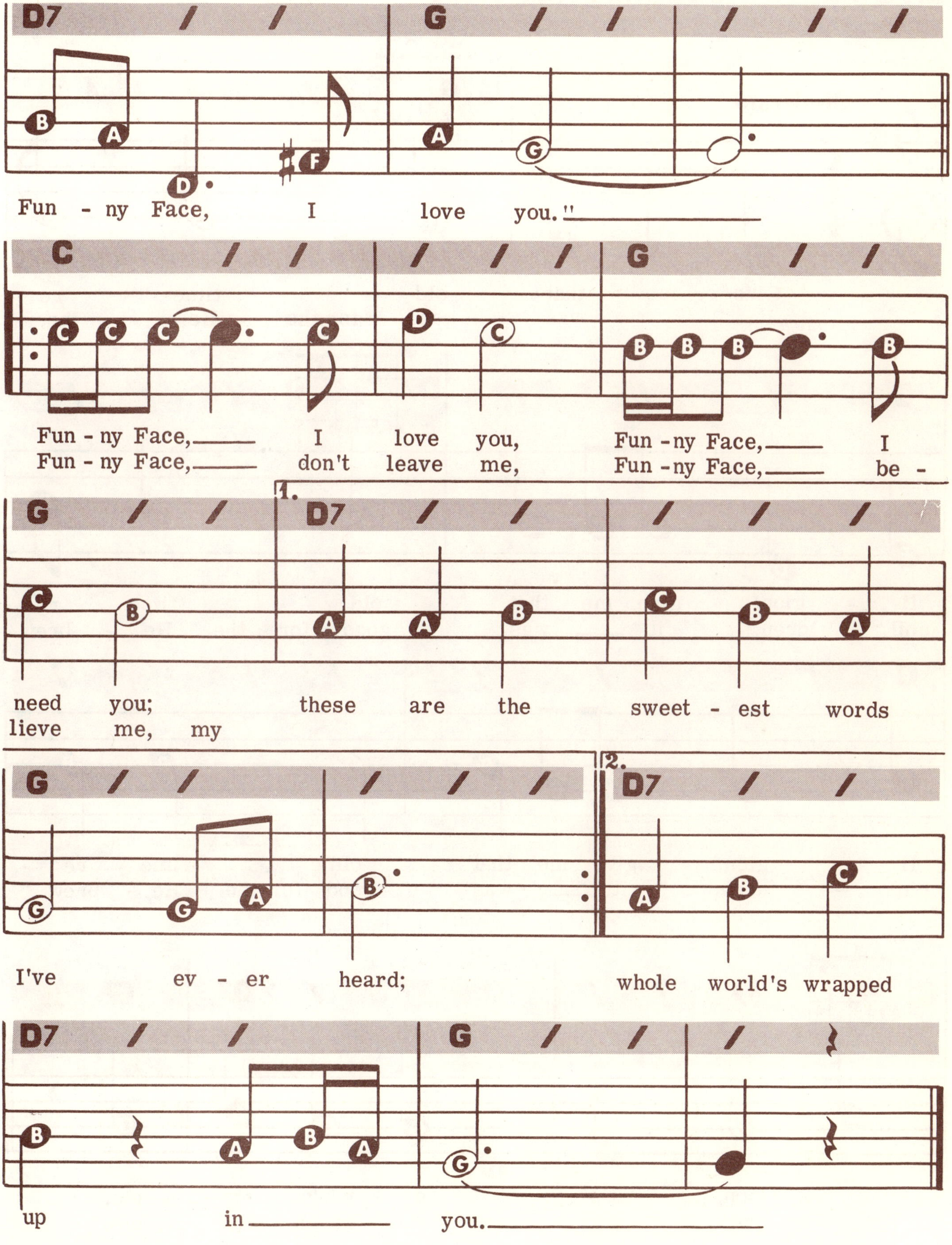

Fun - ny Face, I love you."

Fun - ny Face, I love you,
Fun - ny Face, don't leave me,

Fun - ny Face, I
Fun - ny Face, be -

need you; these are the sweet - est words
lieve me, my

I've ev - er heard;

whole world's wrapped

up in you.

Funny Face-2-2

# GIVE ME THAT OLD TIME RELIGION

TRADITIONAL

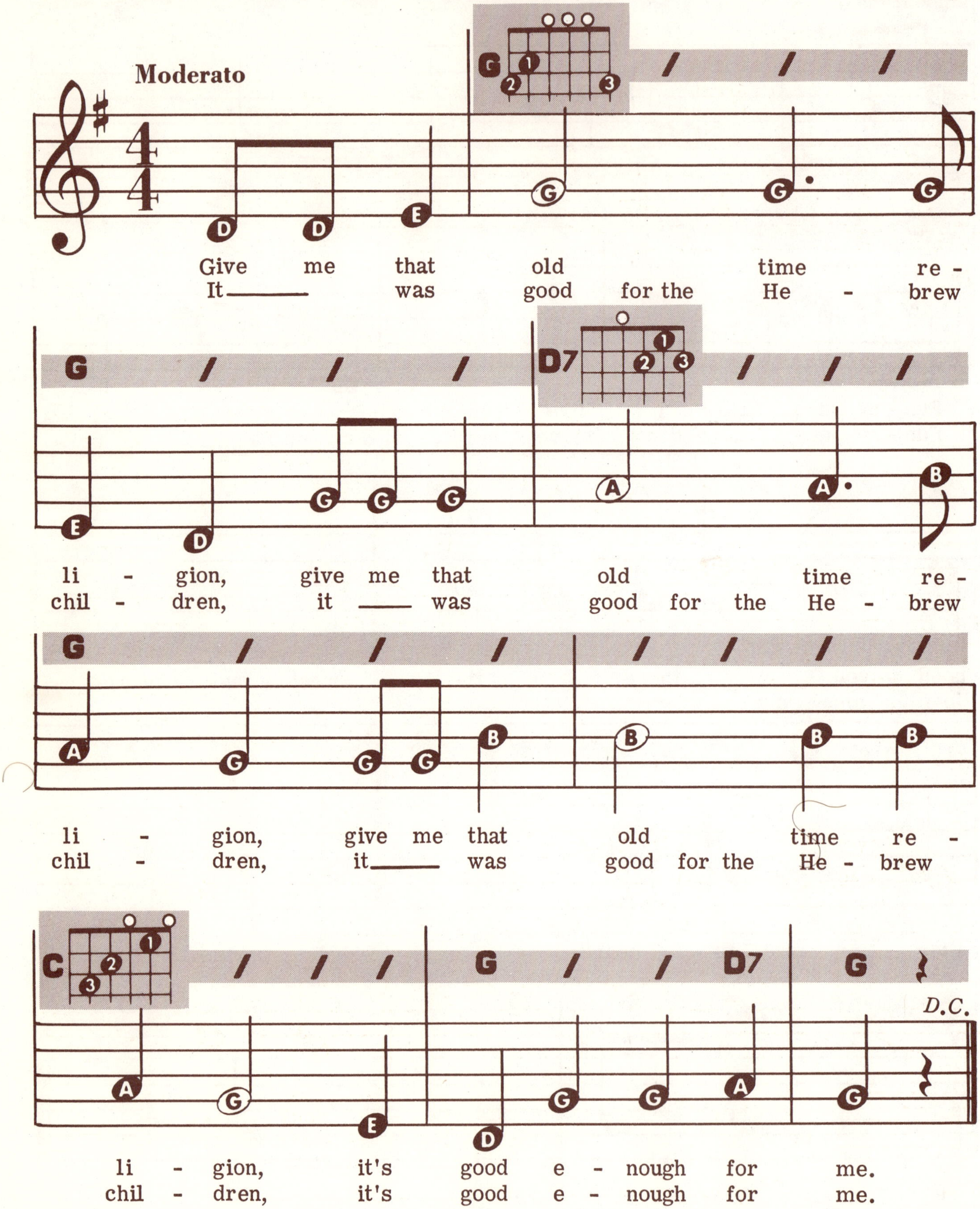

Give me that old time re-
It ___ was good for the He - brew

li - gion, give me that old time re-
chil - dren, it ___ was good for the He - brew

li - gion, give me that old time re -
chil - dren, it___ was good for the He - brew

li - gion, it's good e - nough for me.
chil - dren, it's good e - nough for me.

# GALVESTON

Words and Music by
JIMMY WEBB

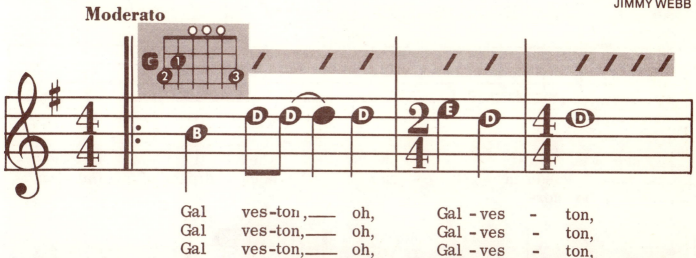

Gal ves-ton,___ oh, Gal - ves - ton,
Gal ves-ton,___ oh, Gal - ves - ton,
Gal ves-ton,___ oh, Gal - ves - ton,

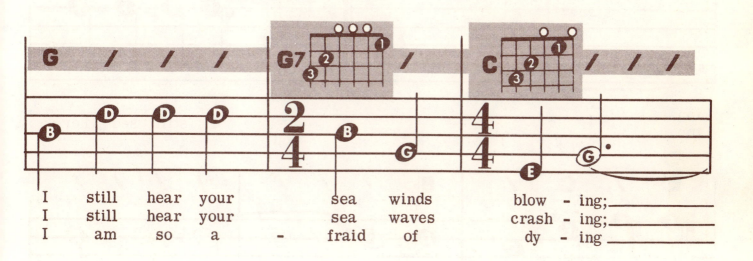

I still hear your sea winds blow - ing;___
I still hear your sea waves crash - ing;___
I am so a - fraid of dy - ing ___

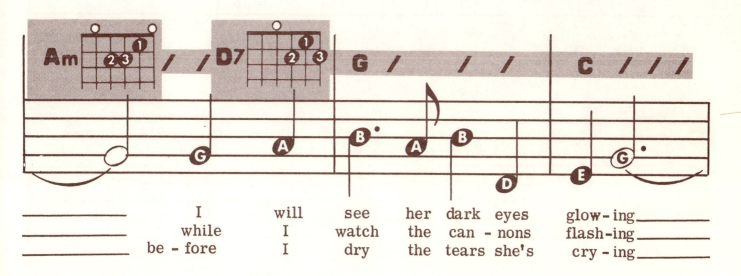

I will see her dark eyes glow-ing___
while I watch the can - nons flash-ing___
be - fore I dry the tears she's cry-ing___

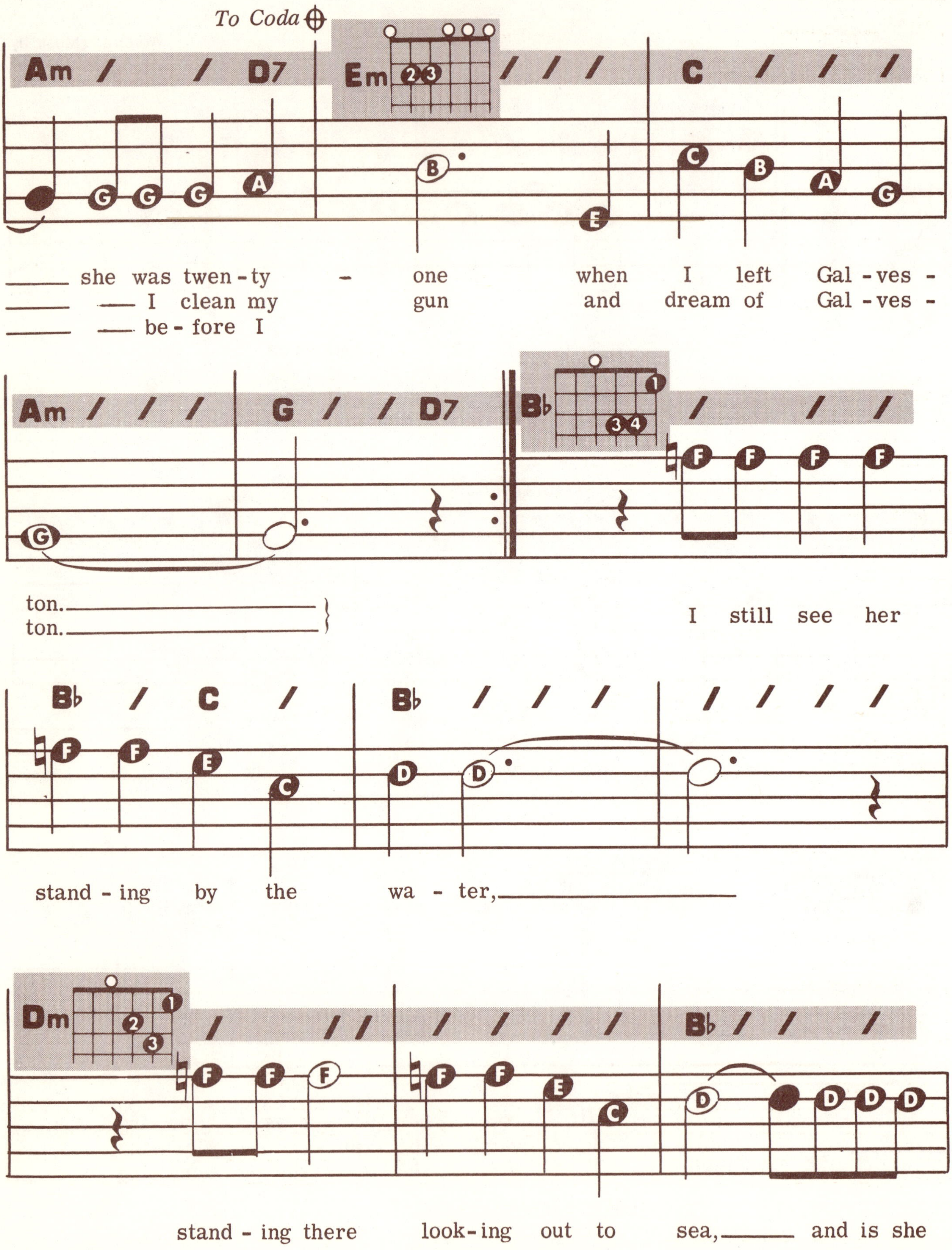

she was twen-ty — one when I left Gal-ves-
— I clean my gun and dream of Gal-ves-
— be-fore I

ton.
ton.

I still see her

stand-ing by the wa-ter,

stand-ing there look-ing out to sea, and is she

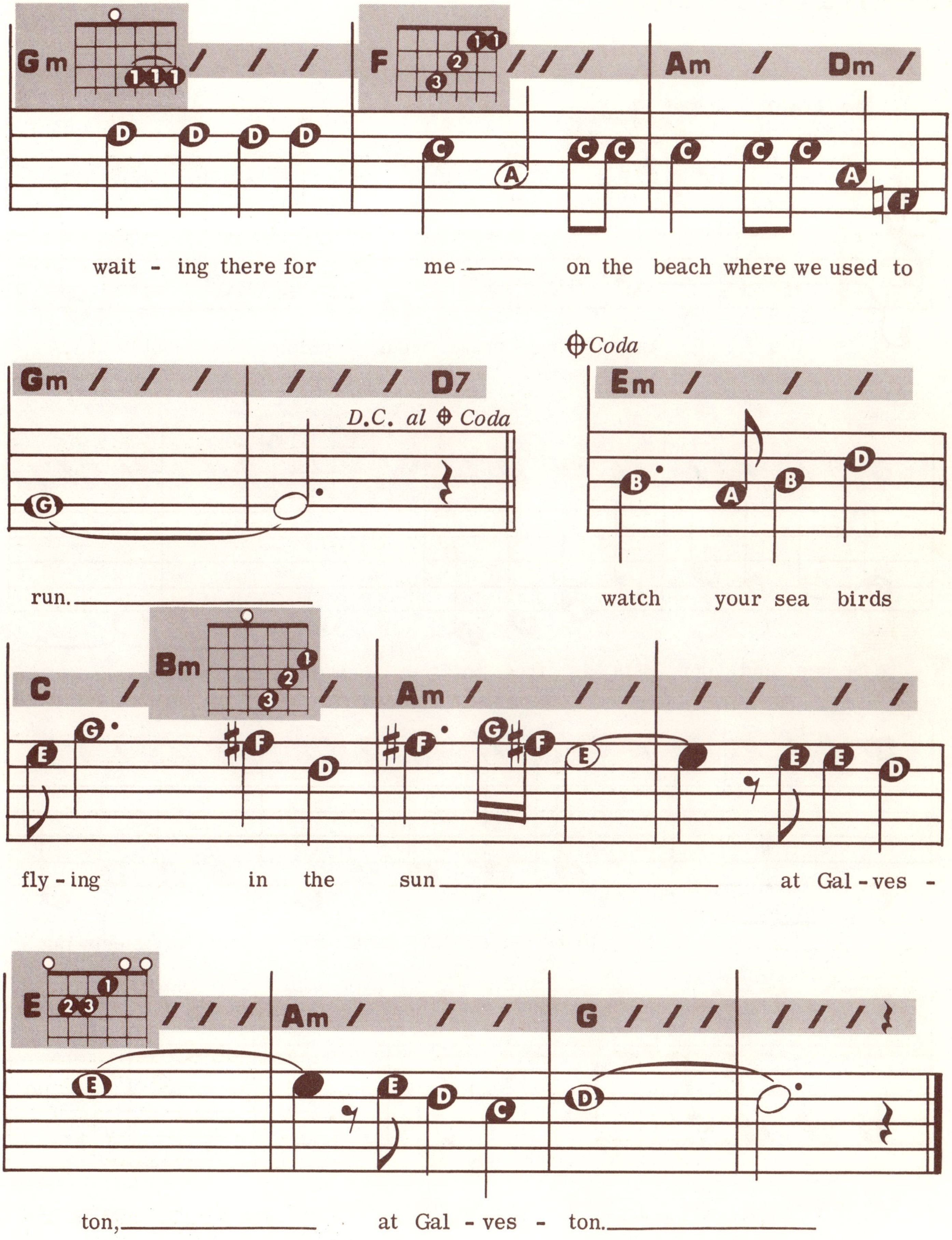

waiting there for me ——— on the beach where we used to run. _____

*D.C. al ⊕ Coda*

⊕ *Coda*

watch your sea birds fly-ing in the sun _____ at Gal-ves-ton, _____ at Gal-ves-ton. _____

Galveston-3-3

# GENTLE ON MY MIND

**Moderato**

By JOHN HARTFORD

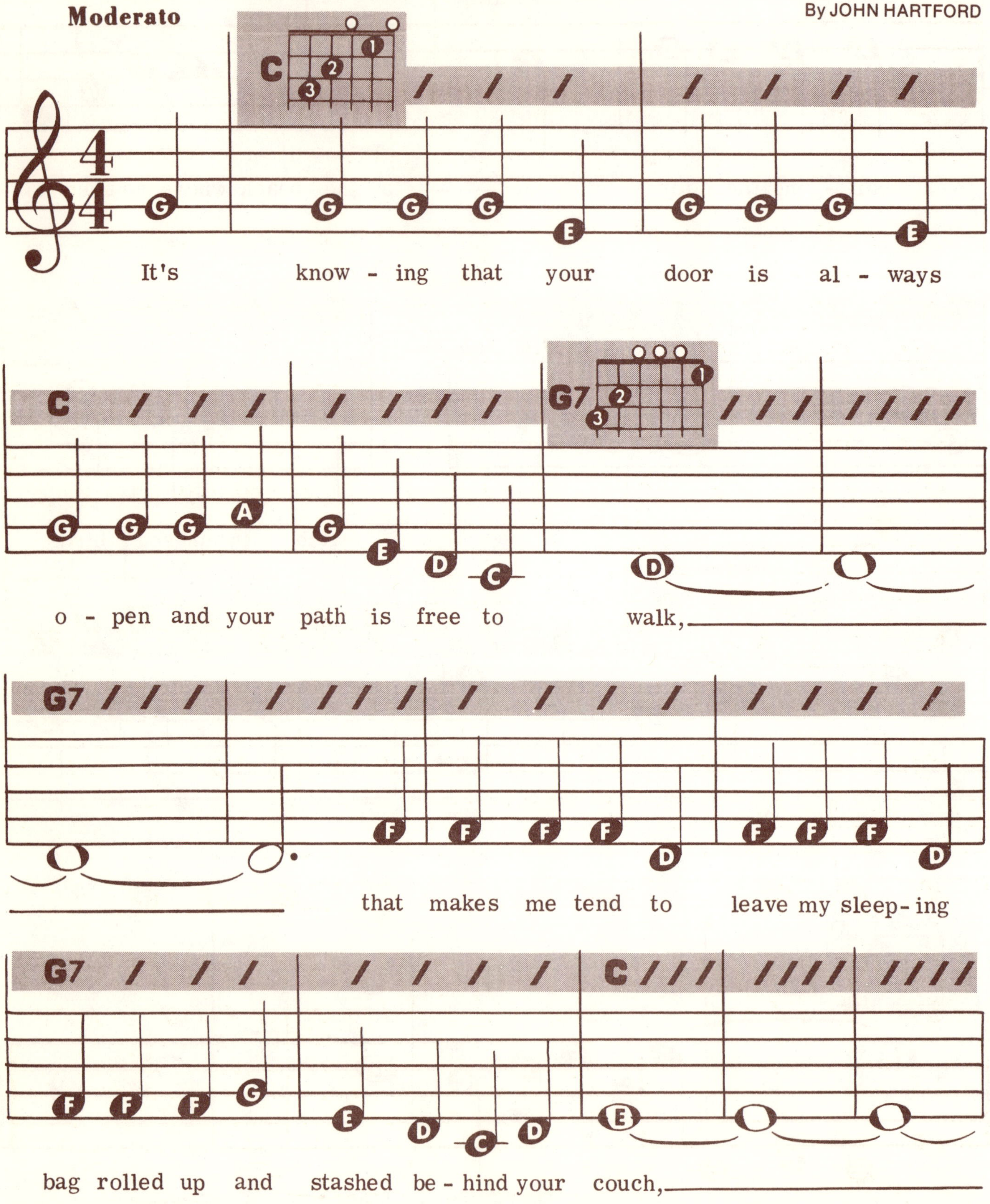

It's know - ing that your door is al - ways o - pen and your path is free to walk, that makes me tend to leave my sleep - ing bag rolled up and stashed be - hind your couch,

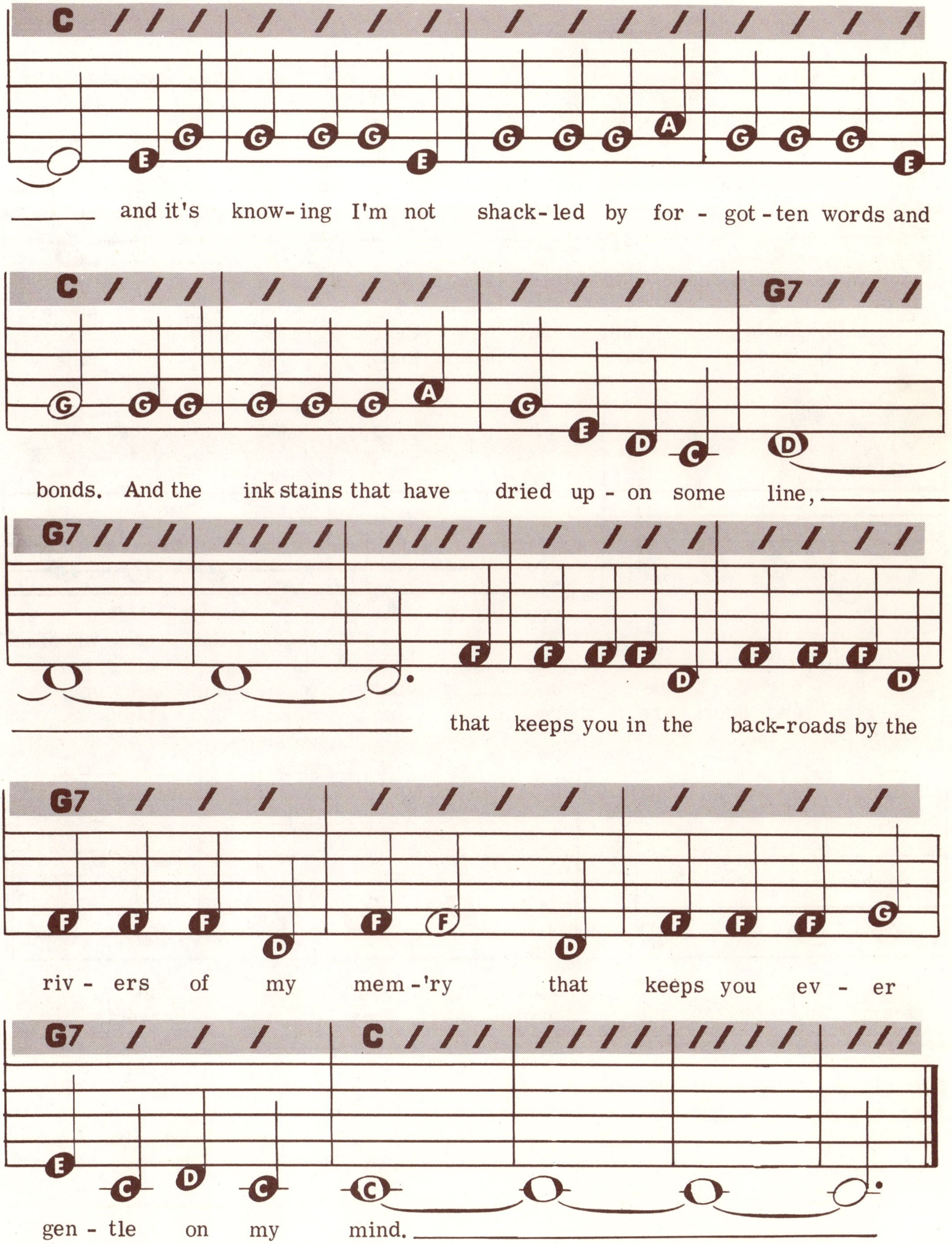
C
and it's know-ing I'm not shack-led by for - got-ten words and
C
G7
bonds. And the ink stains that have dried up - on some line,
G7
that keeps you in the back-roads by the
G7
riv - ers of my mem-'ry that keeps you ev - er
G7
C
gen - tle on my mind.

# GET ON BOARD, LITTLE CHILDREN

SPIRITUAL

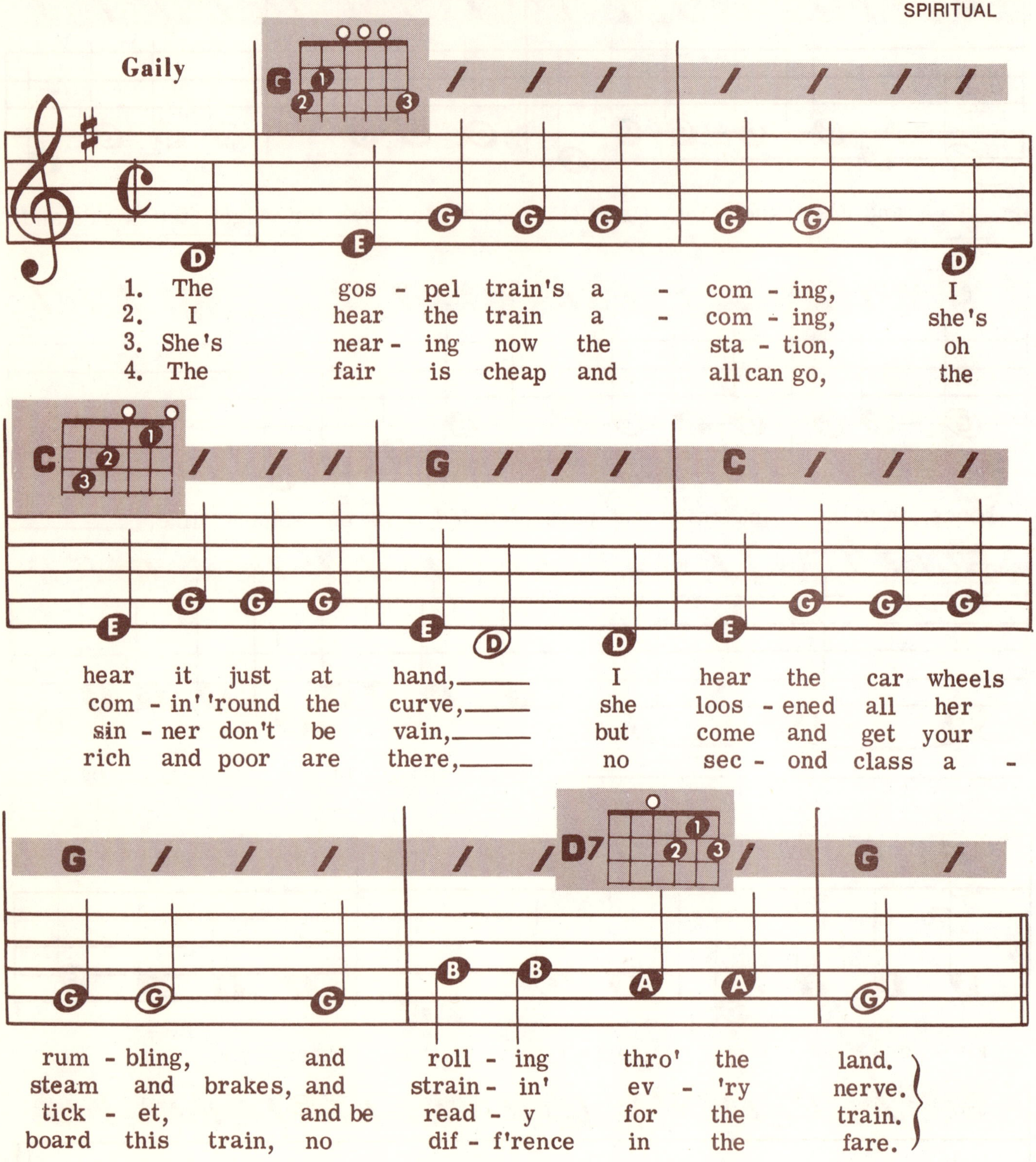

1. The      gos - pel train's a - com - ing,     I
2. I      hear the train a - com - ing,     she's
3. She's      near - ing now the sta - tion,     oh
4. The      fair is cheap and all can go,     the

hear it just at hand, _____ I hear the car wheels
com - in' 'round the curve, _____ she loos - ened all her
sin - ner don't be vain, _____ but come and get your
rich and poor are there, _____ no sec - ond class a -

rum - bling,     and roll - ing thro' the land.
steam and brakes, and strain - in' ev - 'ry nerve.
tick - et,     and be read - y for the train.
board this train, no dif - f'rence in the fare.

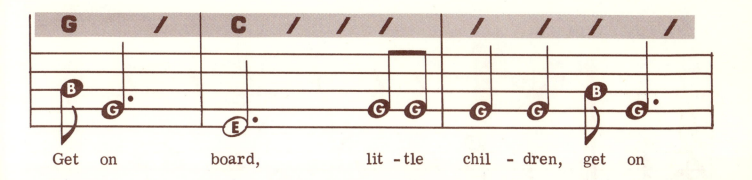

Get on  board,  lit -tle  chil - dren, get on

board,  lit - tle  chil - dren, get on

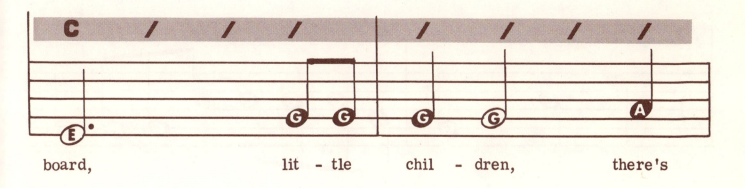

board,  lit - tle  chil - dren,  there's

room  for  man - y - a  more.

Get On Board, Little Children-2-2

# GREEN GREEN

By BARRY McGUIRE
RANDY SPARKS

CHORUS

C / / /     F / / /

Green, green, it's green, they say,____ on the

C / / /     G7 / / /

far side of the hill;_____

C / / /     F / / /

Green, green, I'm go - in' a - way____ to where the

C / G7 /     C / / /

grass is green - er still._____

{ Well, I
{ No, there

**VERSE**

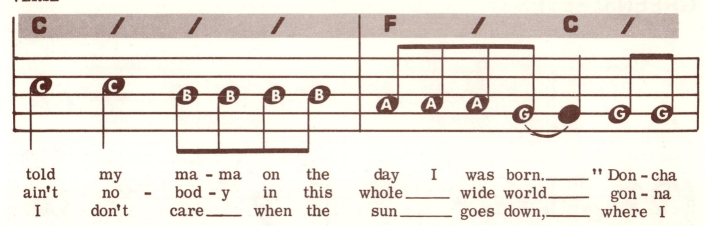

| told | my | ma - ma | on | the | day | I | was born._____ | " Don - cha |
| ain't | no - bod - y | in | this | whole_____ | wide | world_____ | gon - na |
| I | don't | care_____ | when | the | sun_____ | goes down,_____ | where I |

| cry | when | you | see | I'm | gone._____ | | You know there |
| tell | me | how | to | spend | my | time._____ | _____ I'm_____ |
| lay | my_____ | wea - ry | head;_____ | | |

| ain't | no | wom - an | gon - na | set - tle | me down,_____ | I just |
| just | a | good_____ | lov - in' | ram - bl - in' | man_____ | say, |
| Green, | green | val - ley | or a | rock - y | road;_____ | It's |

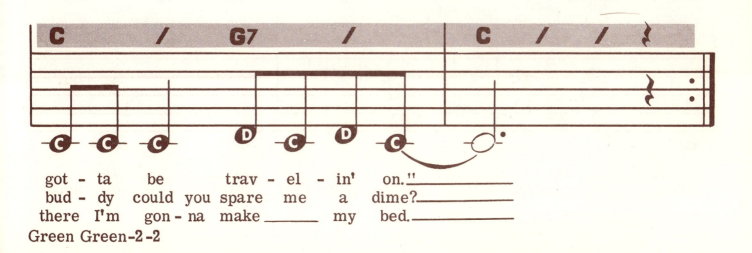

| got - ta | be | trav - el - in' | on."_____ | |
| bud - dy | could | you | spare | me | a | dime?_____ | |
| there | I'm | gon - na | make_____ | my bed._____ | |

Green Green-2 -2

# GREENSLEEVES

OLD ENGLISH FOLK SONG

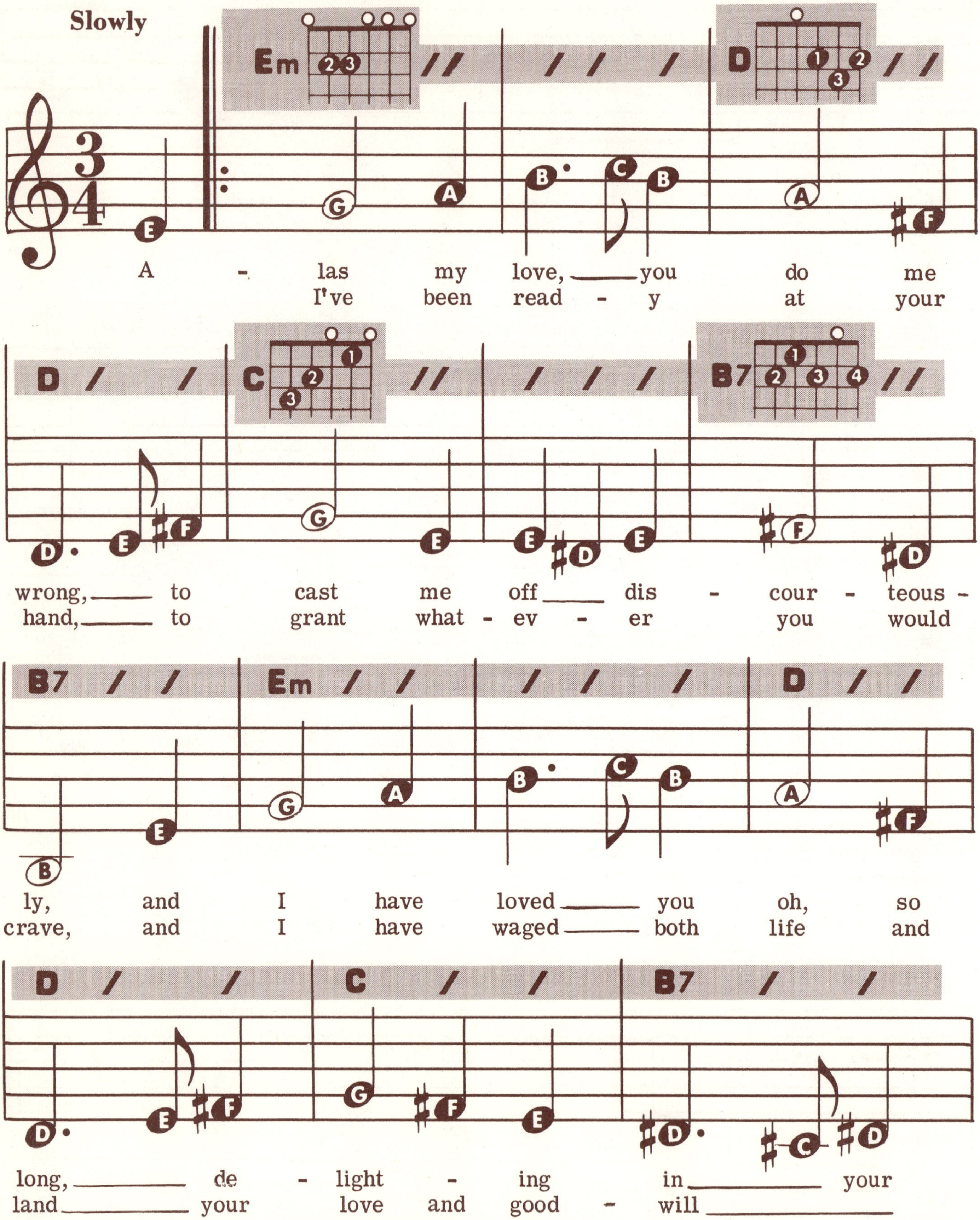

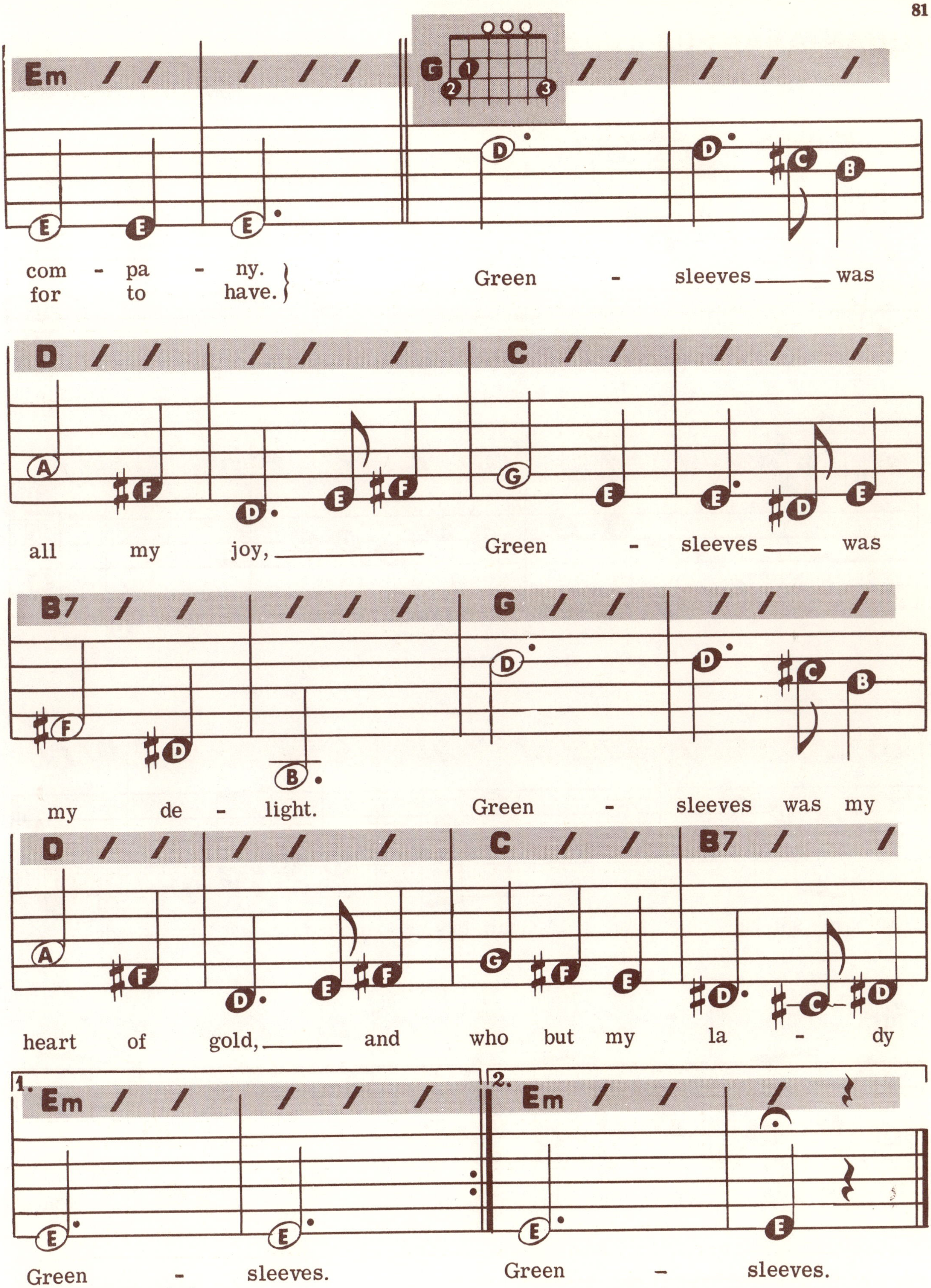
Em
G
1
2
3
D E E E D D C B
com - pa - ny.
for to have.
Green - sleeves was
D
C
A F D E F G E E D E
all my joy,
Green - sleeves was
B7
G
F D B D D C B
my de - light.
Green - sleeves was my
D
C
B7
A F D E F G F E D C D
heart of gold, and who but my la - dy
1.
Em
2.
Em
E E E E
Green - sleeves.
Green - sleeves.

# GUANTANAMERA (Lady Of Guantanamo)

Spanish Words by JOSE MARTI
English Adaptation by BERNARD GASSO (ASCAP)

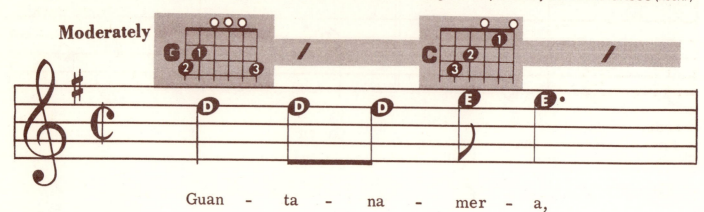

Guan - ta - na - mer - a,

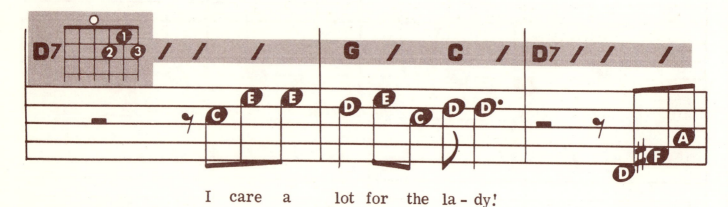

I care a lot for the la - dy!

My in-spi-ra - tion, Guan-ta-na - mo's fair-est la - dy.____

I'm just a man who is try-ing                 to do some

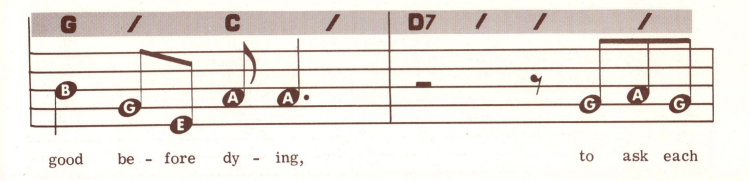

good be - fore dy - ing, to ask each

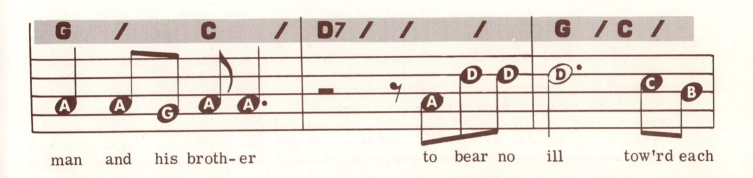

man and his broth - er to bear no ill tow'rd each

oth - er. This life will nev - er be hol -

*D.C. al Fine*

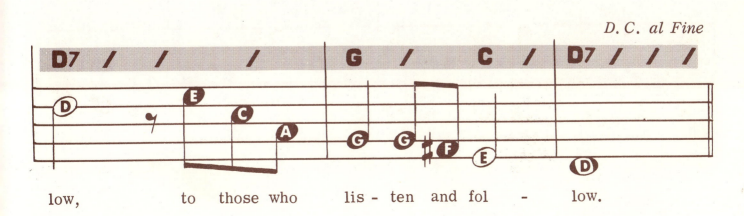

low, to those who lis - ten and fol - low.

Guantanamera-2-2

# GOTTA TRAVEL ON

TRADITIONAL

Done laid a-round, done stayed a-round this ole town too long. Sum-mer's al-most gone and win-ter's com-in' on. Done laid a-round, done stayed a-round this ole town too long and I feel like I got-ta trav-el on.

# A HOT TIME IN THE OLD TOWN TONIGHT

Words by JOE HAYDEN
Music by THEO. A. METZ

**Moderato**

When you hear the___ bells go ding-ling-ling, all join 'round and ___ sweet-ly you must sing. And when the verse is through, in the cho-rus all join in, there'll be a hot time in the old town to-night.___

# THE HAPPIEST GIRL IN THE WHOLE U.S.A.

Words and Music by
DONNA FARGO

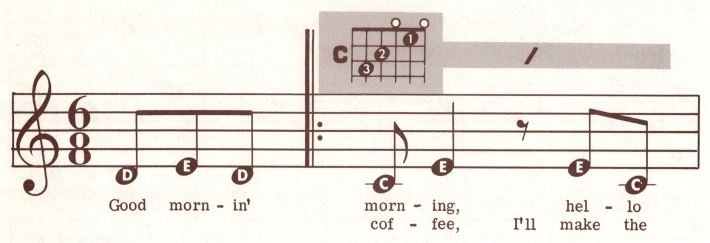

Good morn-in' morn-ing, hel-lo
cof-fee, I'll make the

sun-shine,_____ make up sleep-y head._____
bed,_____I'll fix your lunch and you fix mine. Now

Why'd we move_____ that bo-jan-gle clock so
tell me the truth_____ do these old shoes look

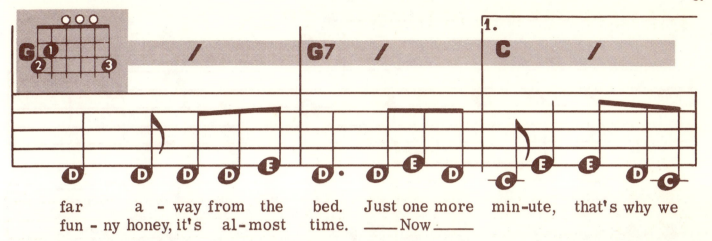

far      a - way from the    bed.   Just one more  min-ute,  that's why we
fun - ny honey, it's al-most    time. ___ Now ___

moved it; _____           one more ___ hug  or  two.     Do you

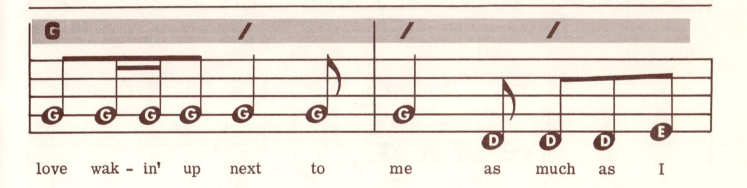

love wak- in' up next  to    me      as   much as   I

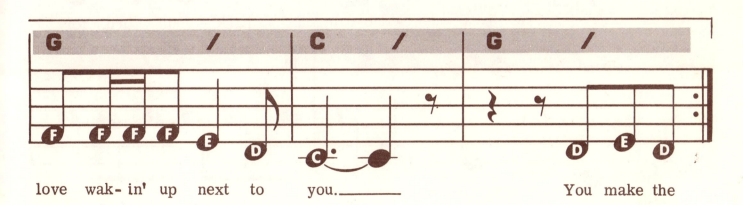

love wak- in' up next to    you. _____        You make the

The Happiest Girl In The Whole U. S. A. -4-2

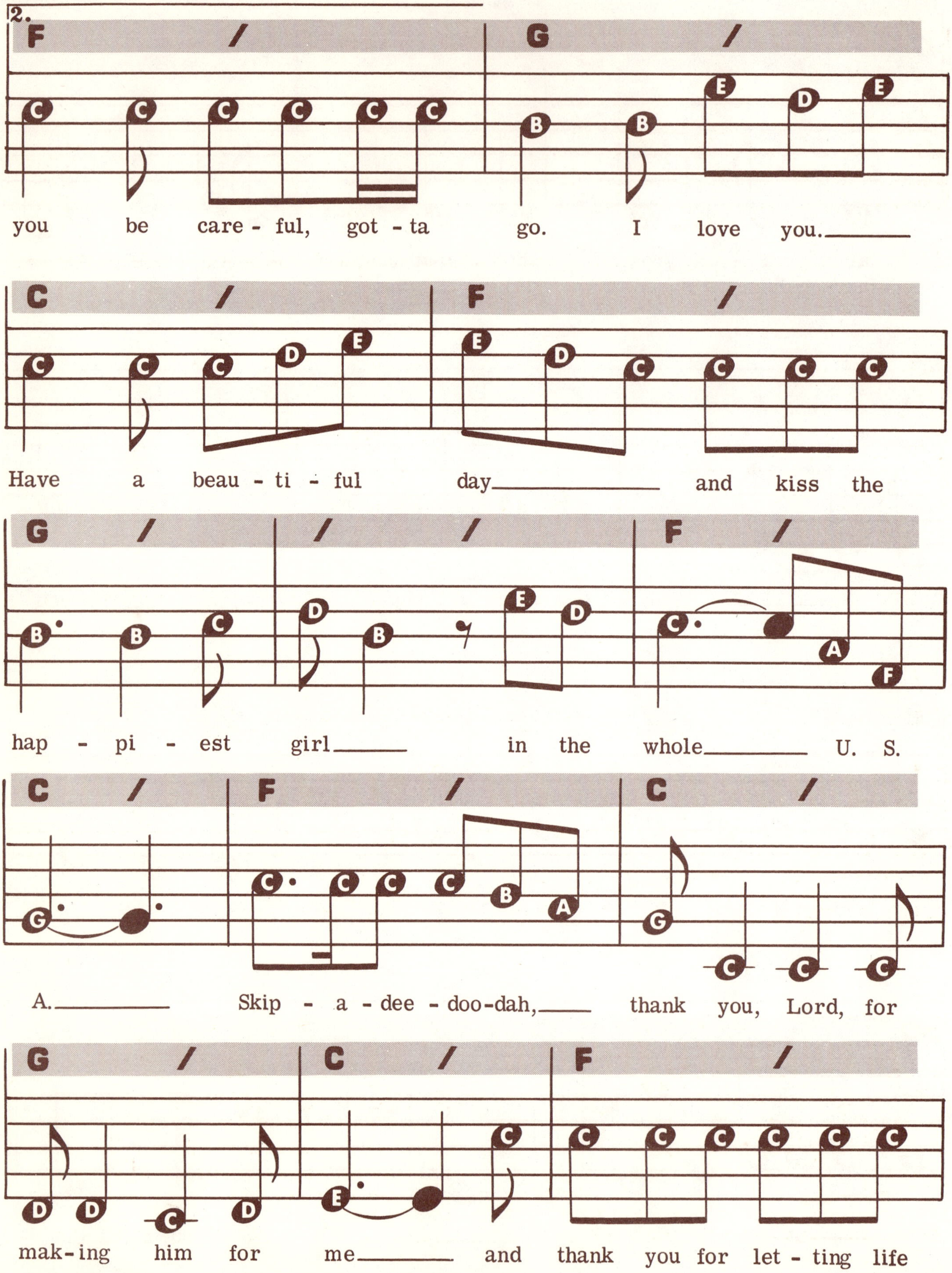
2.
F / G /
you be care - ful, got - ta go. I love you.
C / F /
Have a beau - ti - ful day and kiss the
G / / / F /
hap - pi - est girl in the whole U. S.
C / F / C /
A. Skip - a - dee - doo-dah, thank you, Lord, for
G / C / F /
mak-ing him for me and thank you for let - ting life

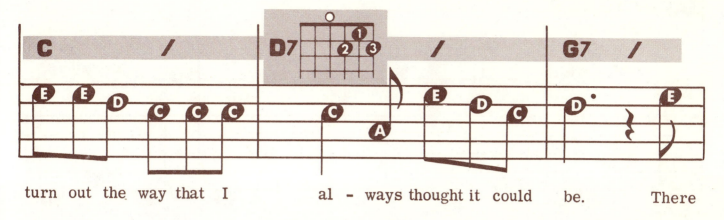

turn out the way that I    al – ways thought it could    be.    There

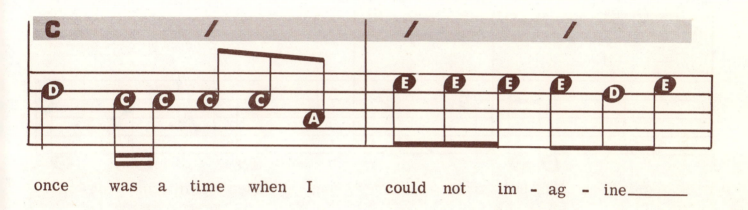

once    was a time when I    could not im – ag – ine_____

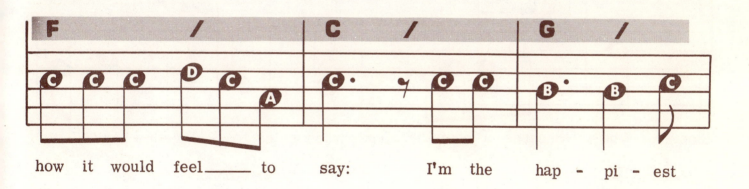

how it would feel____ to    say:    I'm the    hap – pi – est

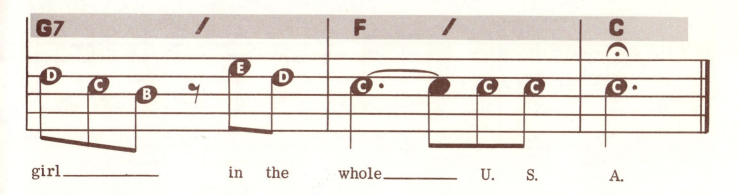

girl_____    in the whole_____ U. S.    A.

The Happiest Girl In The Whole U. S. A. –4–4

# HAPPY TRAILS

By DALE EVANS

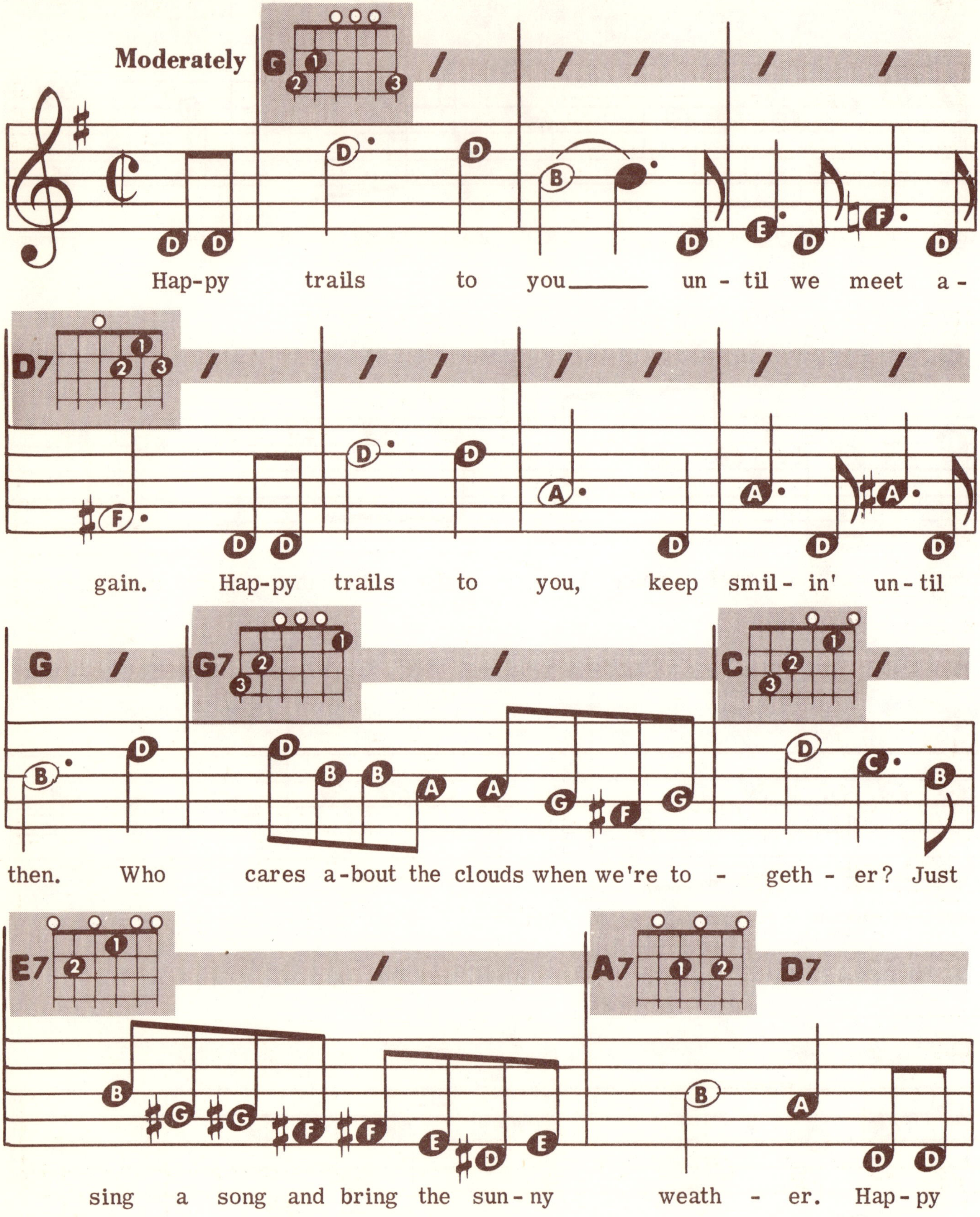

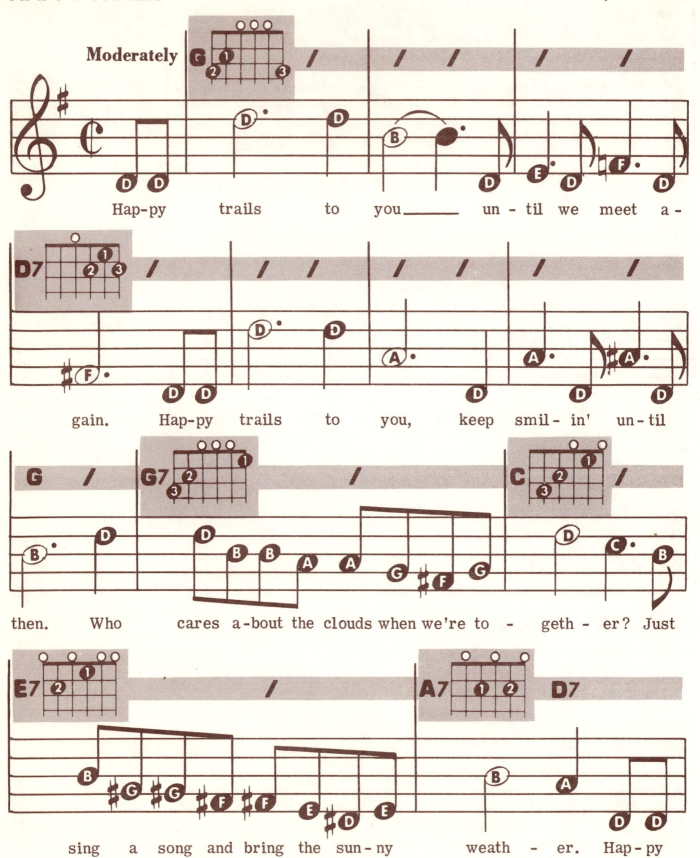

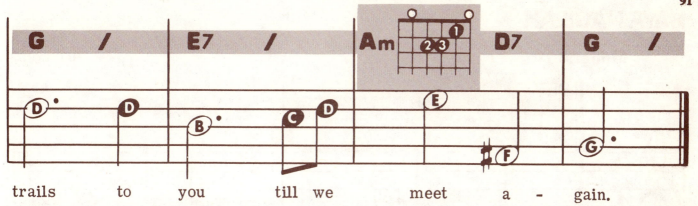

trails   to   you   till   we   meet   a - gain.

# HE'S GOT THE WHOLE WORLD IN HIS HANDS

TRADITIONAL

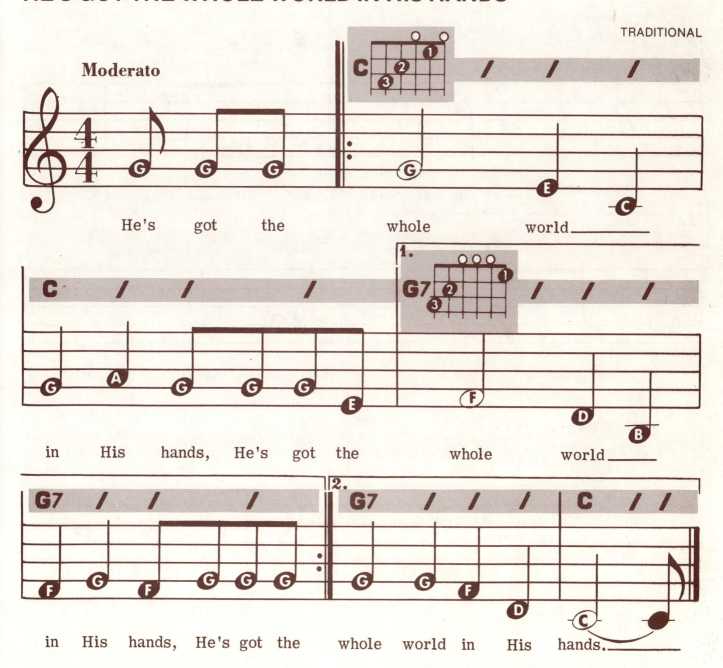

He's   got   the   whole   world _____

in   His   hands,   He's   got   the   whole   world _____

in   His   hands,   He's got the   whole world in   His   hands. _____

# HAVA NAGILAH

**Moderato**

TRADITIONAL

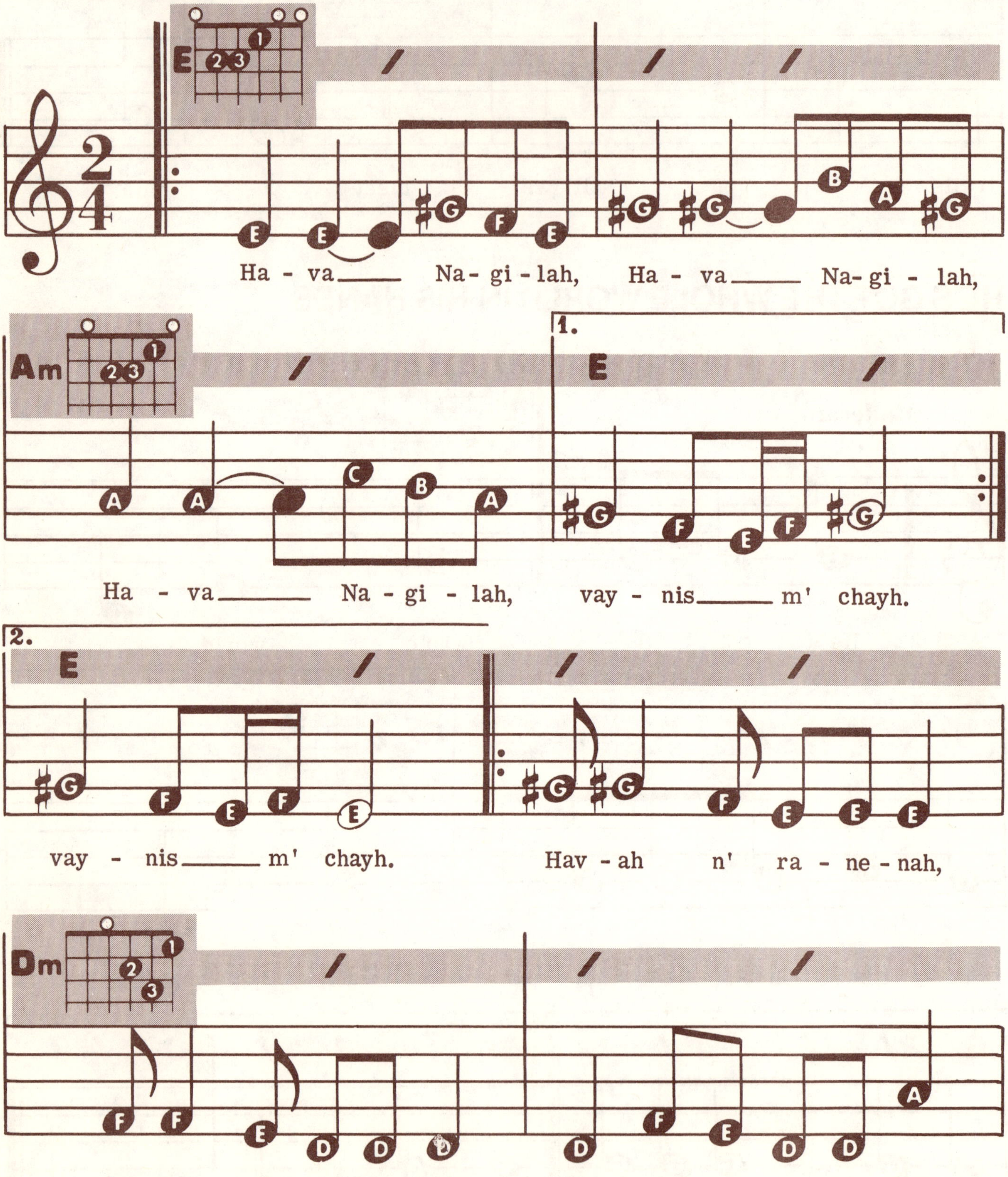

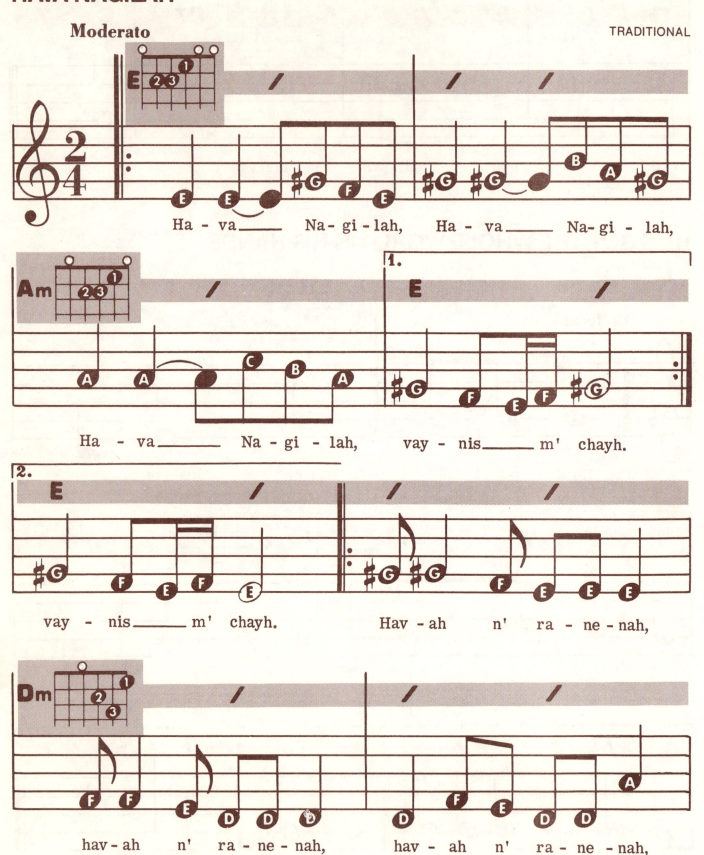

Ha - va____ Na - gi -lah, Ha - va____ Na - gi - lah,

Ha - va____ Na - gi - lah, vay - nis____ m' chayh.

vay - nis____ m' chayh. Hav - ah n' ra - ne - nah,

hav - ah n' ra - ne - nah, hav - ah n' ra - ne - nah,

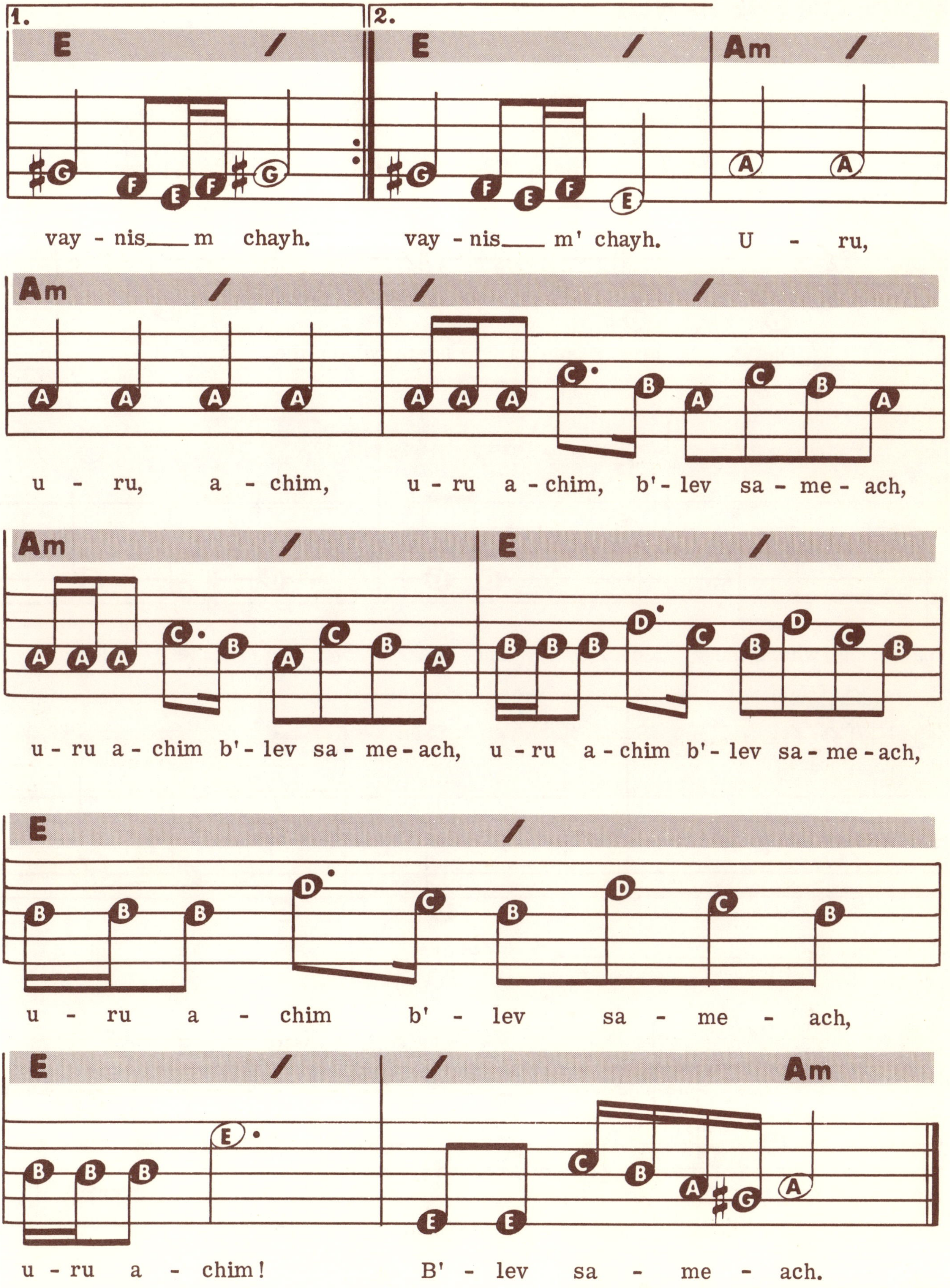

Hava Nagilah-2-2

1.
E
E
Am
vay - nis___ m chayh.
vay - nis___ m' chayh.
U - ru,
Am
u - ru, a - chim,
u - ru a - chim, b'- lev sa - me - ach,
Am
E
u - ru a - chim b'- lev sa - me - ach,
u - ru a - chim b'- lev sa - me - ach,
E
u - ru a - chim b' - lev sa - me - ach,
E
Am
u - ru a - chim!
B' - lev sa - me - ach.

# HOME ON THE RANGE

FOLK SONG

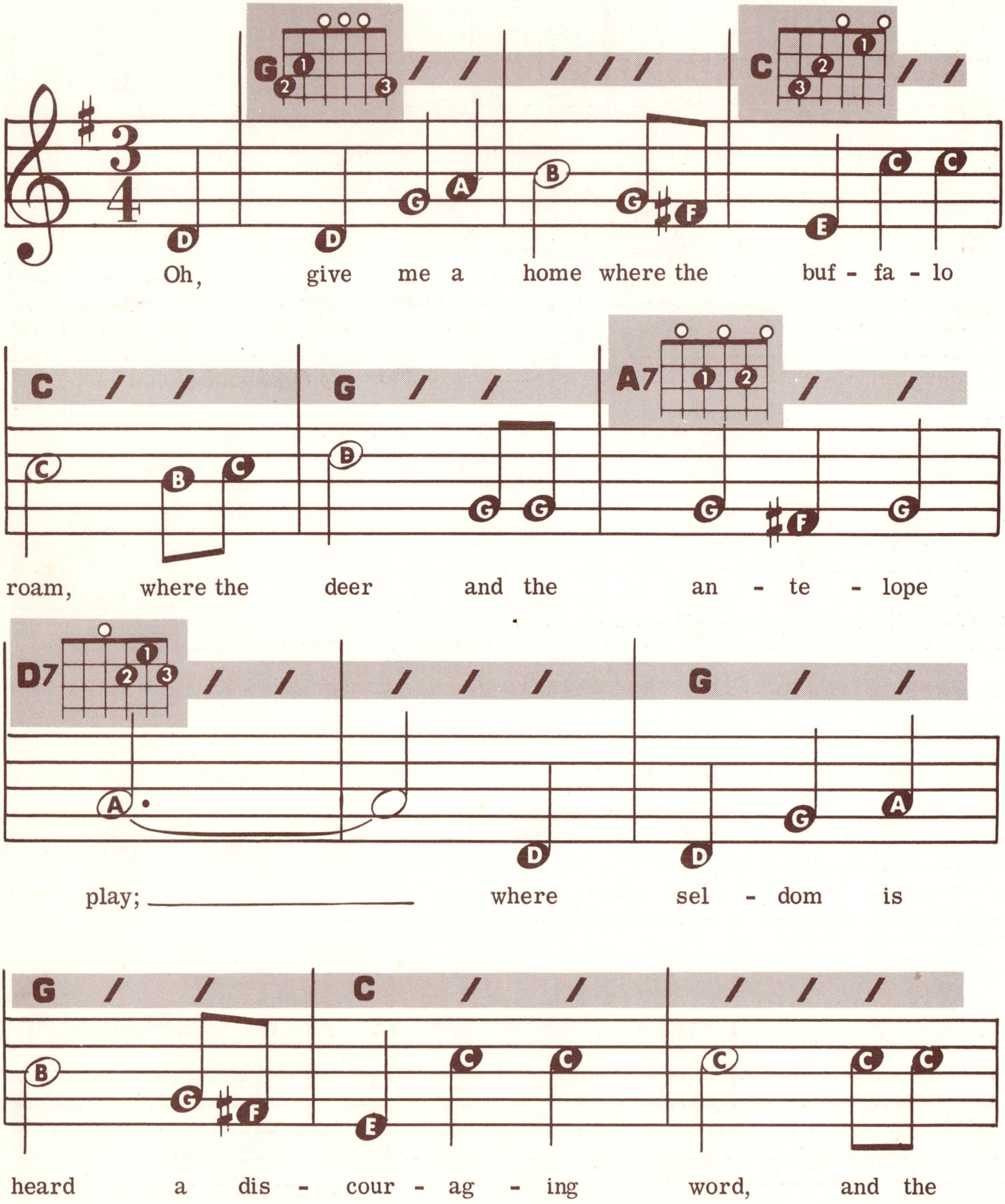

Oh, give me a home where the buf-fa-lo roam, where the deer and the an-te-lope play; _____ where sel-dom is heard a dis-cour-ag-ing word, and the

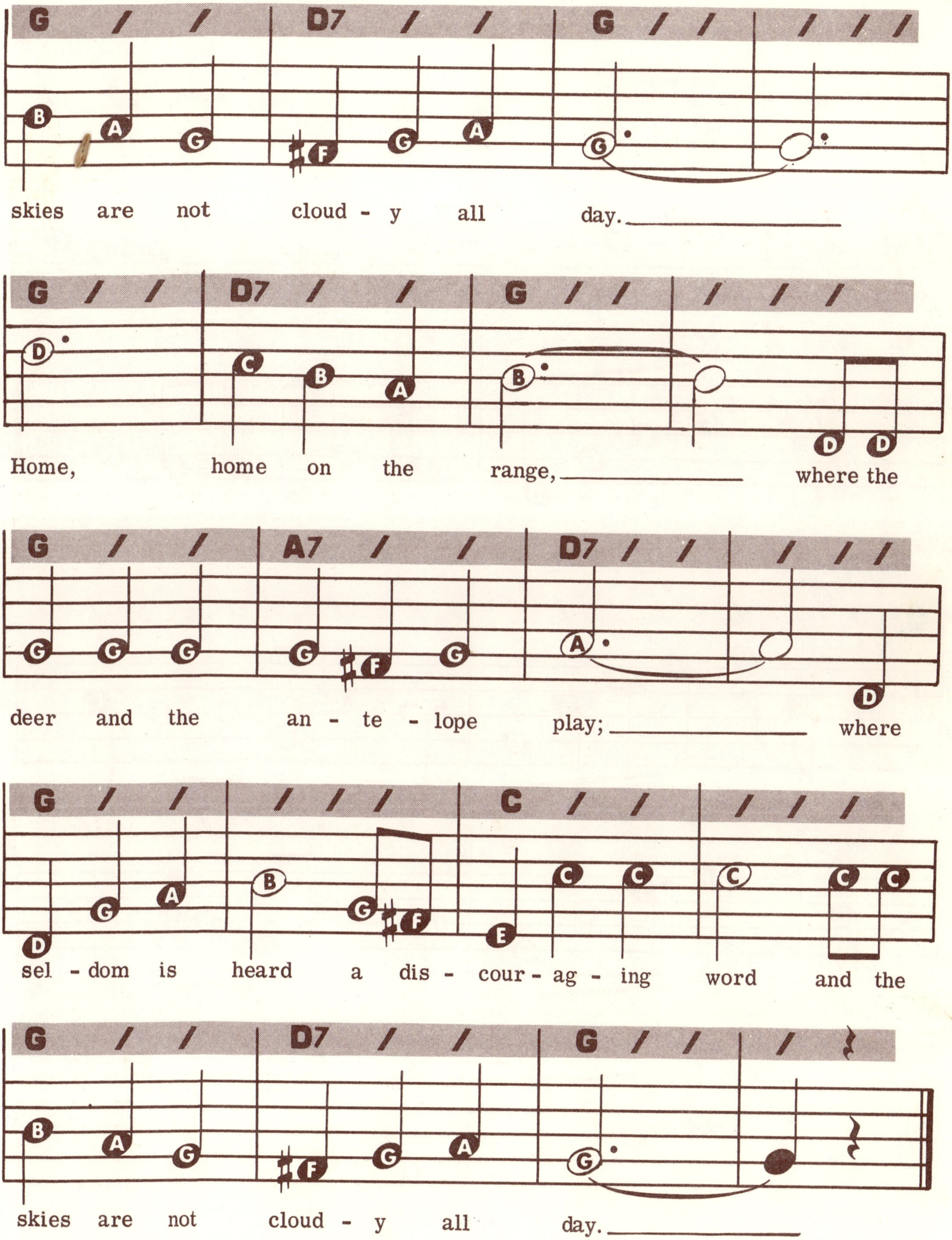

skies    are    not    cloud - y    all    day._____

Home,    home    on    the    range,_____    where the

deer    and    the    an - te - lope    play;_____    where

sel - dom    is    heard    a    dis - cour - ag - ing    word    and the

skies    are    not    cloud - y    all    day._____

Home On The Range -2 -2

# HOOKINIT

By ROY CLARK

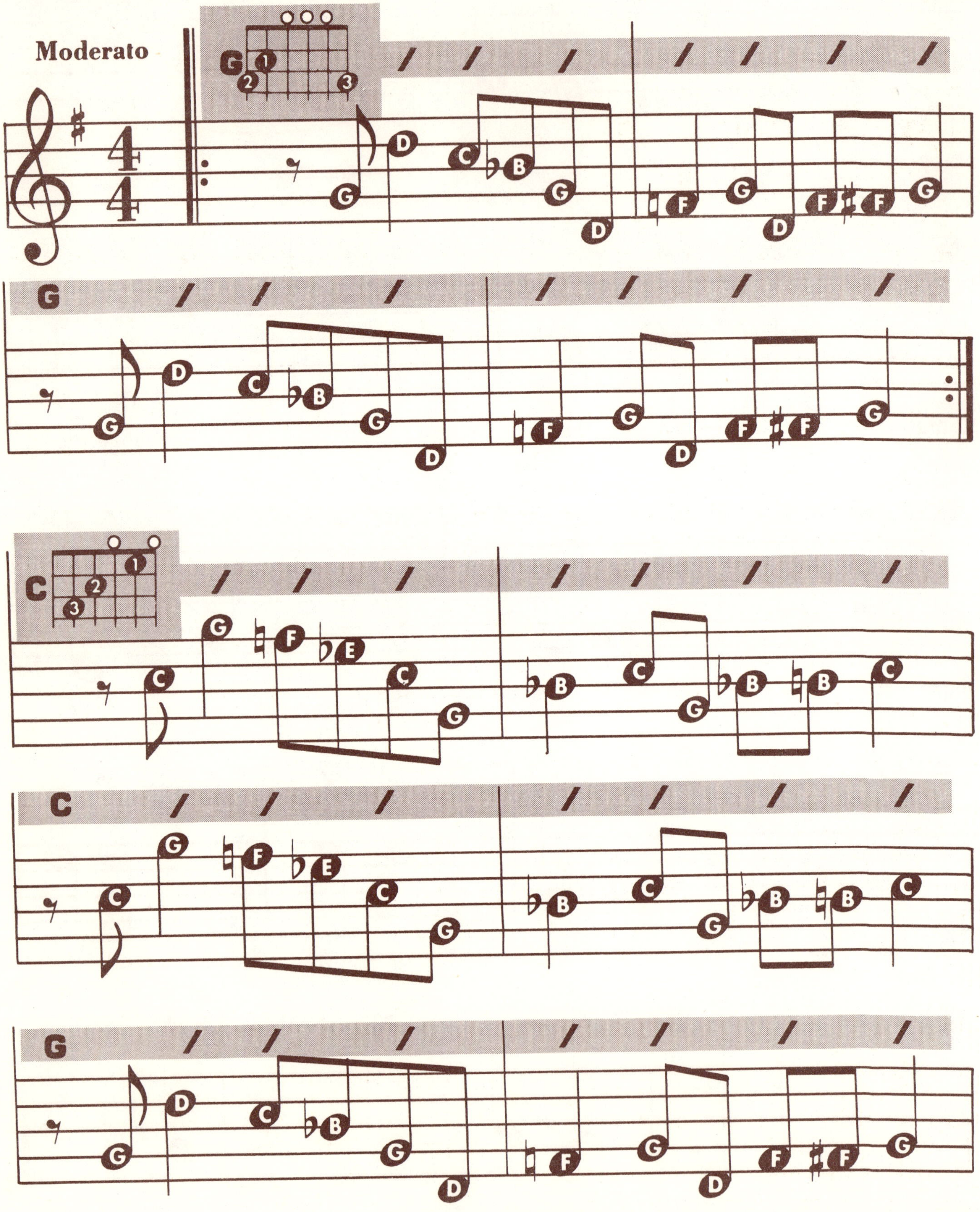

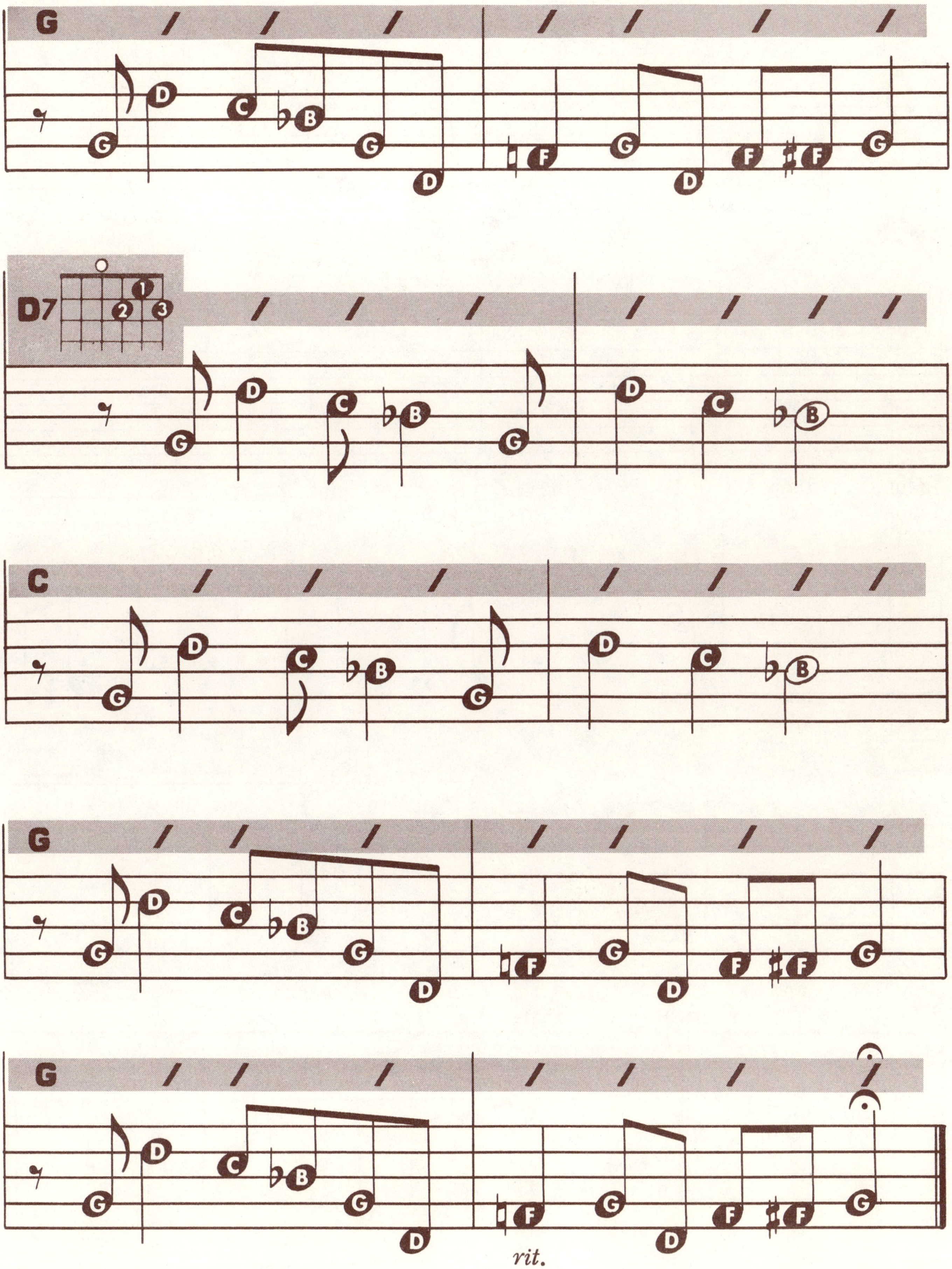

*rit.*

Hookinit-2-2

# THE HOUSE OF THE RISING SUN

TRADITIONAL

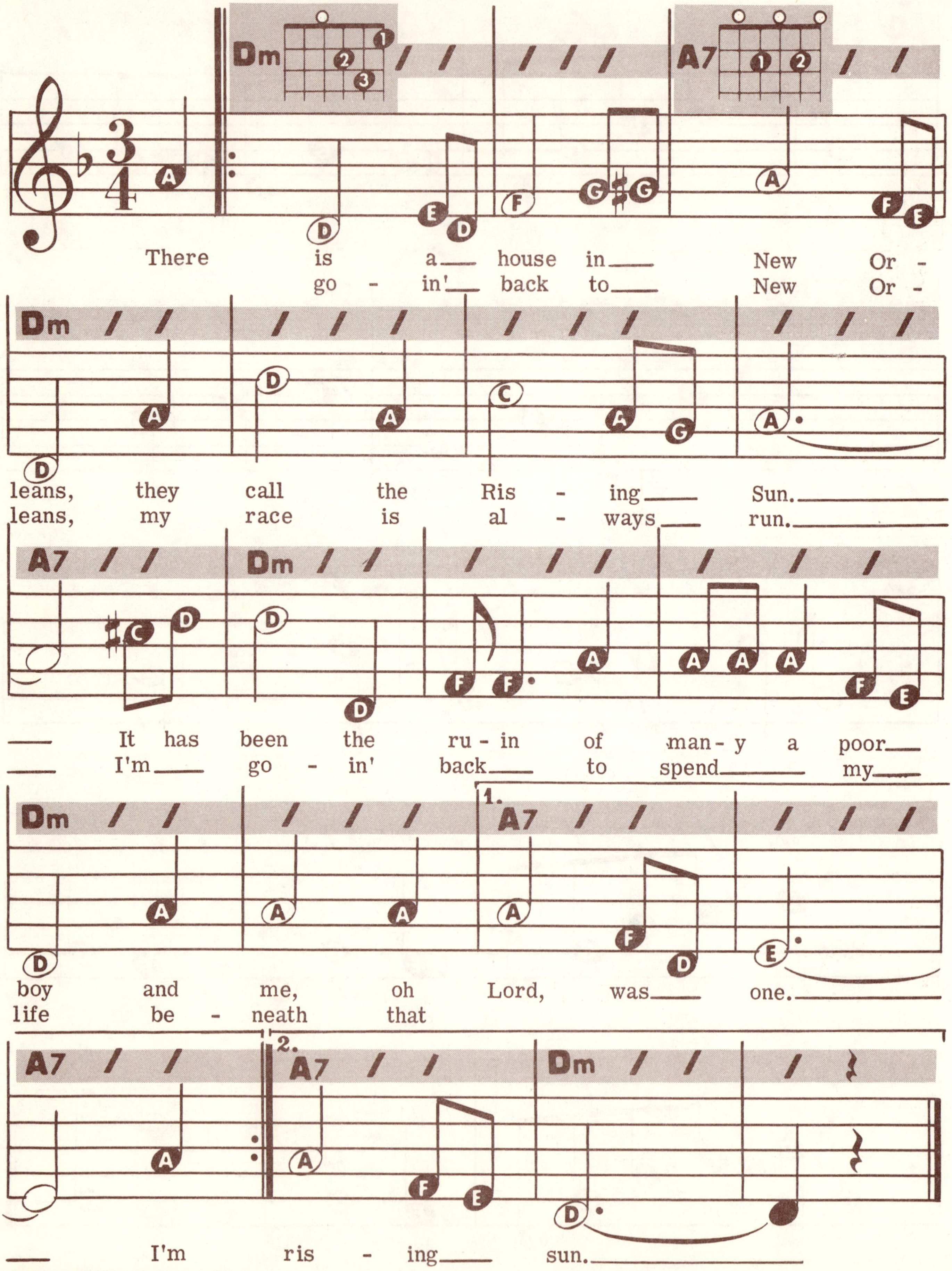

There is a_____ house in_____ New Or -
go - in'_____ back to_____ New Or -

leans, they call the Ris - ing_____ Sun._____
leans, my race is al - ways_____ run._____

_____ It has been the ru - in of man - y a poor_____
_____ I'm_____ go - in' back_____ to spend_____ my_____

boy and me, oh Lord, was_____ one.
life be - neath oh that

I'm ris - ing_____ sun._____

# I'M SO LONESOME I COULD CRY

By HANK WILLIAMS

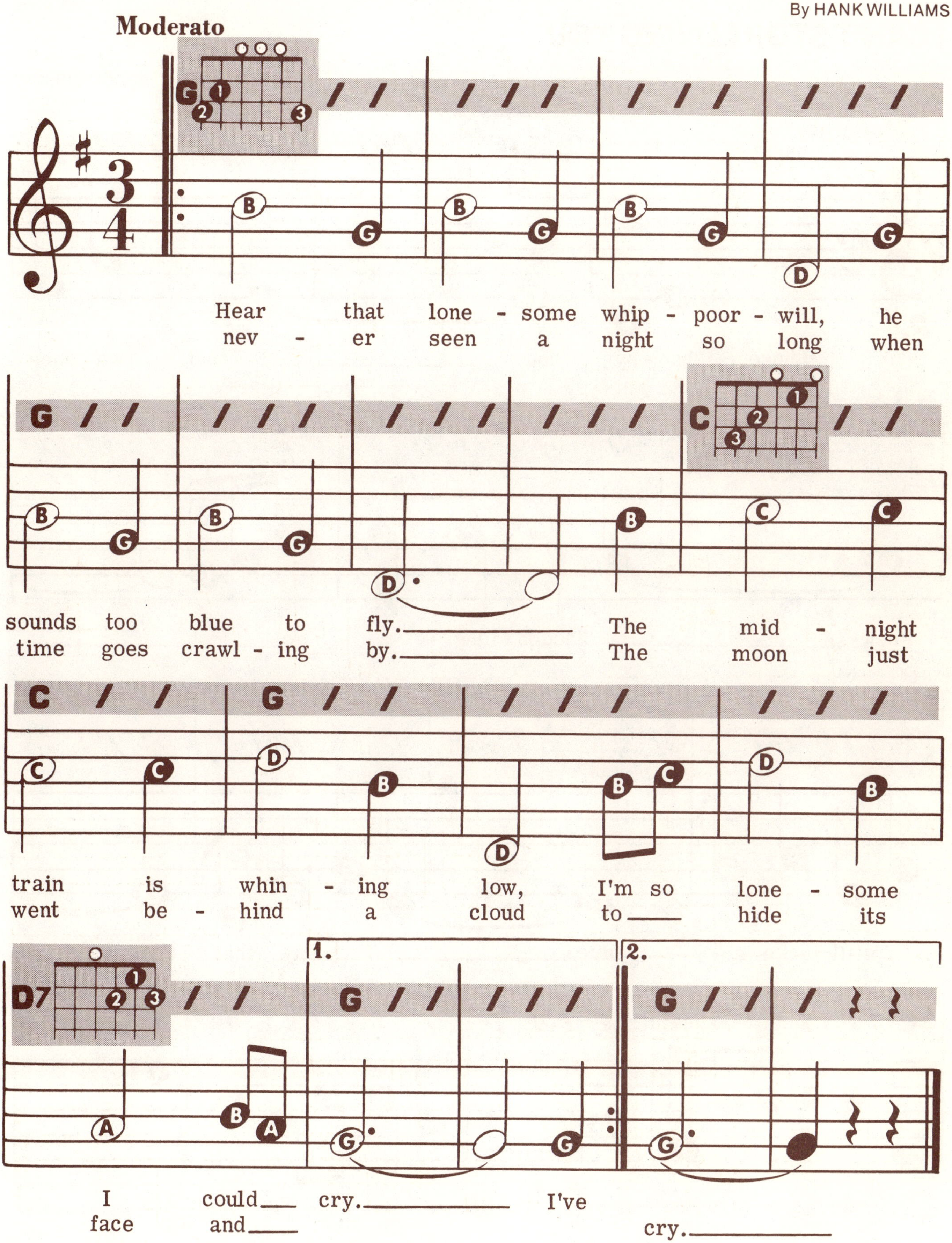

Hear that lone - some whip - poor - will, he
nev - er seen a night so long when

sounds too blue to fly._____ The mid - night
time goes crawl - ing by._____ The moon just

train is whin - ing low, I'm so lone - some
went be - hind a cloud to __ hide its

1.
I could__ cry._____ I've
face and __

2.
cry._____

# I CAN'T STOP LOVING YOU

By DON GIBSON

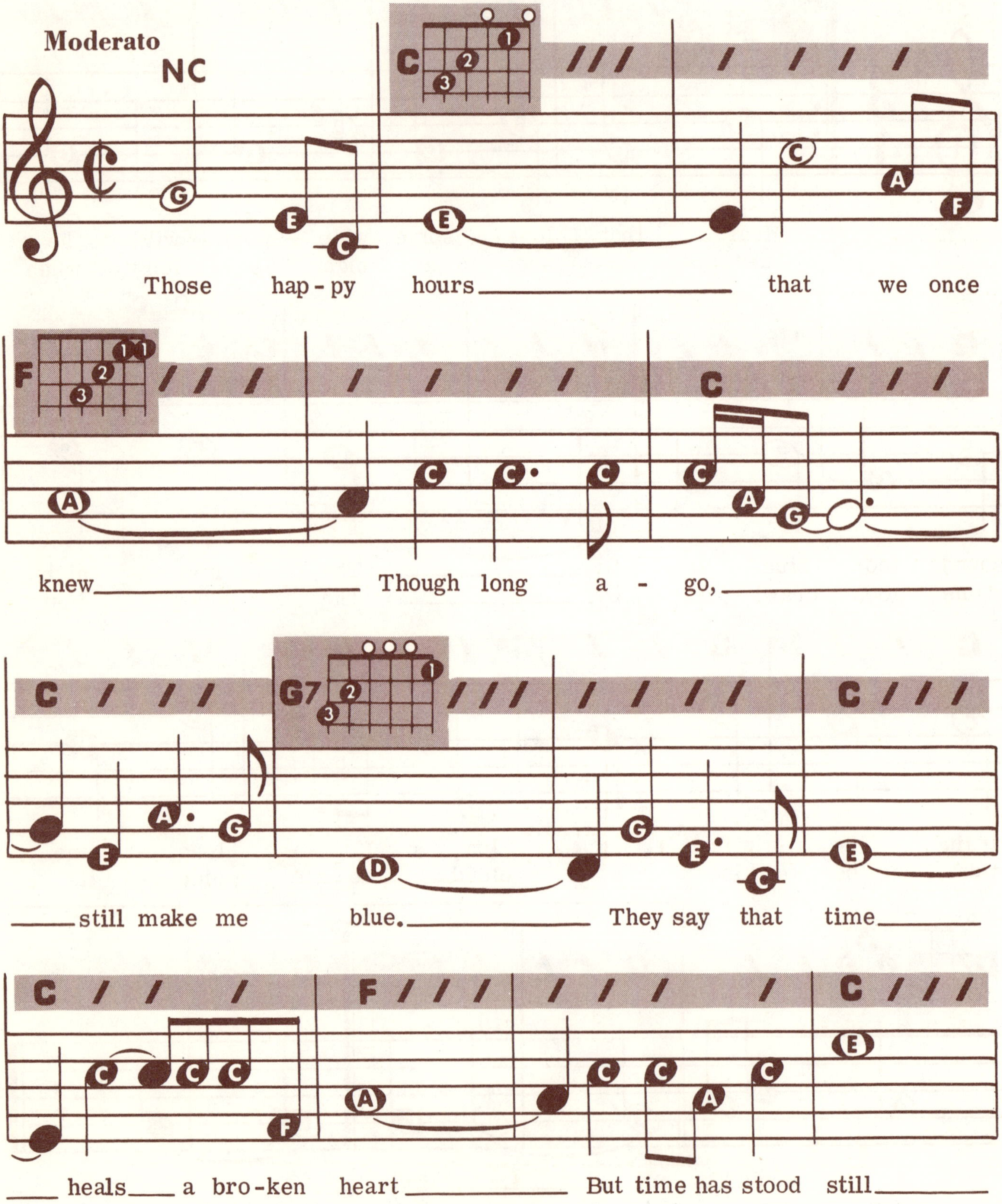

Those hap-py hours _____ that we once knew _____ Though long a - go, _____ still make me blue. _____ They say that time _____ heals ___ a bro-ken heart _____ But time has stood still _____

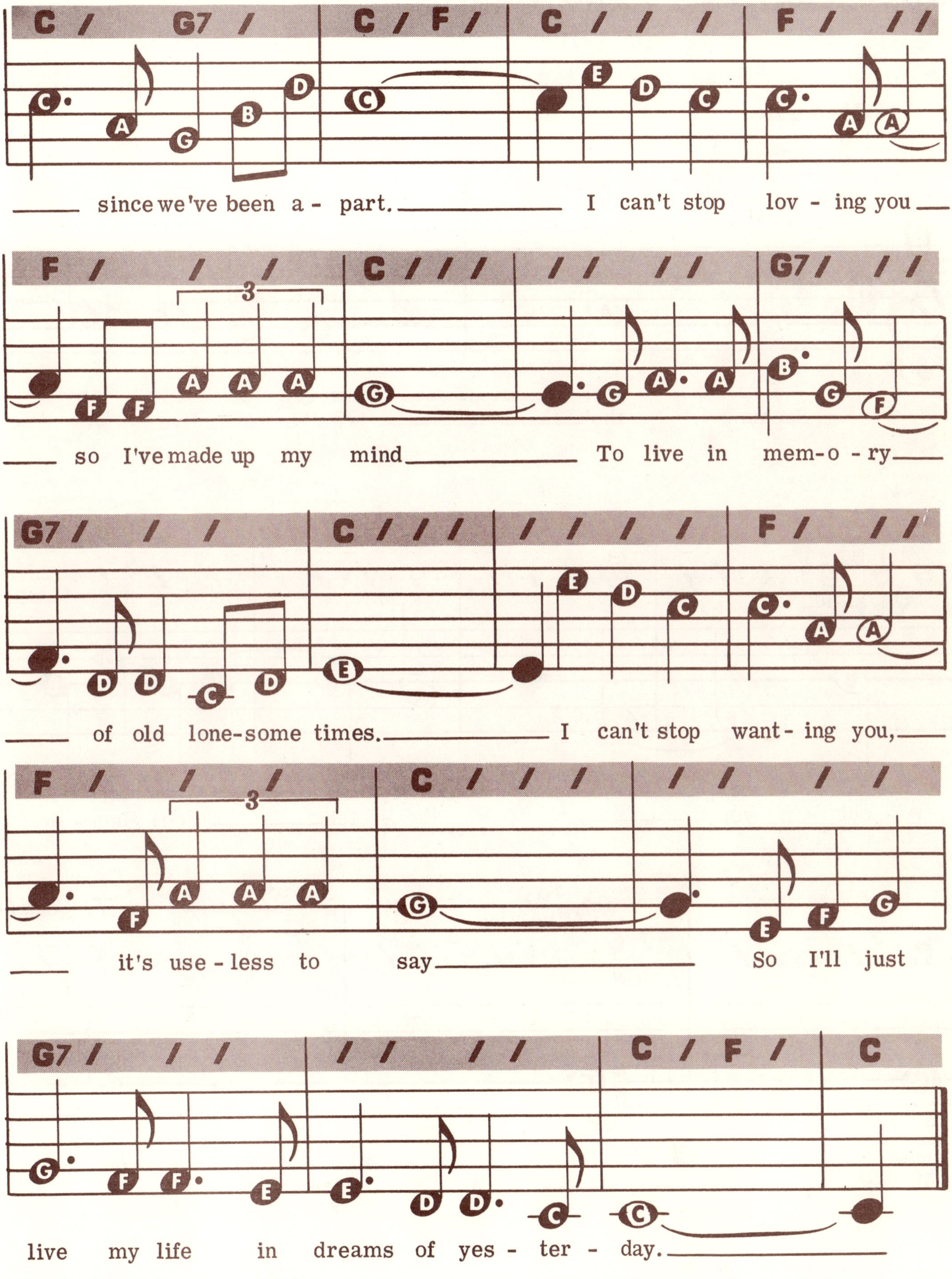
C / G7 / C / F / C / / / F / / /
since we've been a - part. I can't stop lov - ing you
F / / / C / / / / / / / G7 / / /
so I've made up my mind To live in mem-o - ry
G7 / / / C / / / / / / / F / / /
of old lone-some times. I can't stop want - ing you,
F / / / C / / / / / / /
it's use - less to say So I'll just
G7 / / / / / / / C / F / C
live my life in dreams of yes - ter - day.

# IDA, SWEET AS APPLE CIDER

By EDDIE LEONARD and
EDDIE MUNSON

**Moderato**

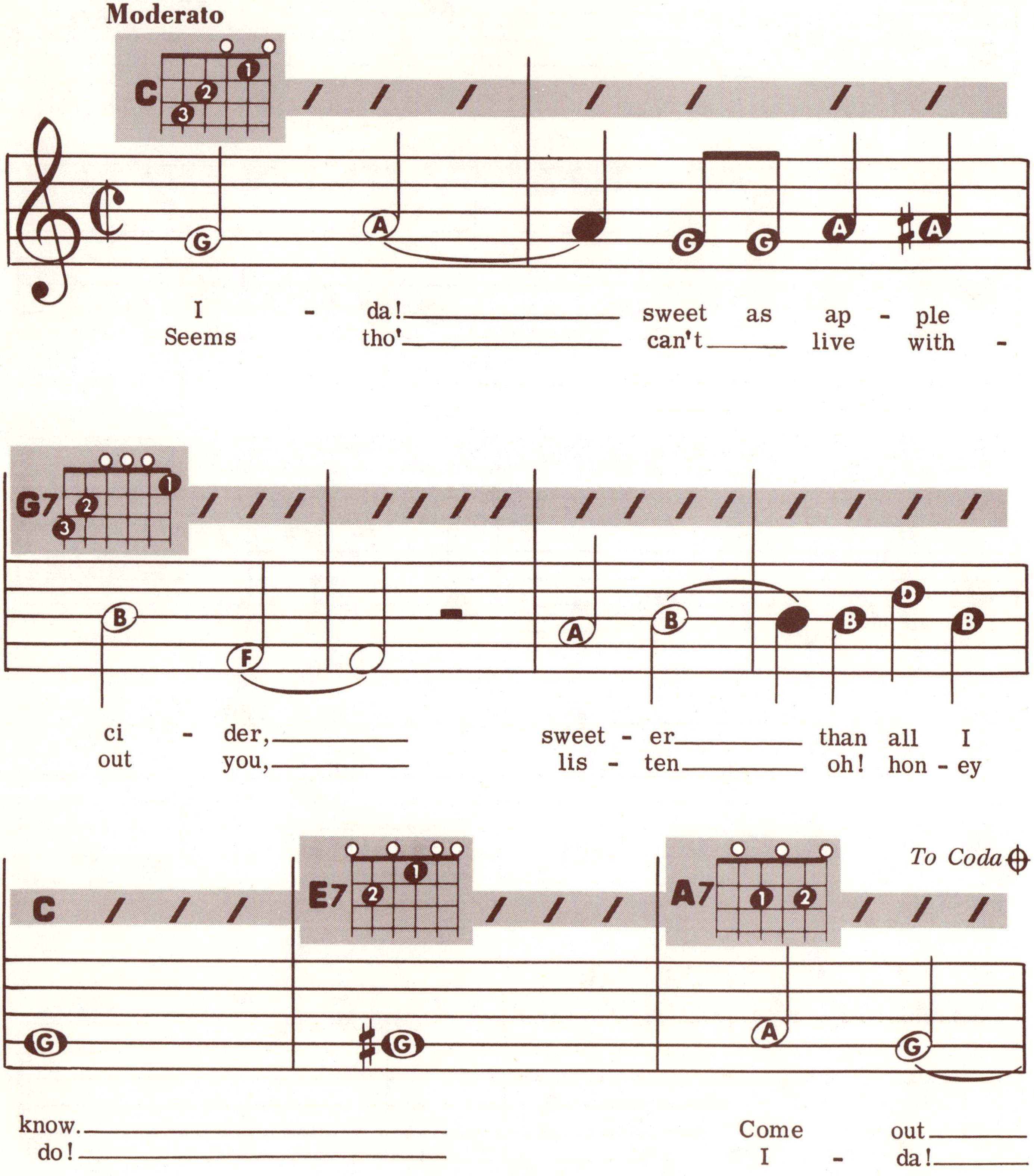

I - da!_____ sweet as ap - ple
Seems tho'_____ can't____ live with -

ci - der,_____ sweet - er_____ than all I
out you,_____ lis - ten_____ oh! hon - ey

know._____
do!_____

Come out_____
I - da!_____

*To Coda* ⊕

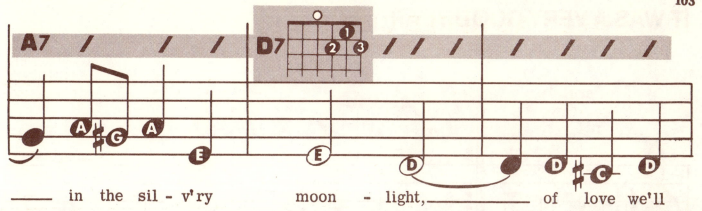

in the sil - v'ry moon - light,_____ of love we'll

D.C. al ⊕ Coda

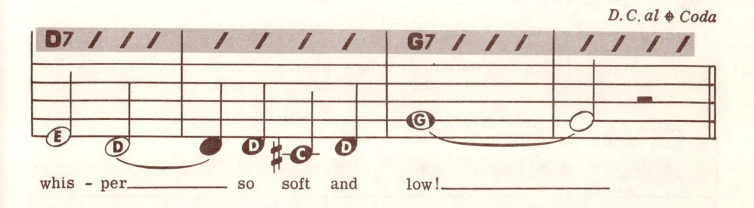

whis - per_____ so soft and low!_____

⊕ Coda

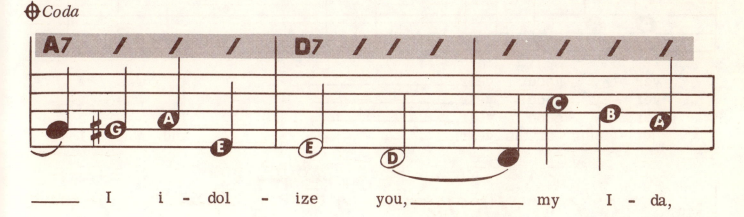

I i - dol - ize you,_____ my I - da,

love you, hon - ey, deed I do._____

Ida, Sweet As Apple Cider-2-2

# IT WAS A VERY GOOD YEAR

Words and Music by
ERVIN DRAKE

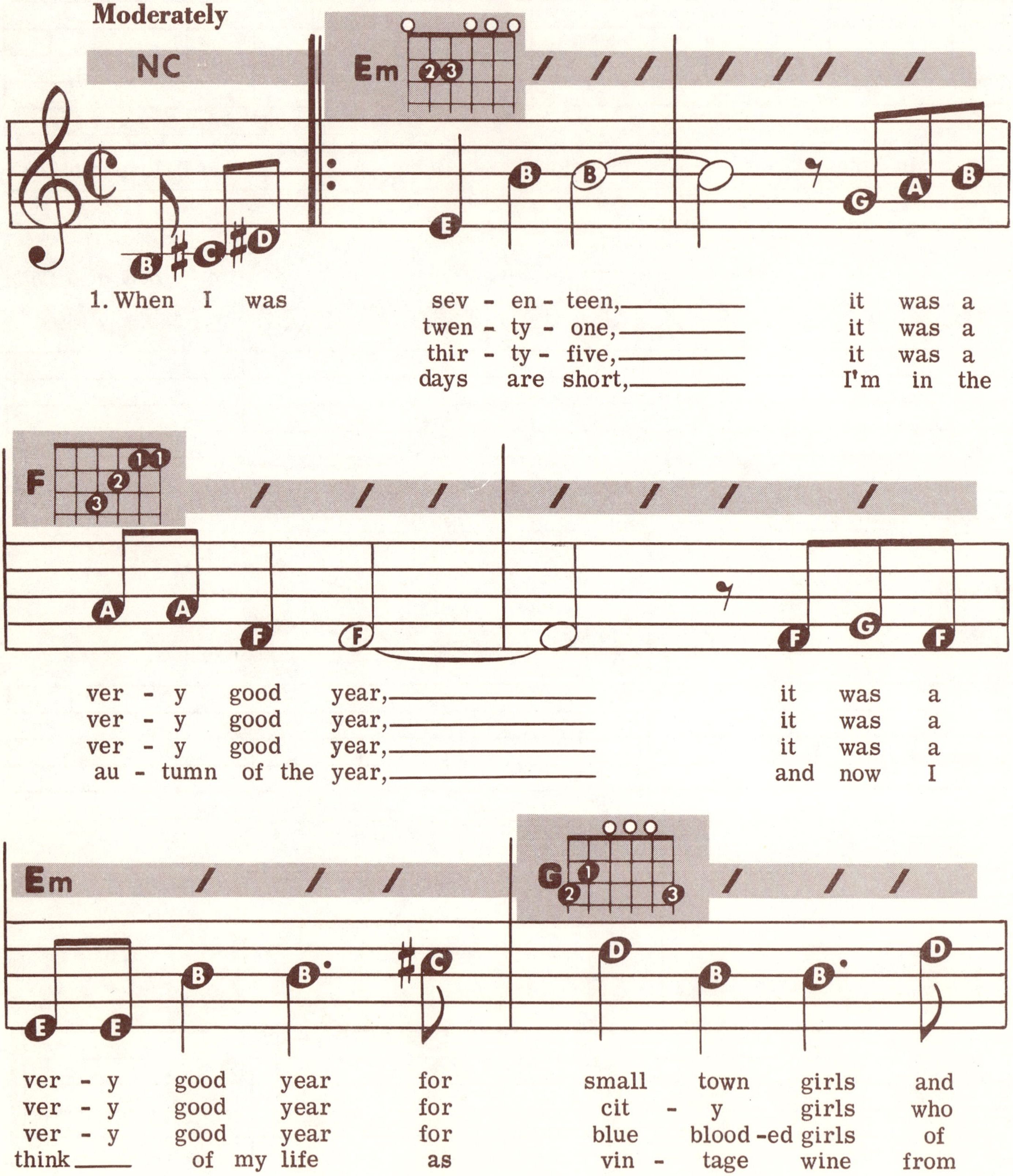

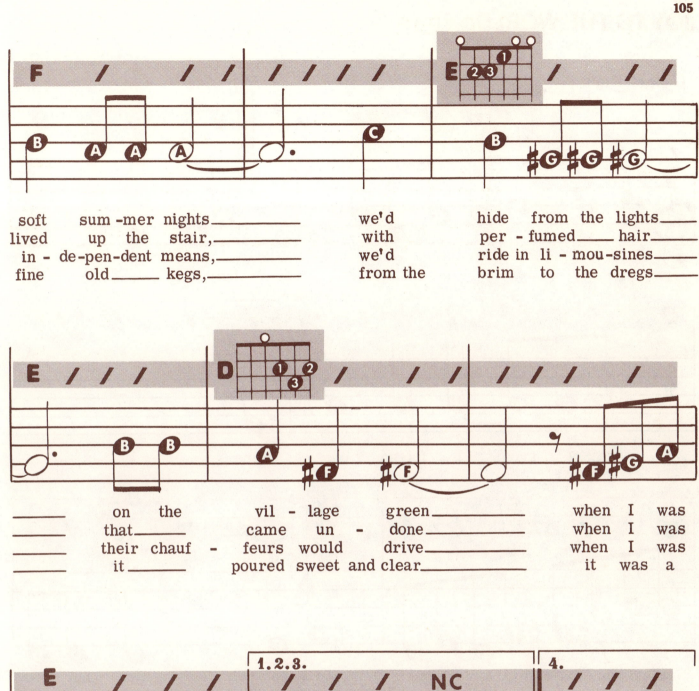

soft    sum-mer nights_____    we'd    hide  from the lights____
lived    up   the   stair,_____    with    per-fumed____ hair____
in-de-pen-dent means,_____    we'd    ride in li-mou-sines____
fine    old____ kegs,_____    from the   brim   to the dregs____

_____    on    the    vil-lage    green_____    when  I  was
_____ that____    came  un-done_____    when  I  was
_____ their chauf-feurs would    drive_____    when  I  was
_____ it____    poured sweet and clear_____    it  was  a

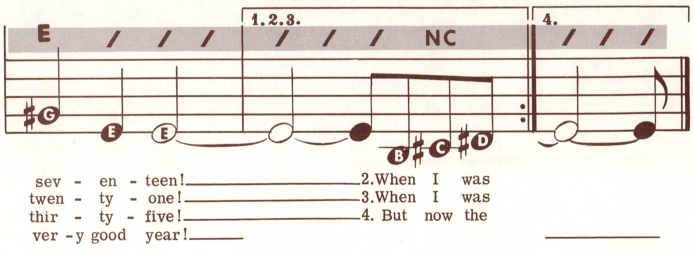

sev - en - teen!_____    2. When  I  was
twen - ty - one!_____    3. When  I  was
thir - ty - five!_____    4. But  now  the
ver -y good  year!_____

It Was A Very Good Year-2-2

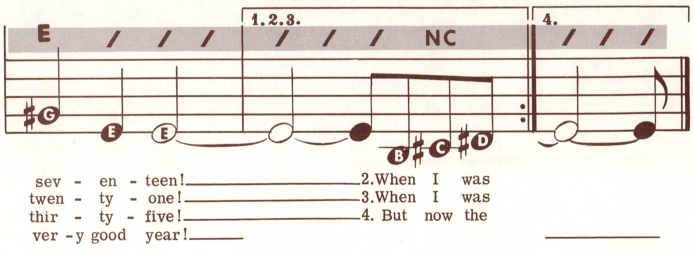

# JOY TO THE WORLD

Words and Music by HOYT AXTON

1. Jer - e - mi - ah was a bull frog____

was a good____ friend of mine.

Nev-er un-der-stood a sin-gle word he said, but I

helped him a - drink - in' his wine. Yes, he

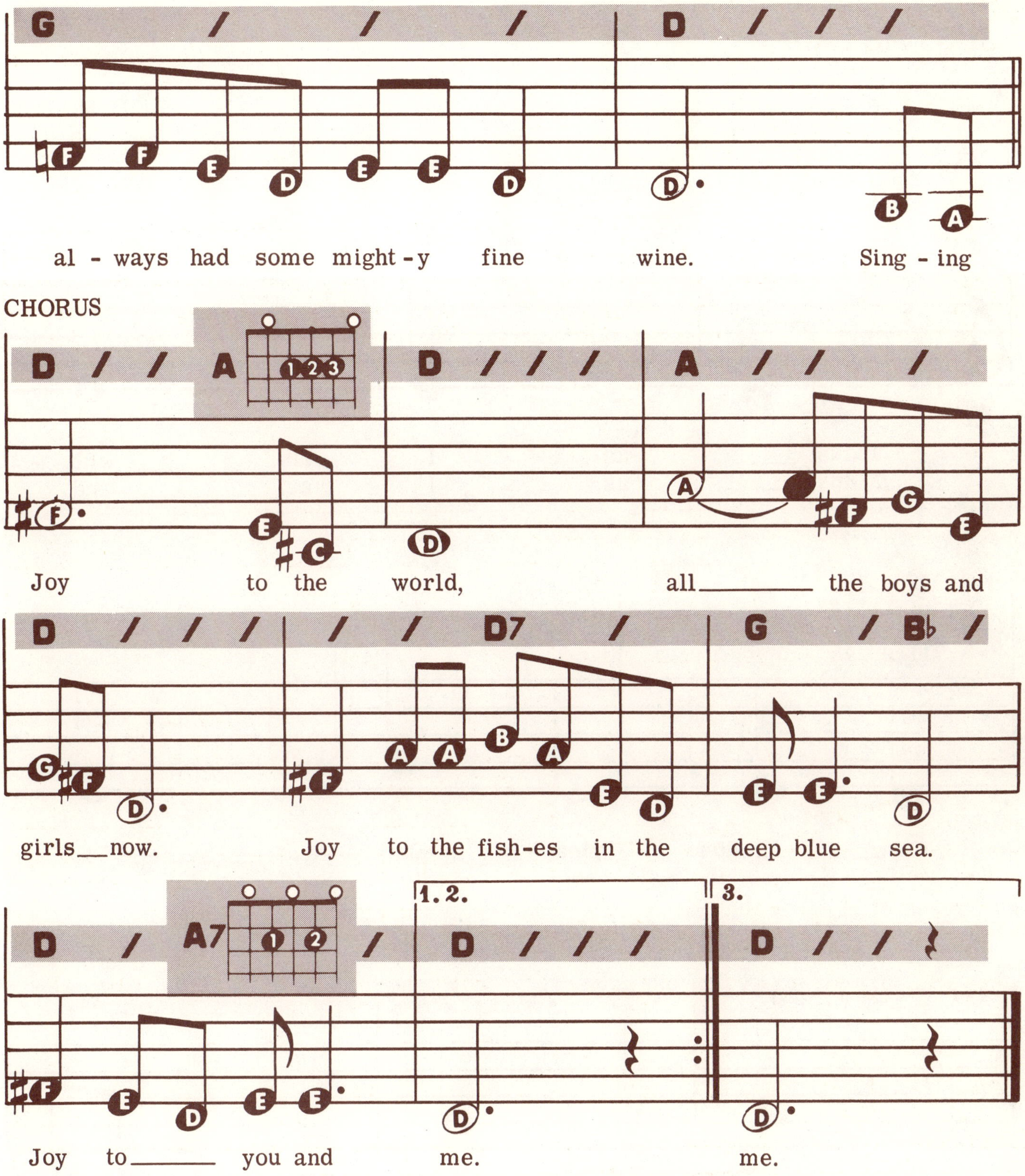

al - ways had some might -y fine wine. Sing - ing

CHORUS

Joy to the world, all_____ the boys and

girls___now. Joy to the fish-es in the deep blue sea.

Joy to_____ you and me. me.

**2.**
If I were the king of the world
Tell you what I'd do.
Throw away the cars and the bars and the wars,
And make sweet love to you.
Yes I'll make sweet love to you. Singing
*(To Chorus)*

**3.**
You know I love the ladies
Love to have my fun.
I'm a high night flyer and a rainbow rider,
A straight shootin' son of a gun.
Yes a straight shootin' son of a gun. Singing
*(To Chorus)*

Joy To The World-2-2

# JUST AS I AM

ELIOTT - BRADBURY

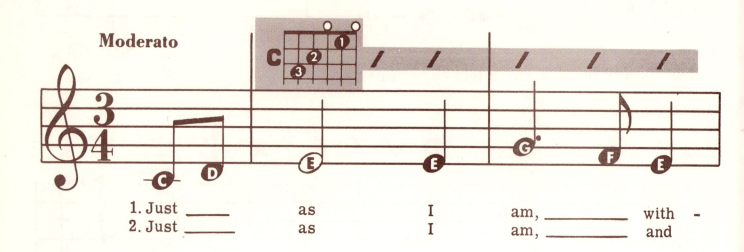

1. Just _____ as I am, _____ with -
2. Just _____ as I am, _____ and

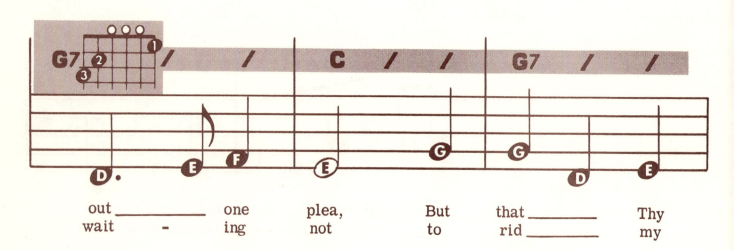

out _____ one plea, But that _____ Thy
wait - ing not to rid _____ my

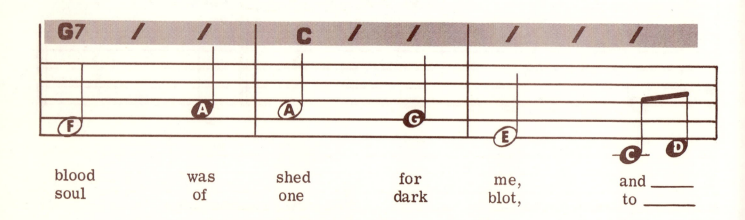

blood was shed for me, and _____
soul of one dark blot, to _____

109

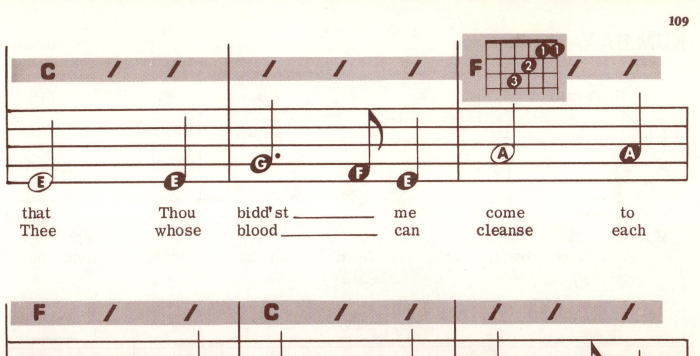

that     Thou   bidd'st _____ me   come   to
Thee   whose   blood _____ can   cleanse   each

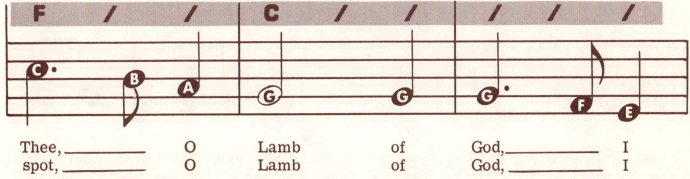

Thee, _____ O   Lamb   of   God, _____ I
spot, _____ O   Lamb   of   God, _____ I

come,    I    come! _____
come,    I    come! _____    O

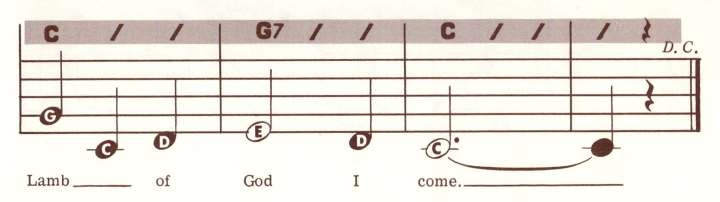

Lamb _____ of   God   I   come. _____

*D. C.*

Just As I Am -2 -2

# KUM BA YAH

TRADITIONAL

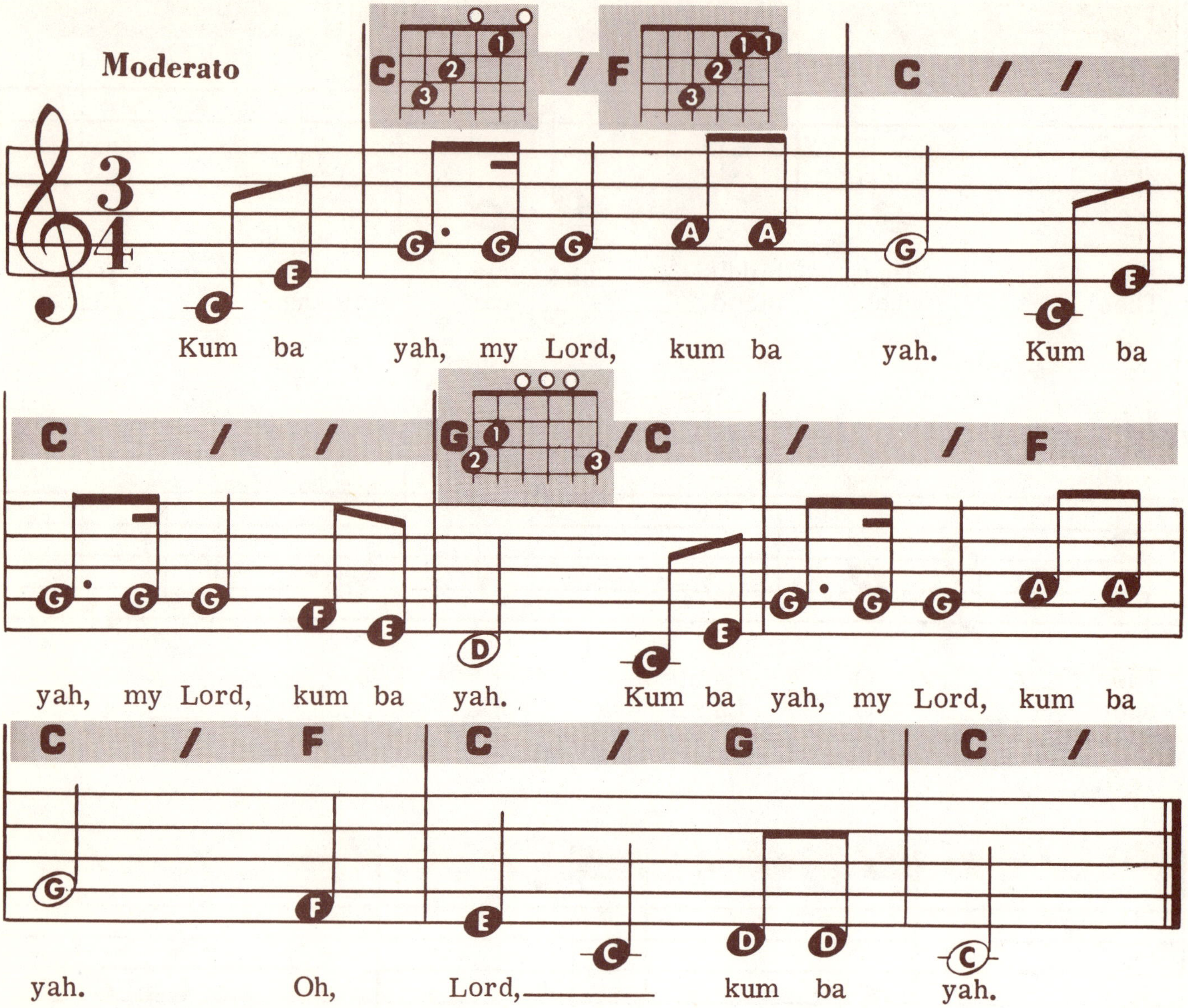

Moderato

Kum ba yah, my Lord, kum ba yah. Kum ba
yah, my Lord, kum ba yah. Kum ba yah, my Lord, kum ba
yah. Oh, Lord, _____ kum ba yah.

# LITTLE BROWN JUG

TRADITIONAL

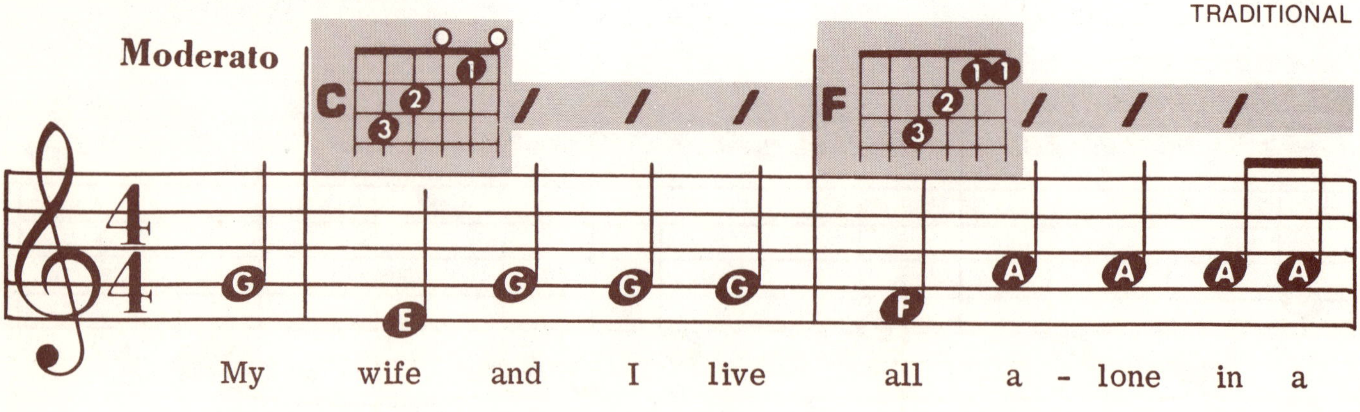

Moderato

My wife and I live all a - lone in a

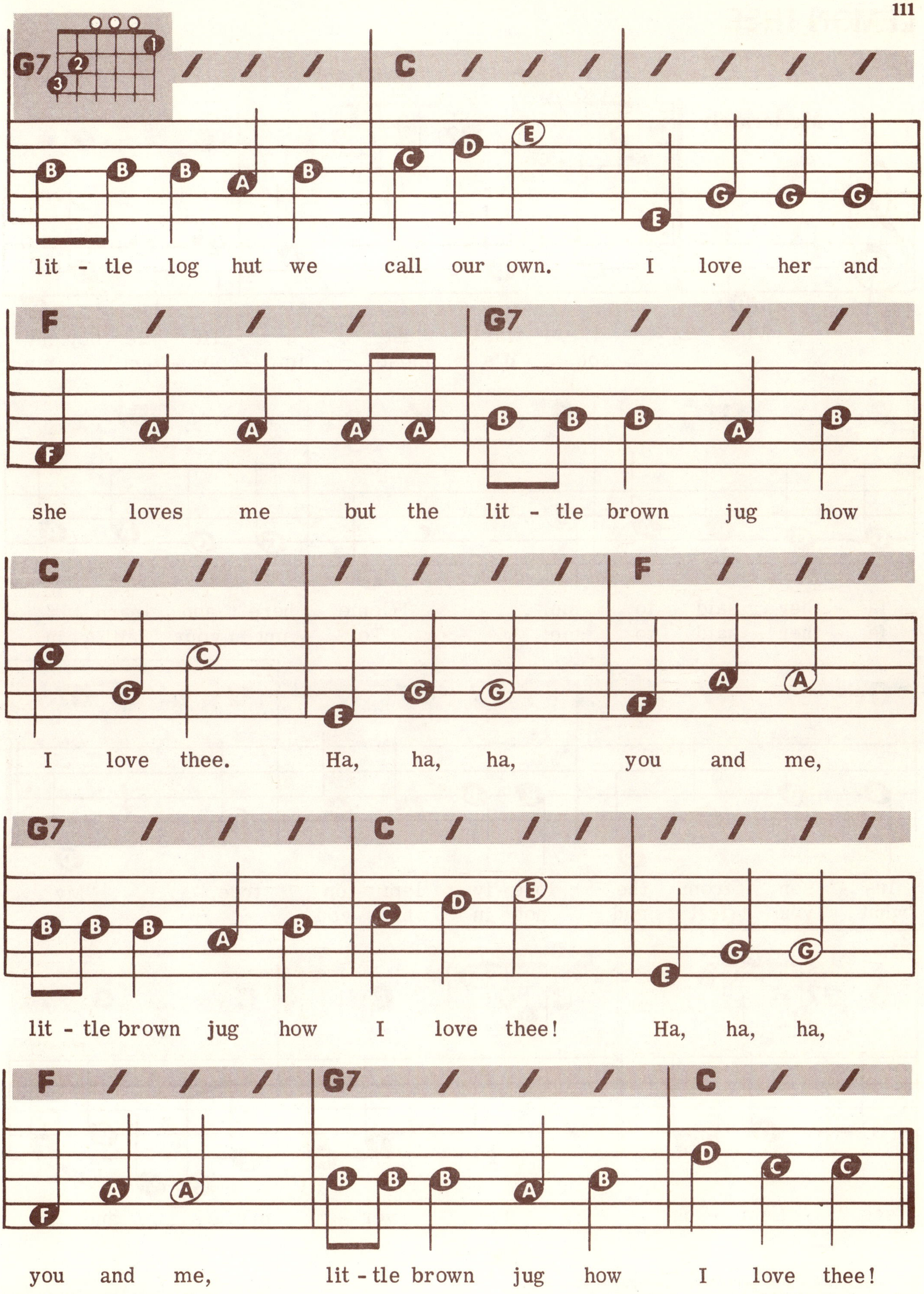

Little Brown Jug-2-2

# LEMON TREE

By WILL HOLT

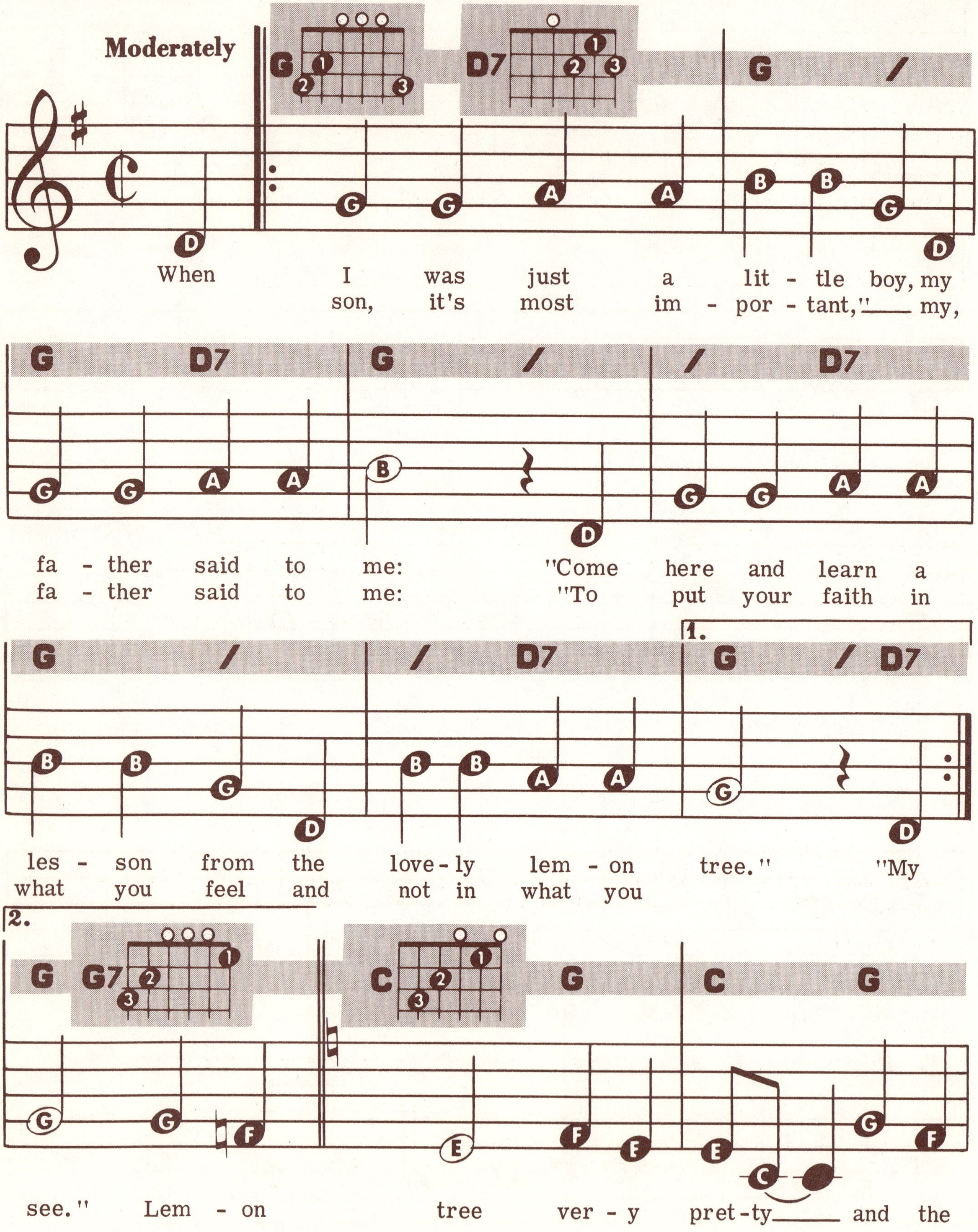

Moderately

When I was just a lit-tle boy, my
son, it's just most im-por-tant," my,

fa-ther said to me: "Come here and learn a
fa-ther said to me: "To put your faith in

les-son from the love-ly lem-on tree." "My
what you feel and not in what you

see." Lem-on tree ver-y pret-ty___ and the

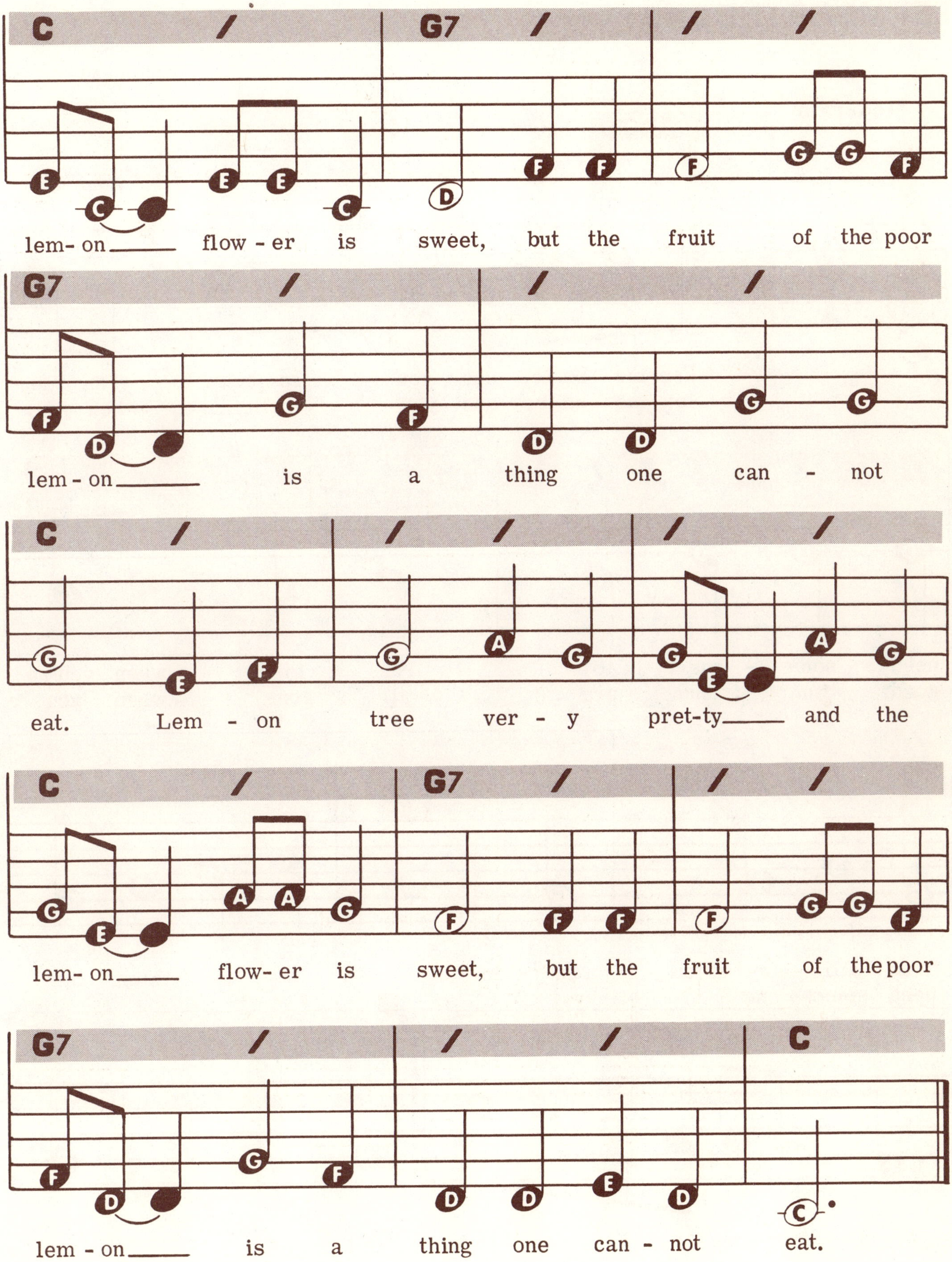
C G7
lem- on flow - er is sweet, but the fruit of the poor
G7
lem - on is a thing one can - not
C
eat. Lem - on tree ver - y pret-ty and the
C G7
lem- on flow- er is sweet, but the fruit of the poor
G7 C
lem - on is a thing one can - not eat.

# LET ME BE THE ONE

By JIMBEAU HINSON

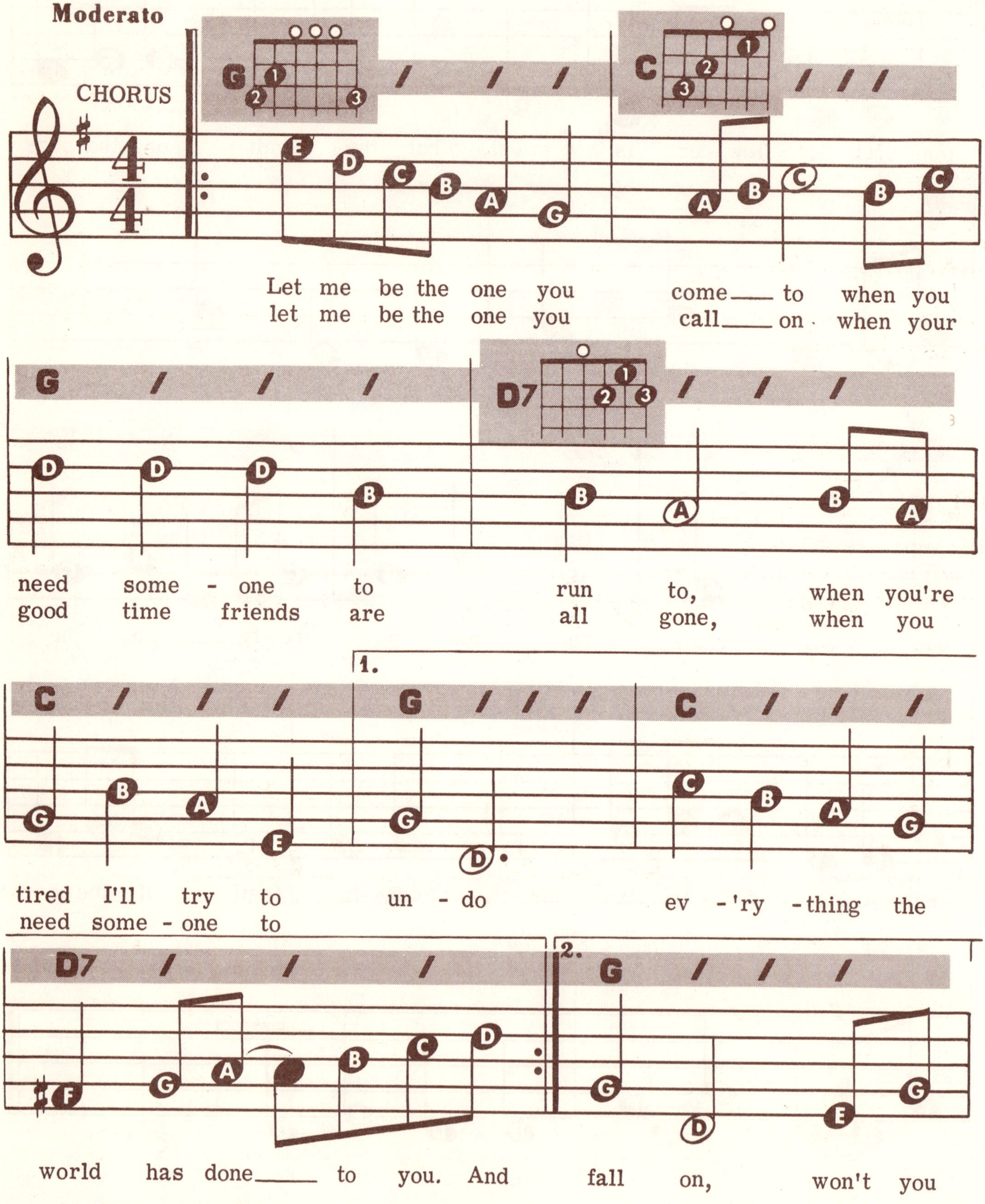

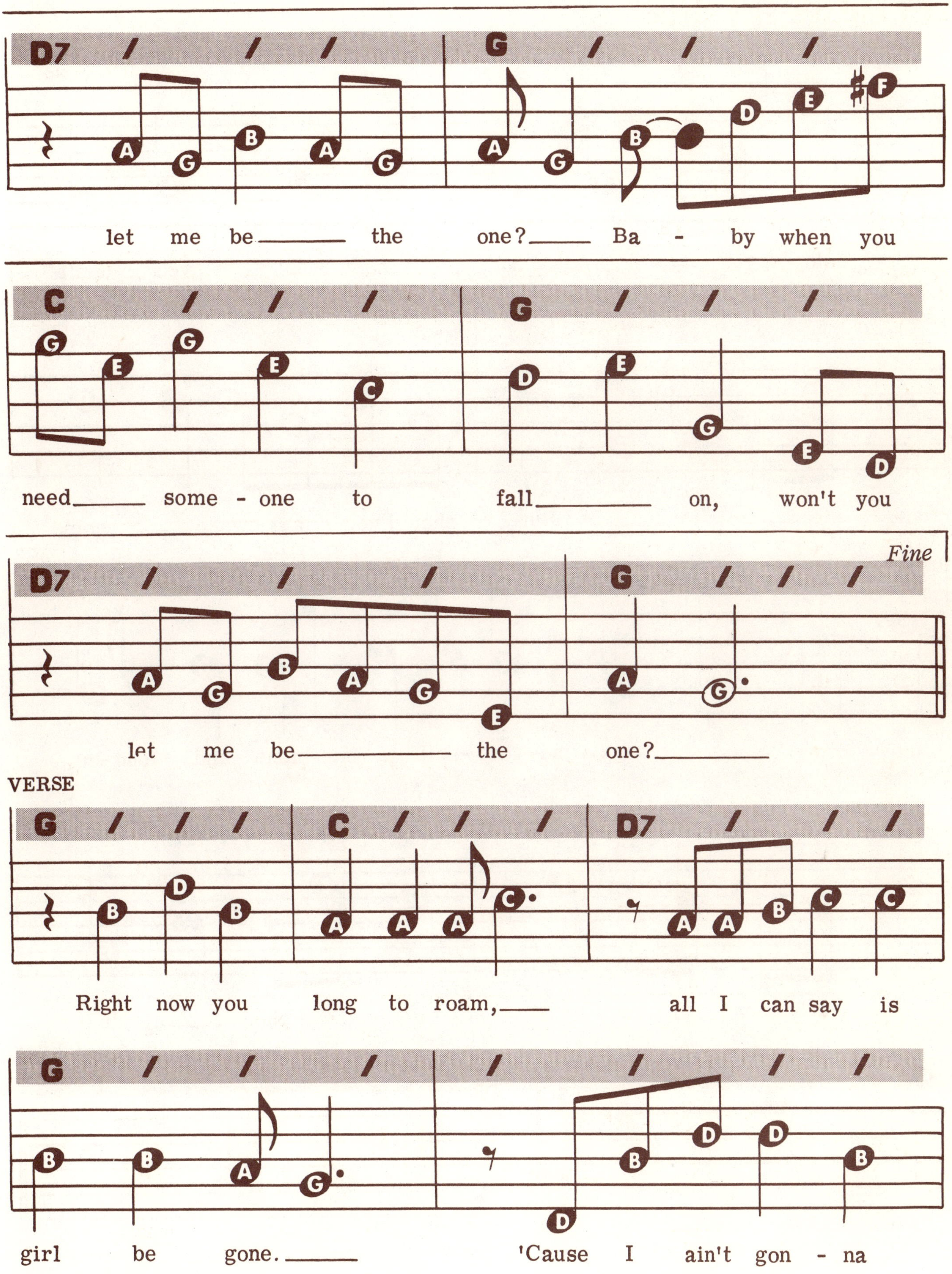
D7 G
let me be the one? Ba - by when you
C G
need some - one to fall on, won't you
D7 G Fine
let me be the one?
VERSE
G C D7
Right now you long to roam, all I can say is
G
girl be gone. 'Cause I ain't gon - na

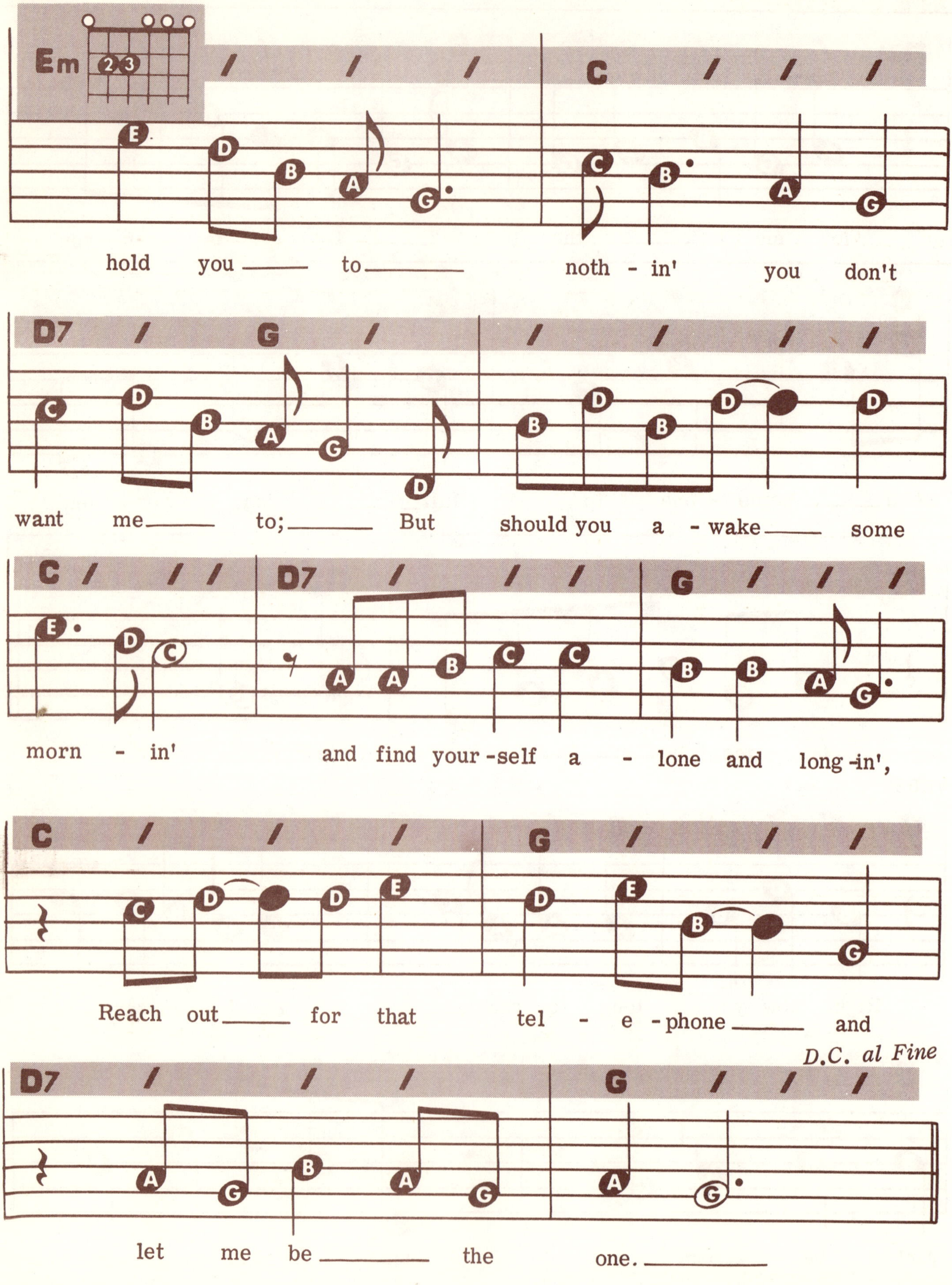
Em
2 3
C
E
D
B
A
G
C
B
A
G
hold you to
noth - in' you don't
D7
G
C
D
B
A
G
D
B
D
B
D
D
want me to; But
should you a - wake some
C
D7
G
E
D
C
A
A
B
C
C
B
B
A
G
morn - in'
and find your - self a - lone and long -in',
C
G
C
D
D
E
D
E
B
G
Reach out for that
tel - e - phone and
D.C. al Fine
D7
G
A
G
B
A
G
A
G
let me be the
one.

# LI'L LIZA JANE

**TRADITIONAL**

**Moderato**

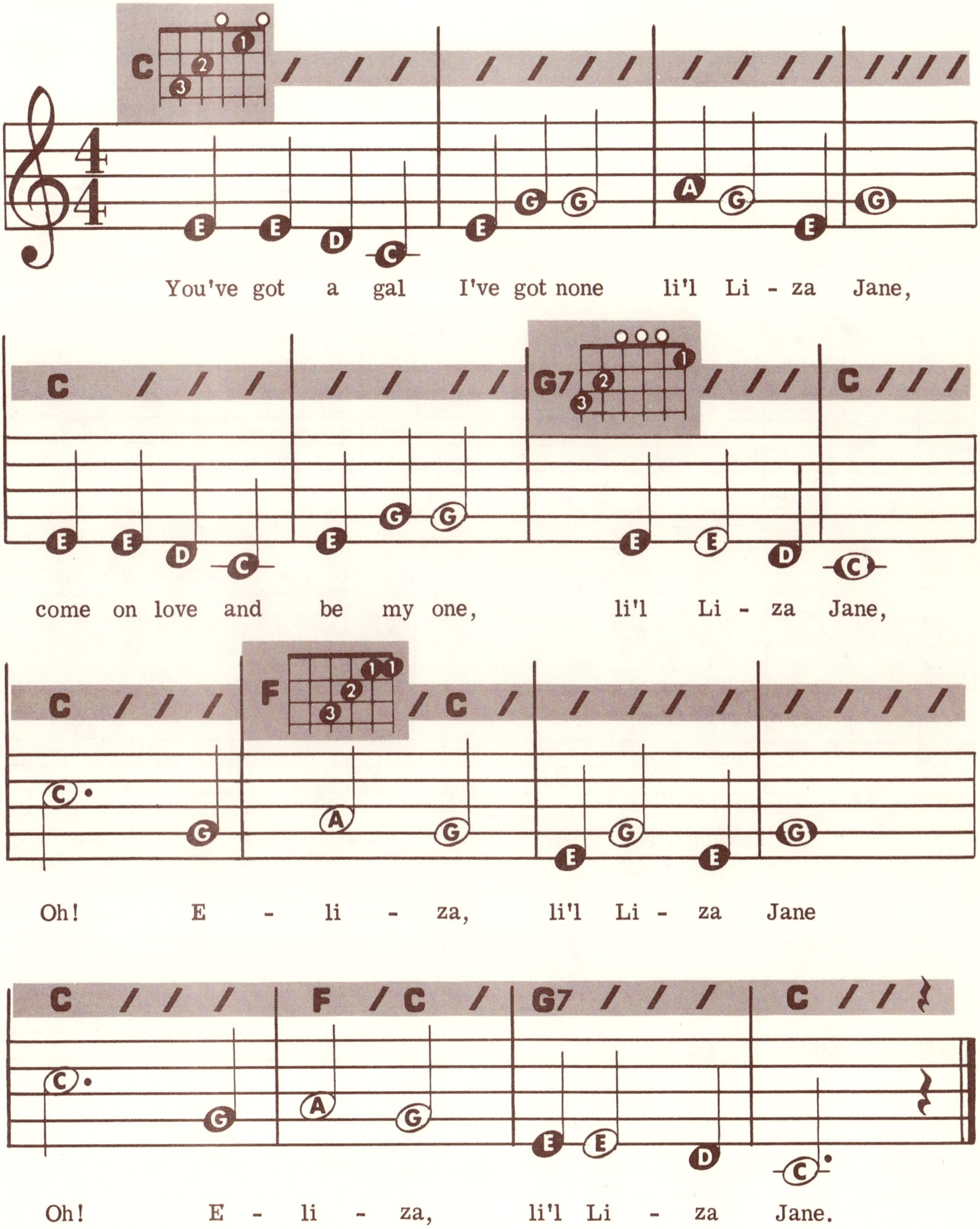

You've got a gal I've got none li'l Li - za Jane,

come on love and be my one, li'l Li - za Jane,

Oh! E - li - za, li'l Li - za Jane

Oh! E - li - za, li'l Li - za Jane.

# (Nothin' Clings To Me)
# LIKE MY MORNIN' GLORY DO

By JIMBEAU HINSON

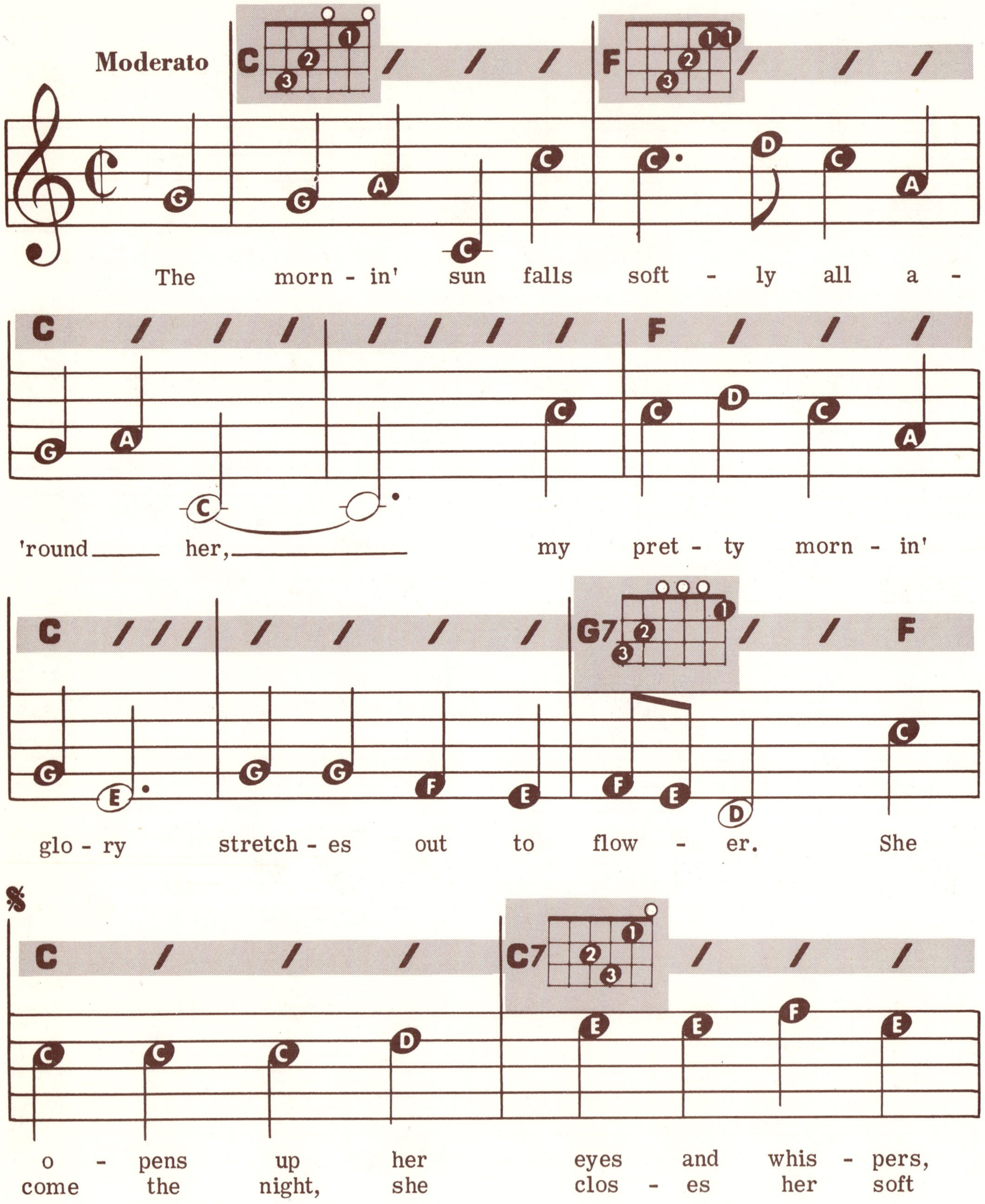

The morn - in' sun falls soft - ly all a - 'round ____ her, ____ my pret - ty morn - in' glo - ry stretch - es out to flow - er. She

o - pens up her eyes and whis - pers,
come the night, she clos - es her soft

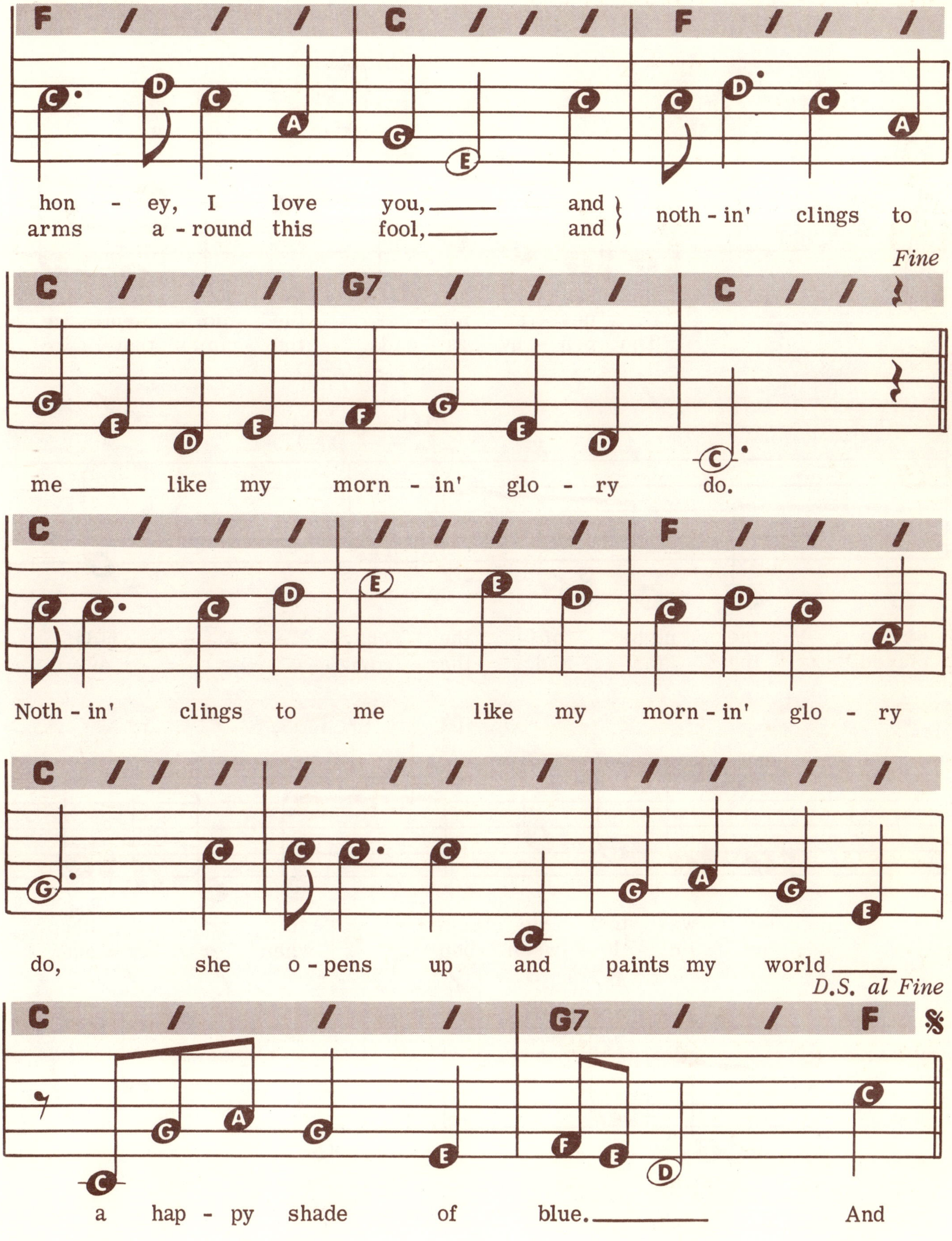
F C F
hon - ey, I love you, and
arms a - round this fool, and
noth - in' clings to
Fine
C G7 C
me like my morn - in' glo - ry do.
C F
Noth - in' clings to me like my morn - in' glo - ry
C
do, she o - pens up and paints my world
D.S. al Fine
C G7 F
a hap - py shade of blue. And

# MAGIC MOMENTS

By HAL DAVID and BURT BACHARACH

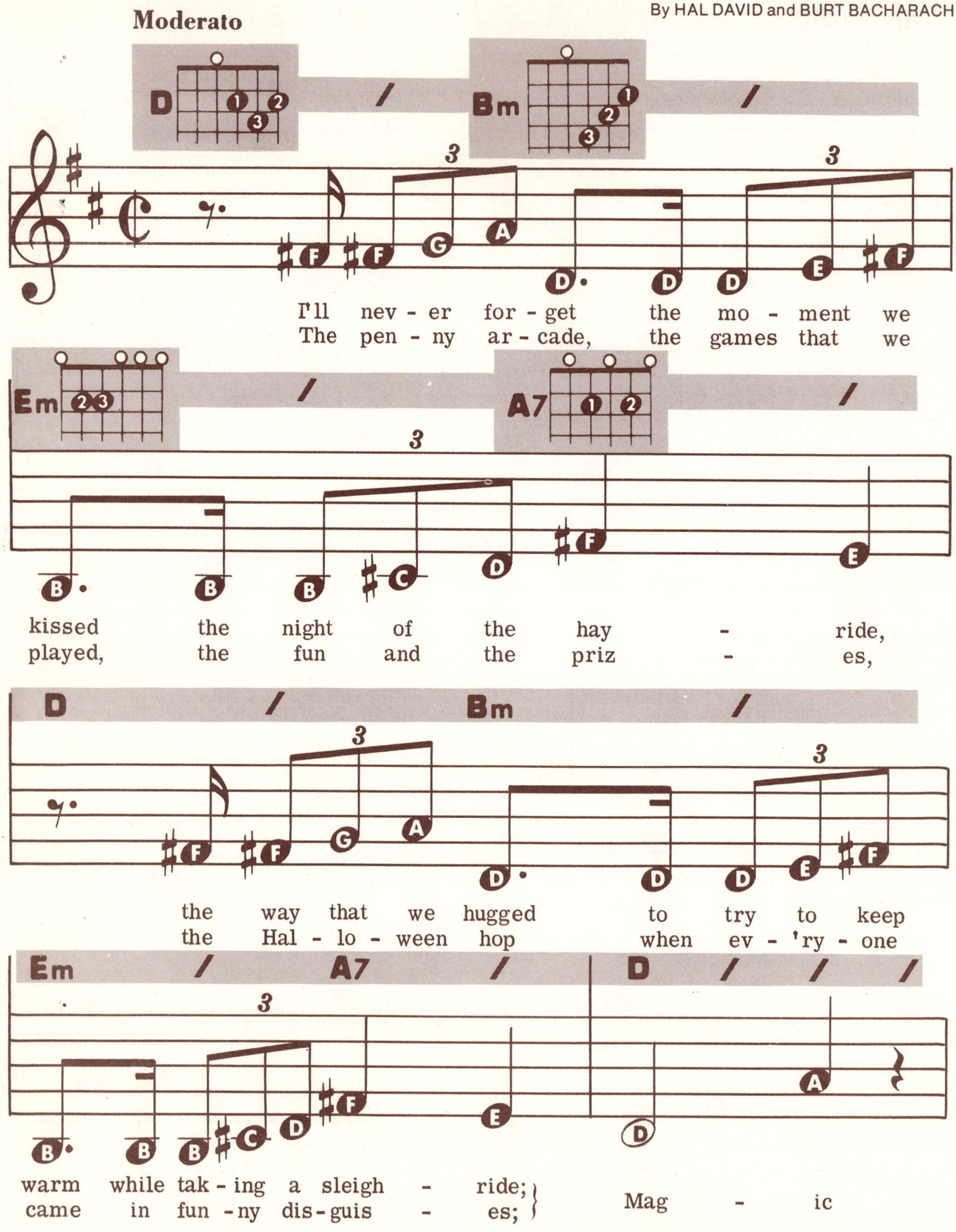

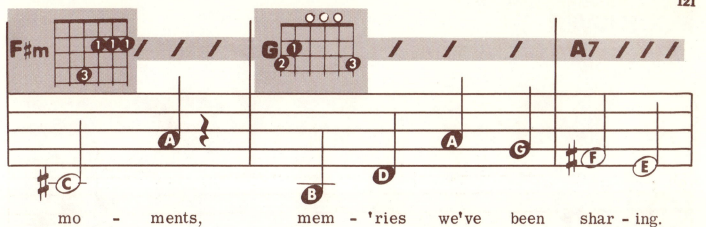

mo — ments,    mem – 'ries we've been shar - ing.

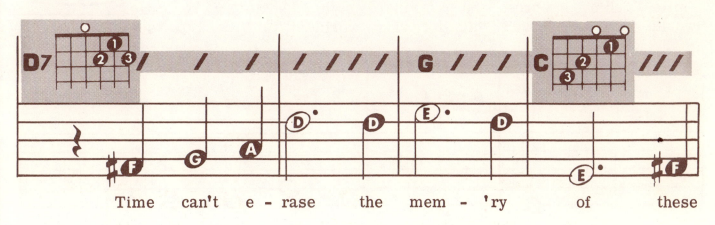

Mag - ic    mo – ments,    when two hearts are    car - ing.

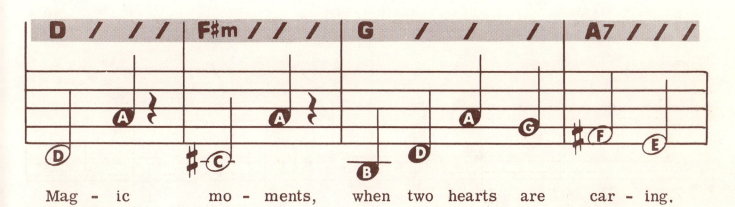

Time    can't e - rase    the    mem – 'ry    of    these

*D.C.*

mag - ic    mo – ments    filled    with    love.

Magic Moments -2 -2

*From the Paramount Picture "BREAKFAST AT TIFFANY'S"*

# MOON RIVER

By JOHNNY MERCER
and HENRY MANCINI

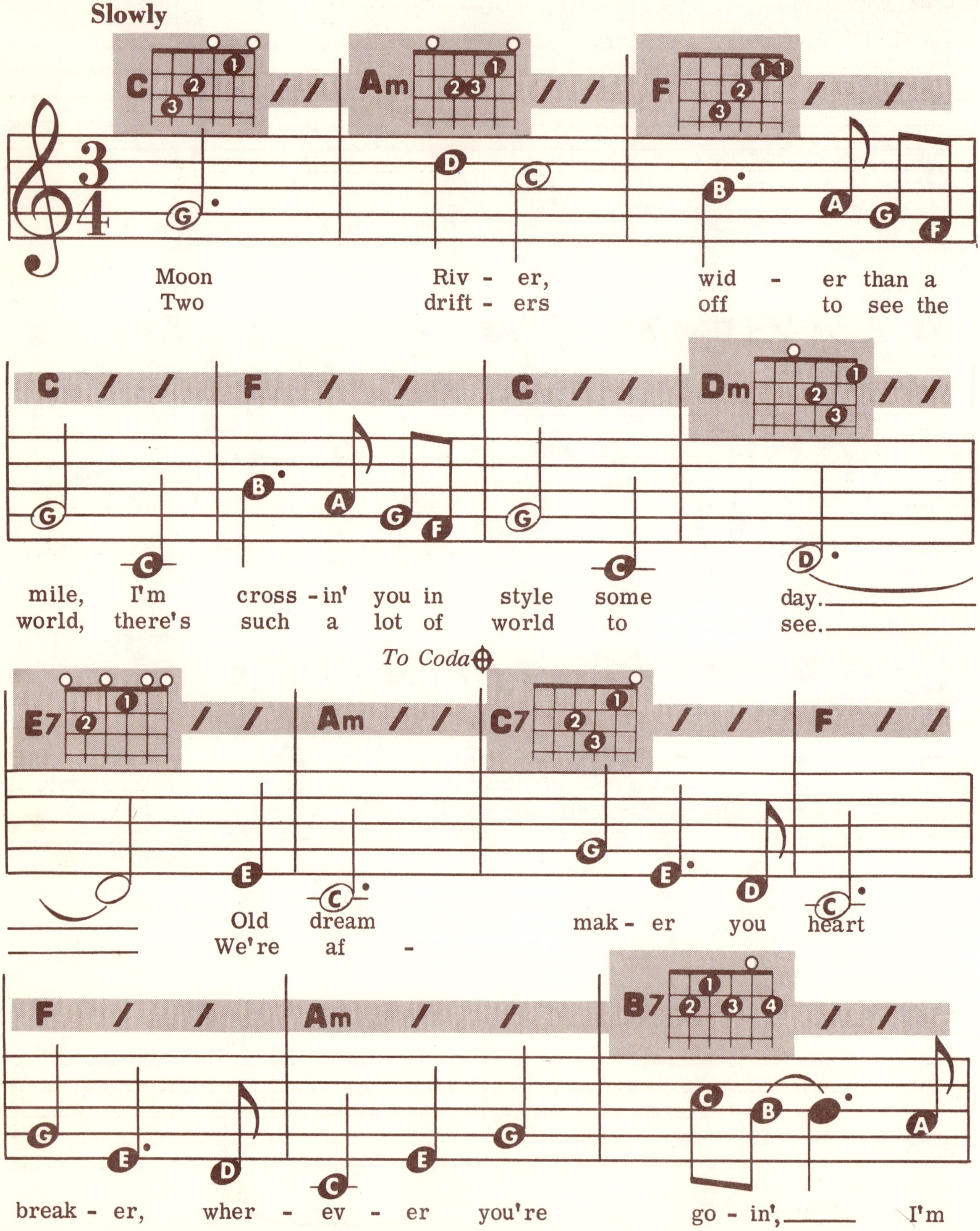

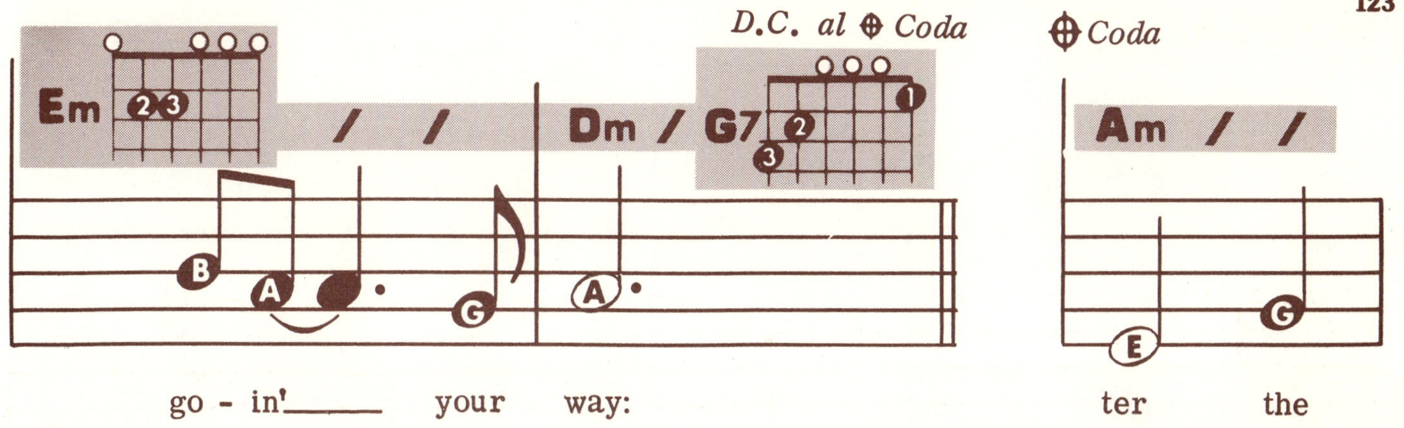

go - in'___ your way:

ter the

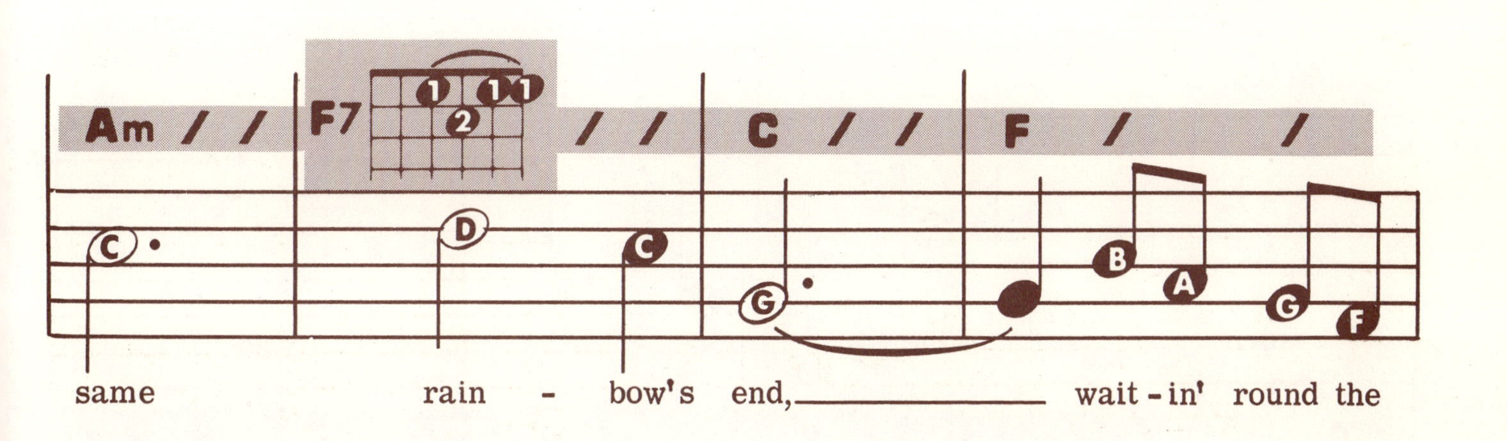

same rain - bow's end,_____ wait-in' round the

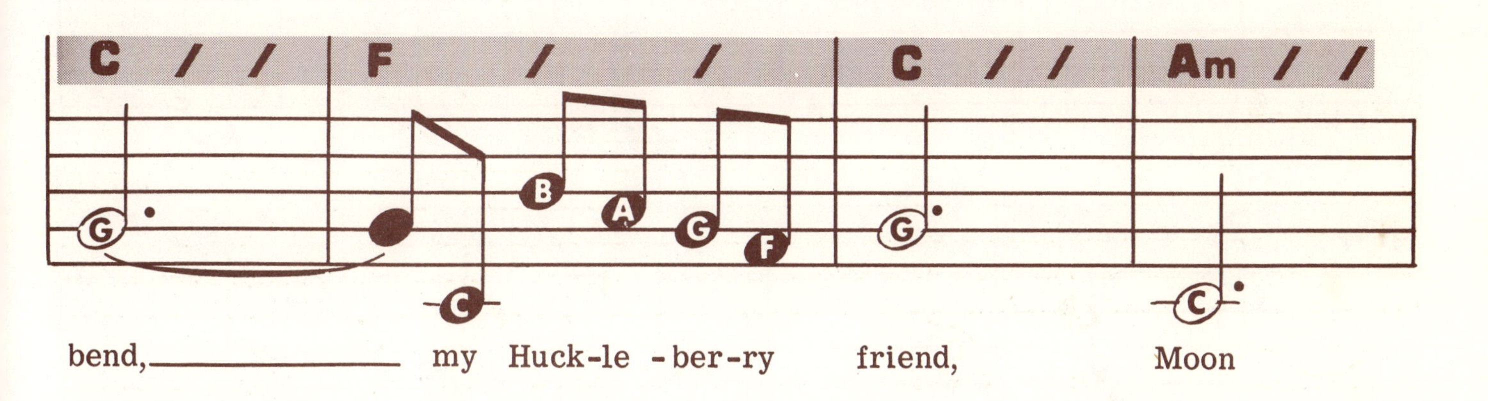

bend,_____ my Huck-le -ber-ry friend, Moon

Riv - er_____ and me._____

Moon River-2-2

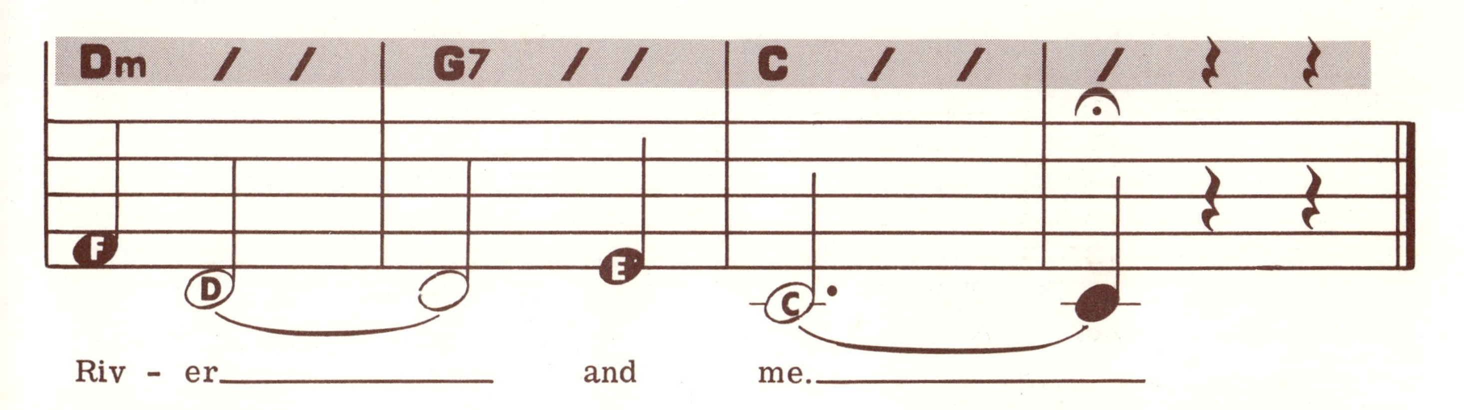

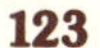

# MORNING HAS BROKEN

Words by ELEANOR FARJEON
*Musical Arrangements by* GEORGE VOLPE

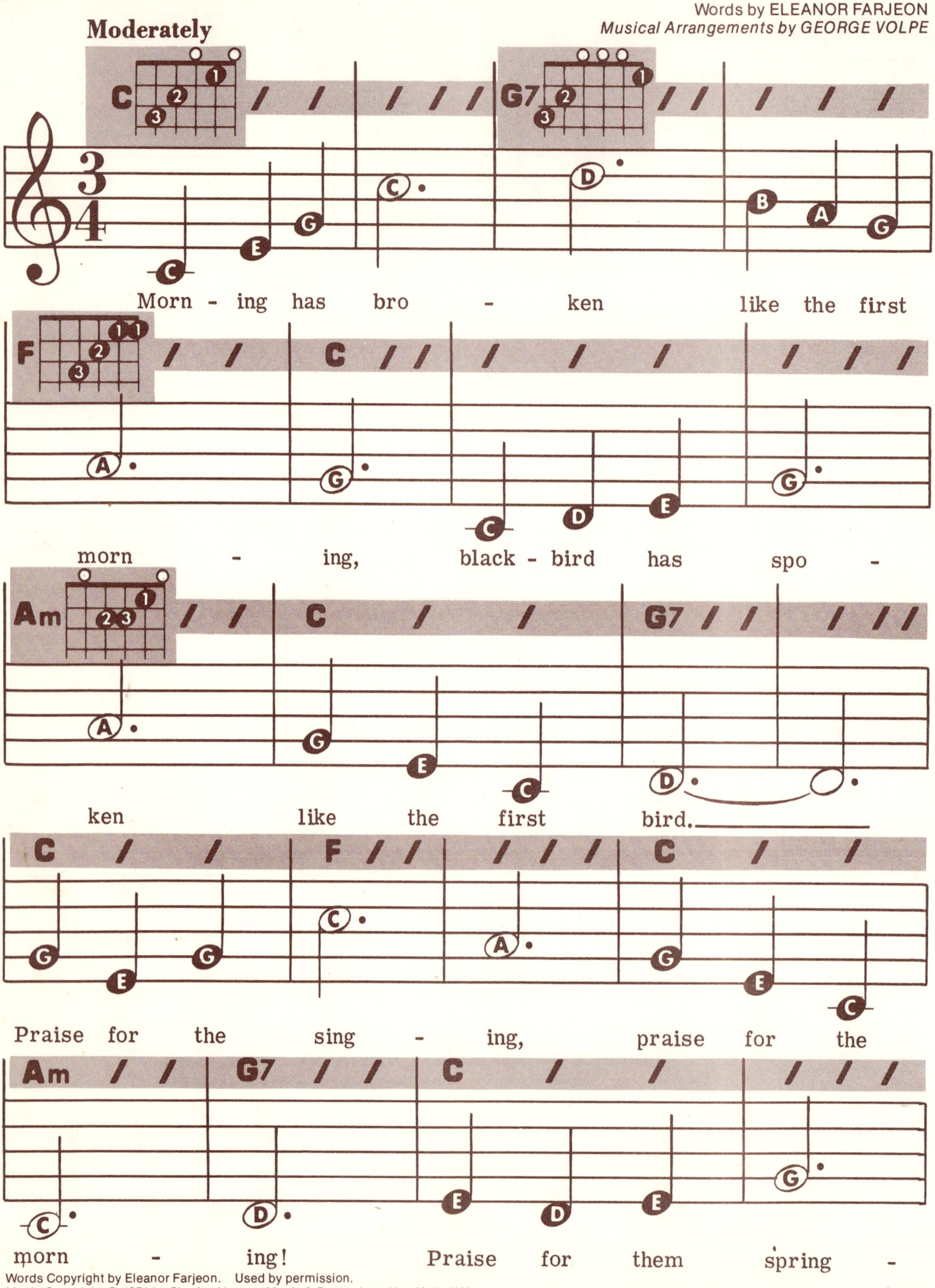

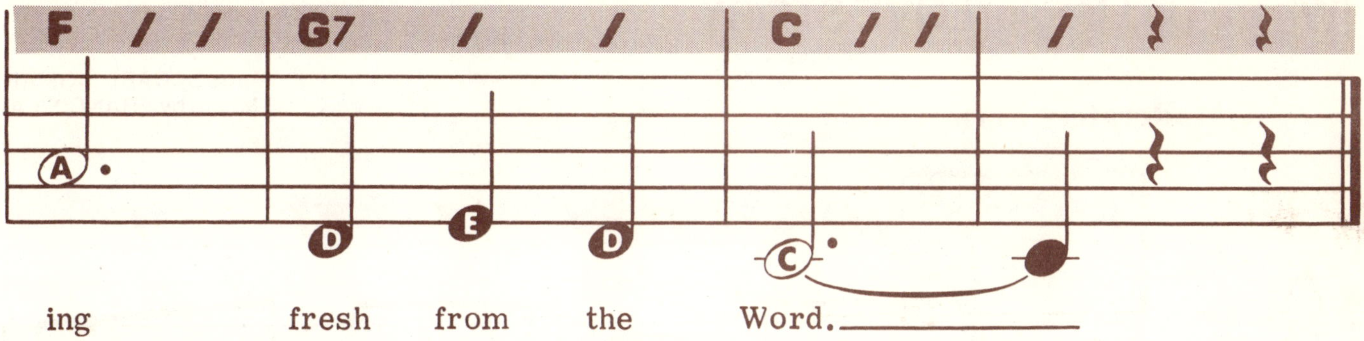

ing        fresh    from    the    Word._____

Morning Has Broken-2-2

## MICHAEL, ROW THE BOAT ASHORE

TRADITIONAL

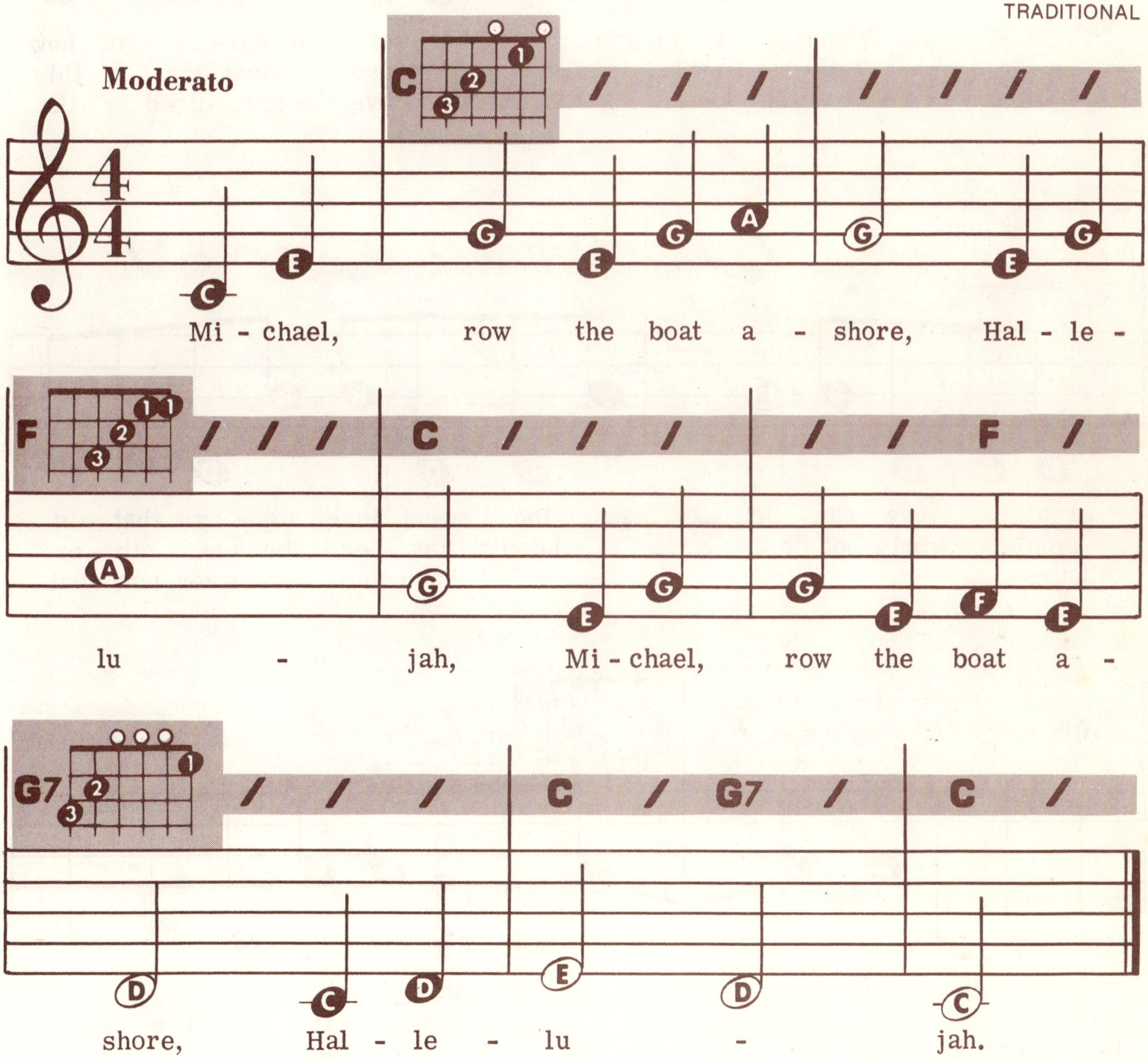

Mi - chael,        row      the    boat  a - shore,    Hal - le -

lu  -        jah,    Mi - chael,    row    the    boat  a -

shore,    Hal - le - lu  -        jah.

*From the Paramount Picture "LOVE STORY"*

# (Where Do I Begin) LOVE STORY

Words by CARL SIGMAN
Music by FRANCIS LAI

**Moderately Slow**

Where do I be-gin_____ to tell the sto-ry of how
With her first hel-lo_____ she gave a mean-ing of this
How long does it last?_____ Can love be meas-ured by the

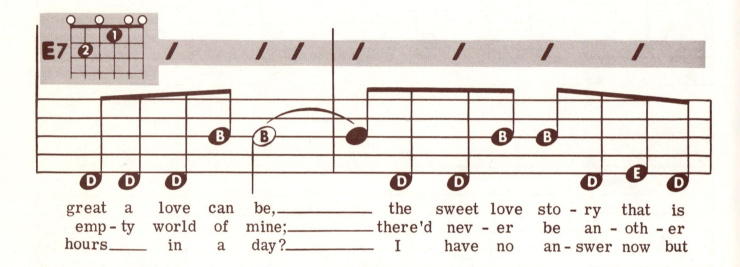

great a love can be,_____ the sweet love sto-ry that is
emp-ty world of mine;_____ there'd nev-er be an-oth-er
hours_____ in a day?_____ I have no an-swer now but

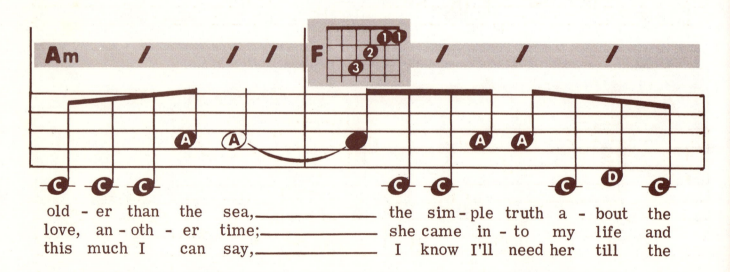

old-er than the sea,_____ the sim-ple truth a-bout the
love, an-oth-er time;_____ she came in-to my life and
this much I can say,_____ I know I'll need her till the

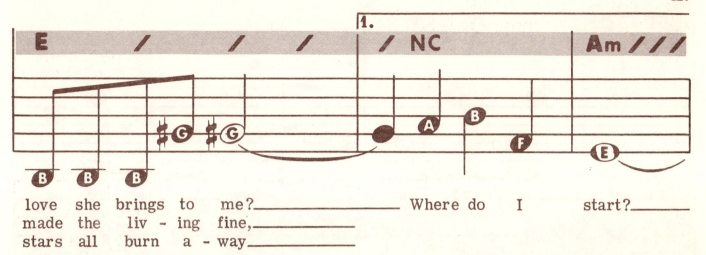

love she brings to me?_____ Where do I start?_____
made the liv - ing fine,_____
stars all burn a - way_____

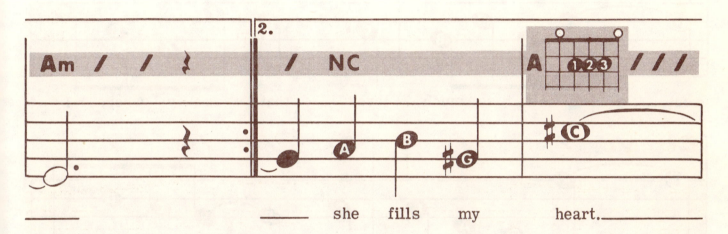

_____ _____ she fills my heart._____

To next strain 3. *Fine*

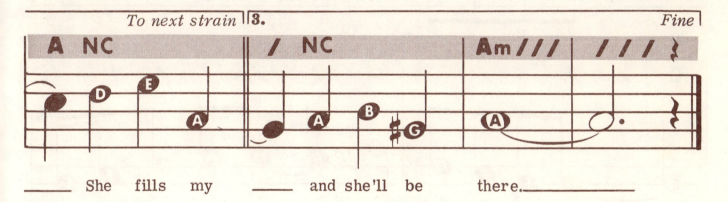

____ She fills my ____ and she'll be there._____

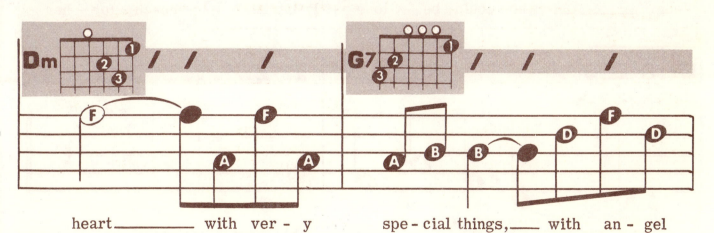

heart_____ with ver - y sp e- cial things,___ with an - gel

Where Do I Begin-3-2

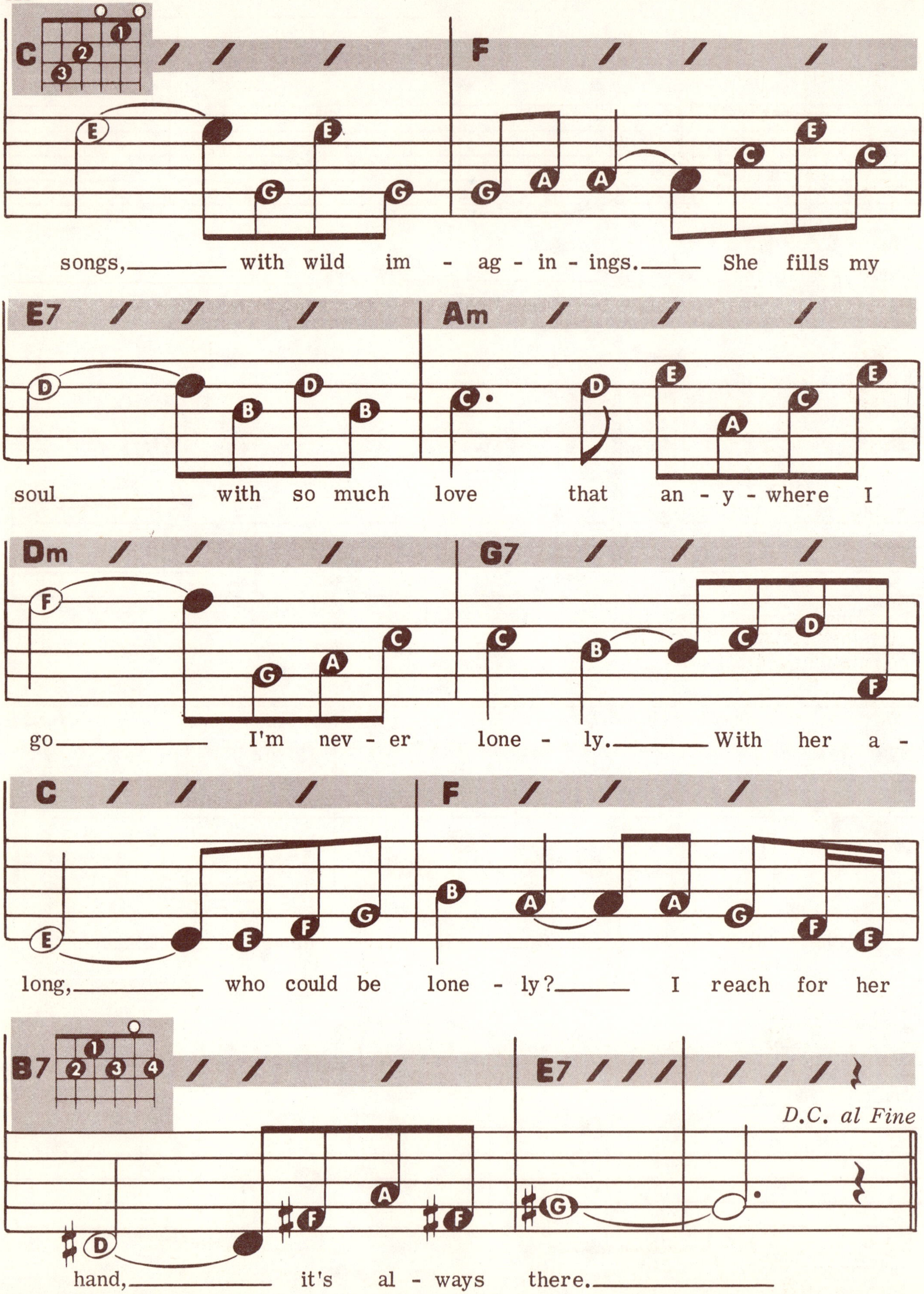

Where Do I Begin-3-3

C
F
A
A
C
C
songs, with wild im - ag - in - ings. She fills my
E7
Am
C
A
C
soul with so much love that an - y - where I
Dm
G7
F
A
C
C
C
F
go I'm nev - er lone - ly. With her a -
C
F
F
A
A
F
long, who could be lone - ly? I reach for her
B7
E7
D.C. al Fine
F
A
F
hand, it's al - ways there.

# NEARER, MY GOD, TO THEE

ADAMS - MASON

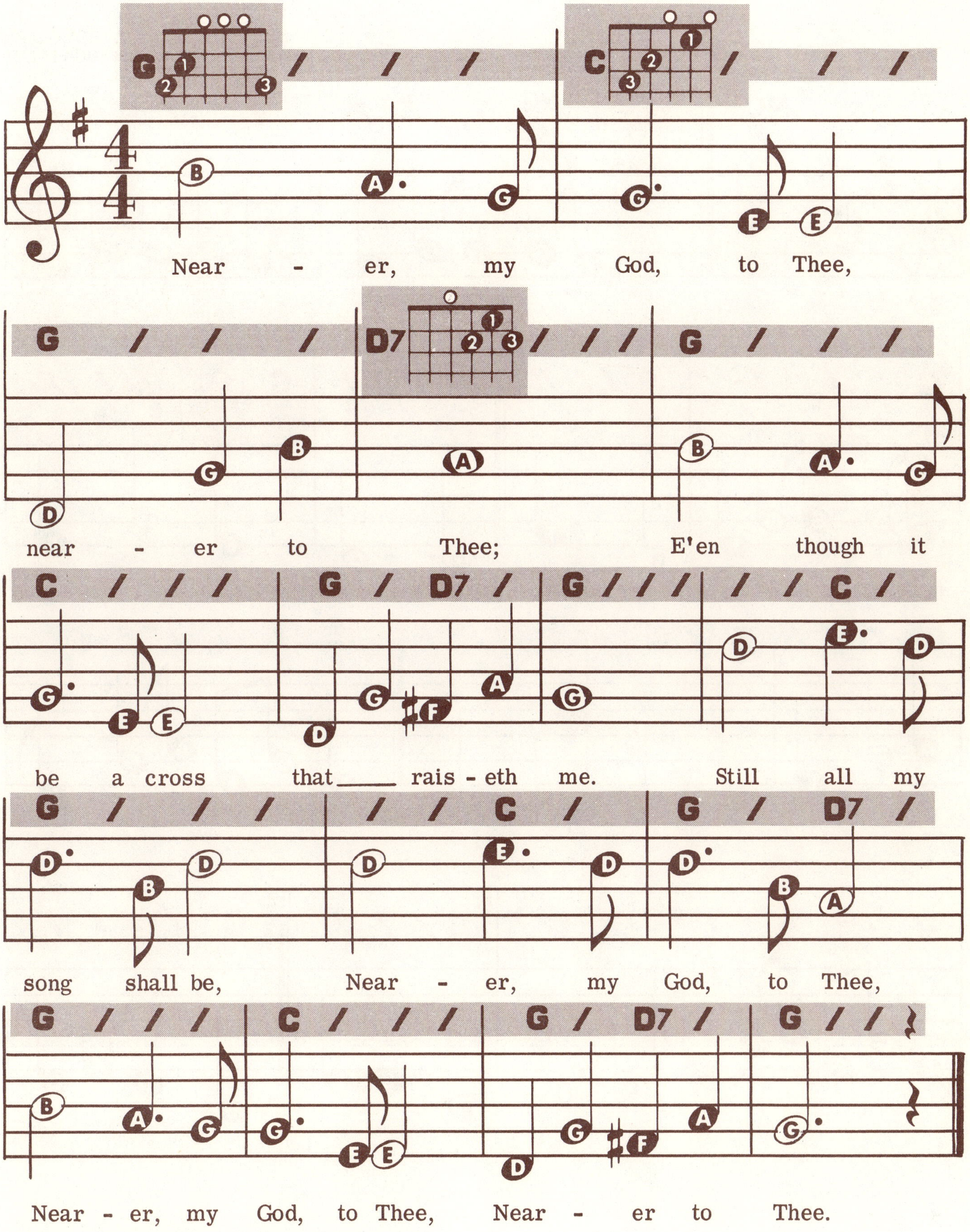

Near - er, my God, to Thee,

near - er to Thee; E'en though it

be a cross that _____ rais - eth me. Still all my

song shall be, Near - er, my God, to Thee,

Near - er, my God, to Thee, Near - er to Thee.

45853

# NIGHTCAP

By ROY CLARK
and BUCK TRENT

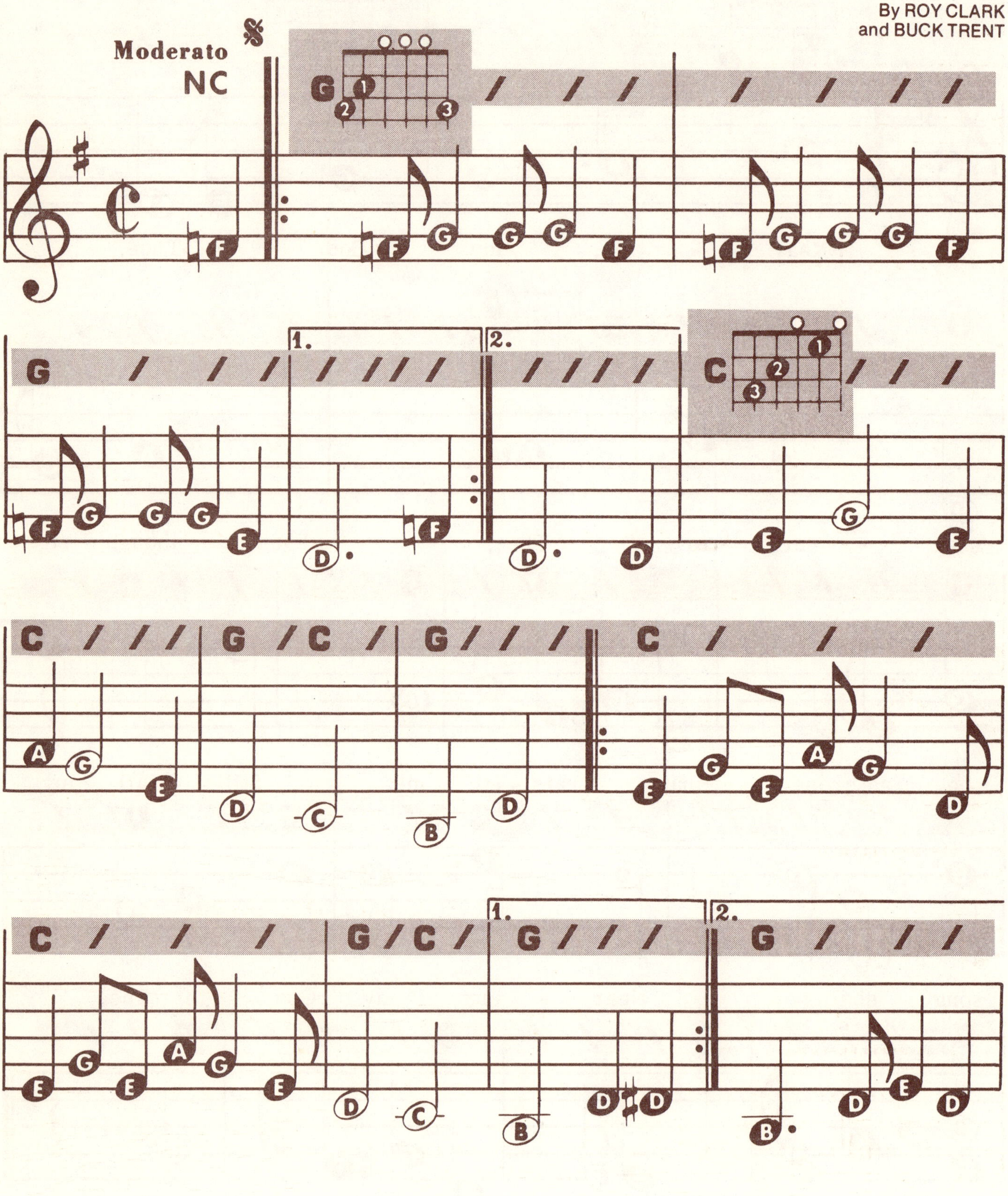

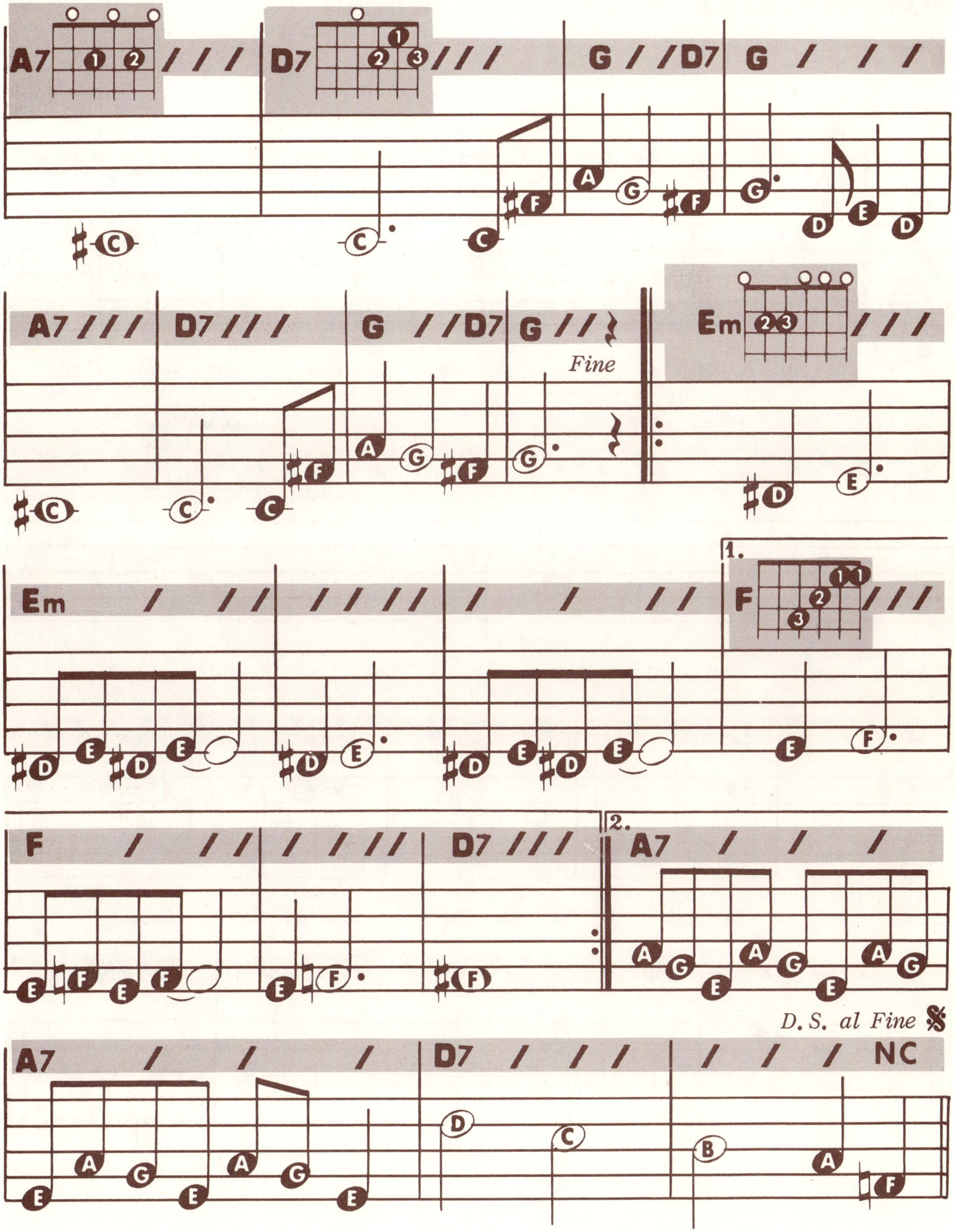

Nightcap-2-2

A7 / / /
D7 / / /
G / / D7
A7 / / /
D7 / / /
G / / D7
Fine
Em / / /
Em / / /
1.
F / / /
F / / /
D7 / / /
A7 / / /
D. S. al Fine
A7 / / /
D7 / / /
NC

# NOBODY KNOWS THE TROUBLE I'VE SEEN

TRADITIONAL

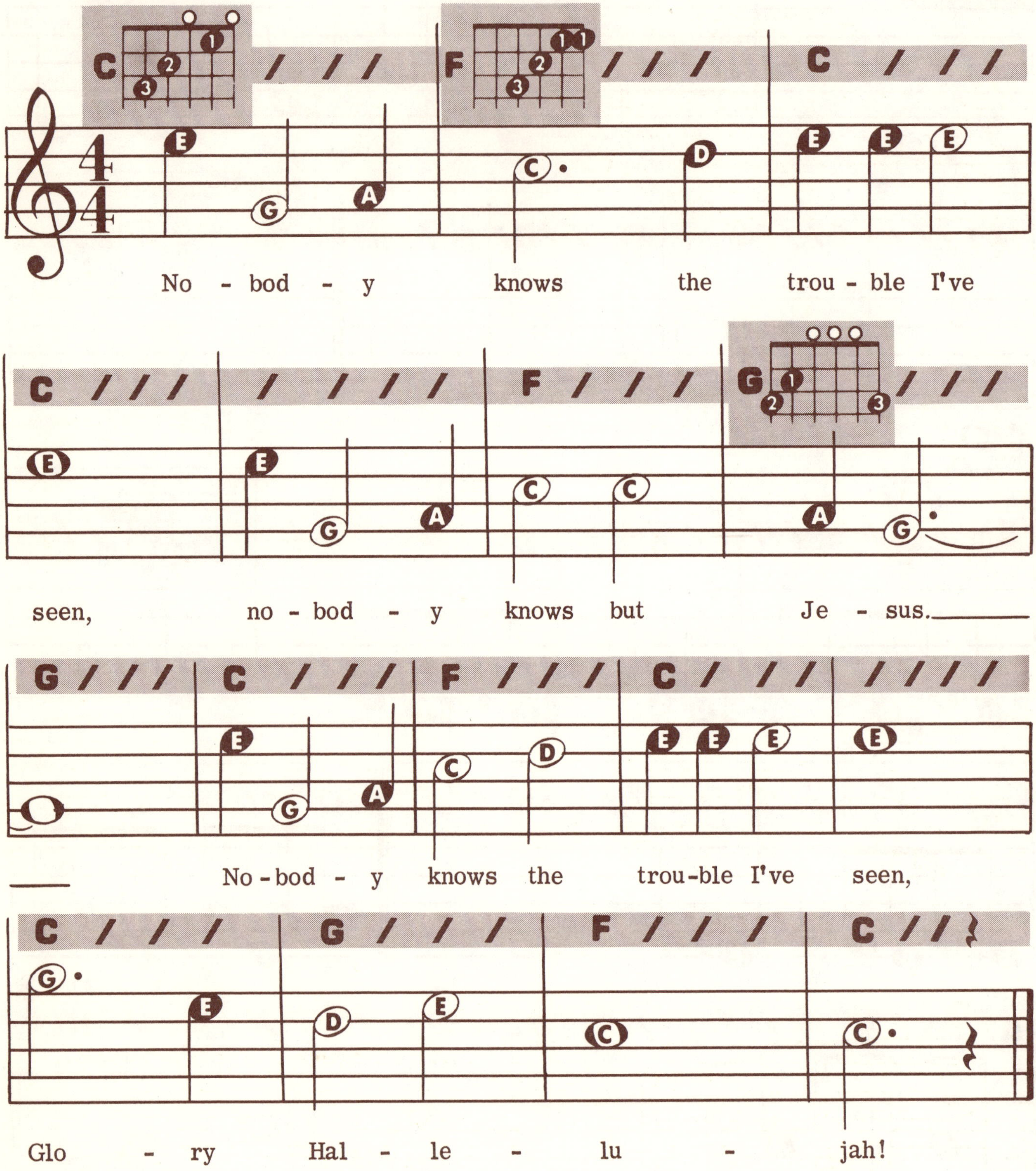

# PAIR OF FIVES

By ROY CLARK
and BUCK TRENT

**Moderato**

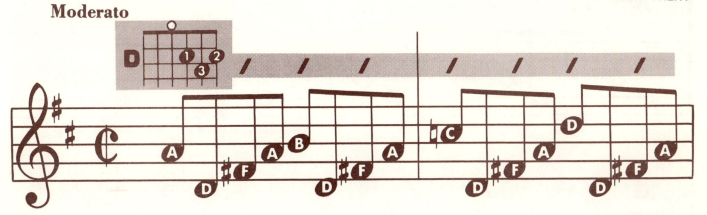

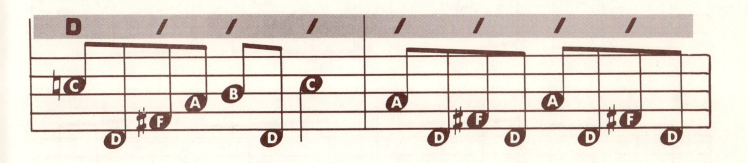

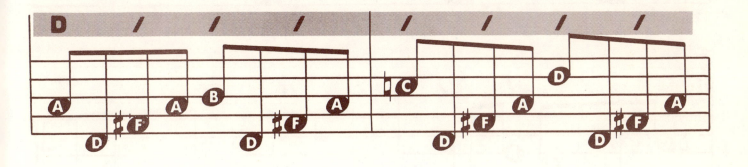

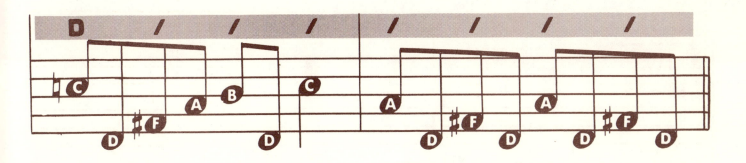

134

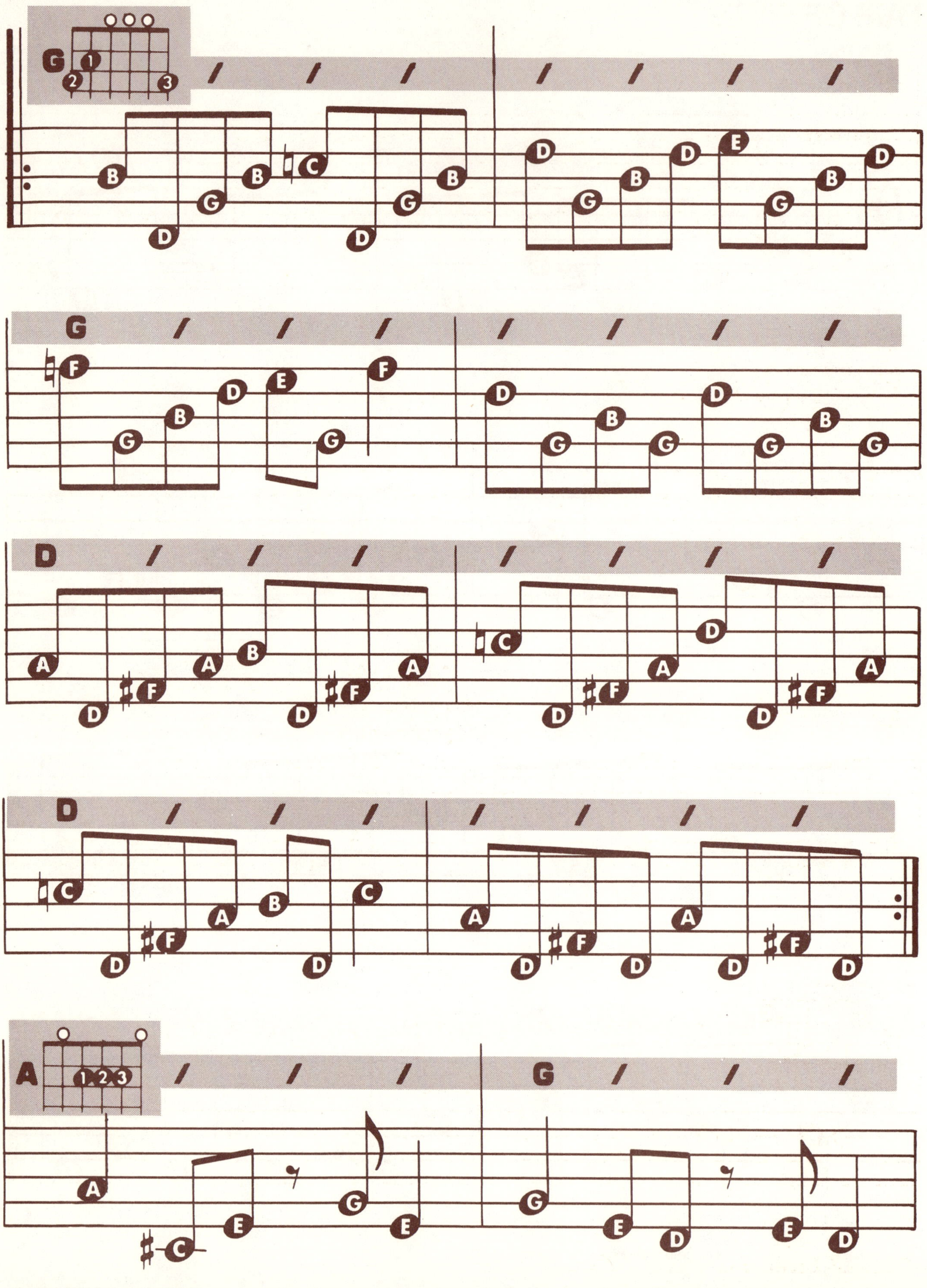

Pair Of Fives-3-2

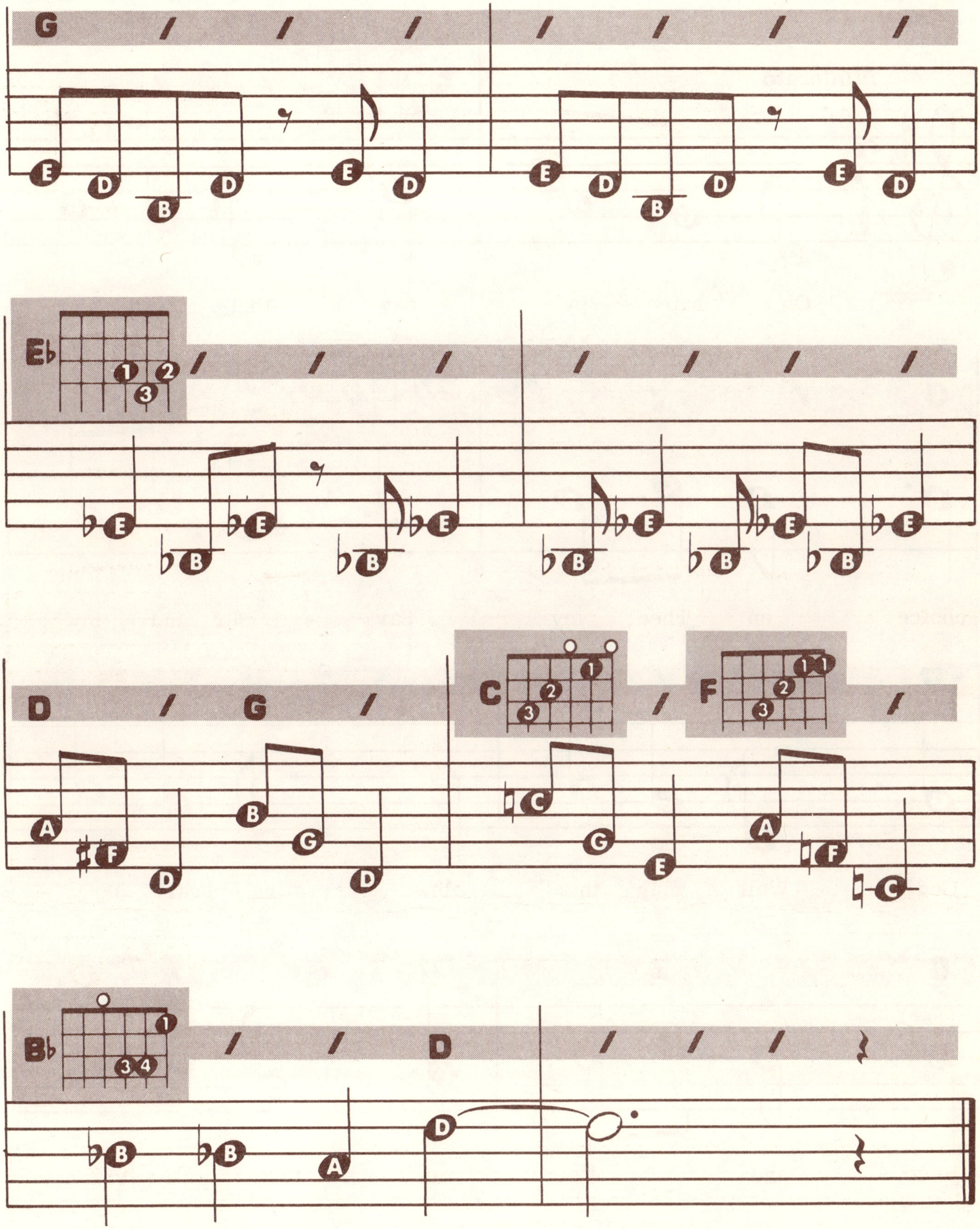

Pair Of Fives-3-3

G
D
B
D
D
D
B
D
D
1
2
♭B
♭B
♭B
♭B
♭B
D
G
C
1
2
1
1
2
D
B
G
D
♮C
G
♮C
B♭
1
4
D
♭B
♭B
D

# OH HAPPY DAY

Words by PHILIP DODDRIDGE
Music by E.F. RIMBAULT

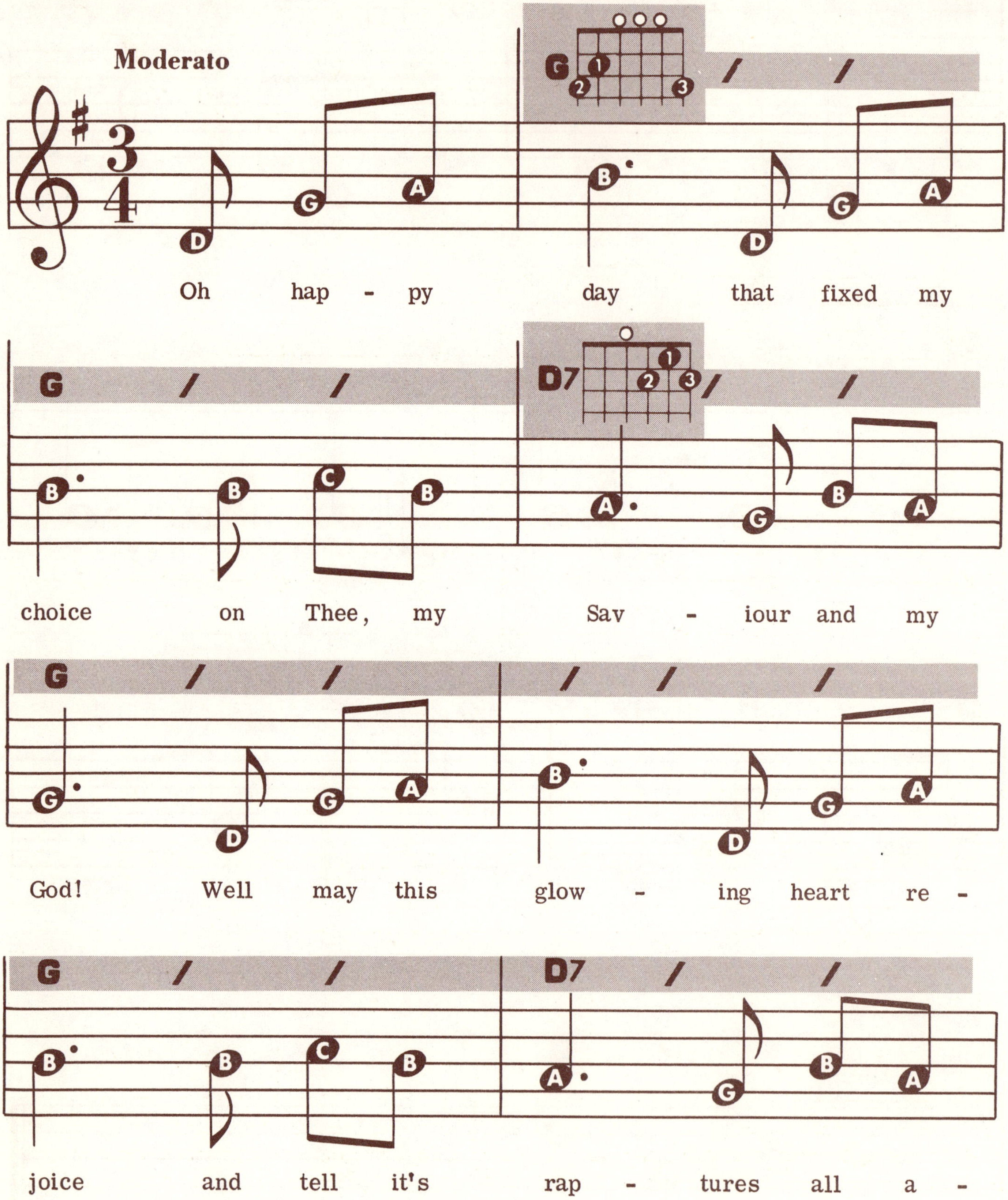

Oh hap - py day that fixed my choice on Thee, my Sav - iour and my God! Well may this glow - ing heart re - joice and tell it's rap - tures all a -

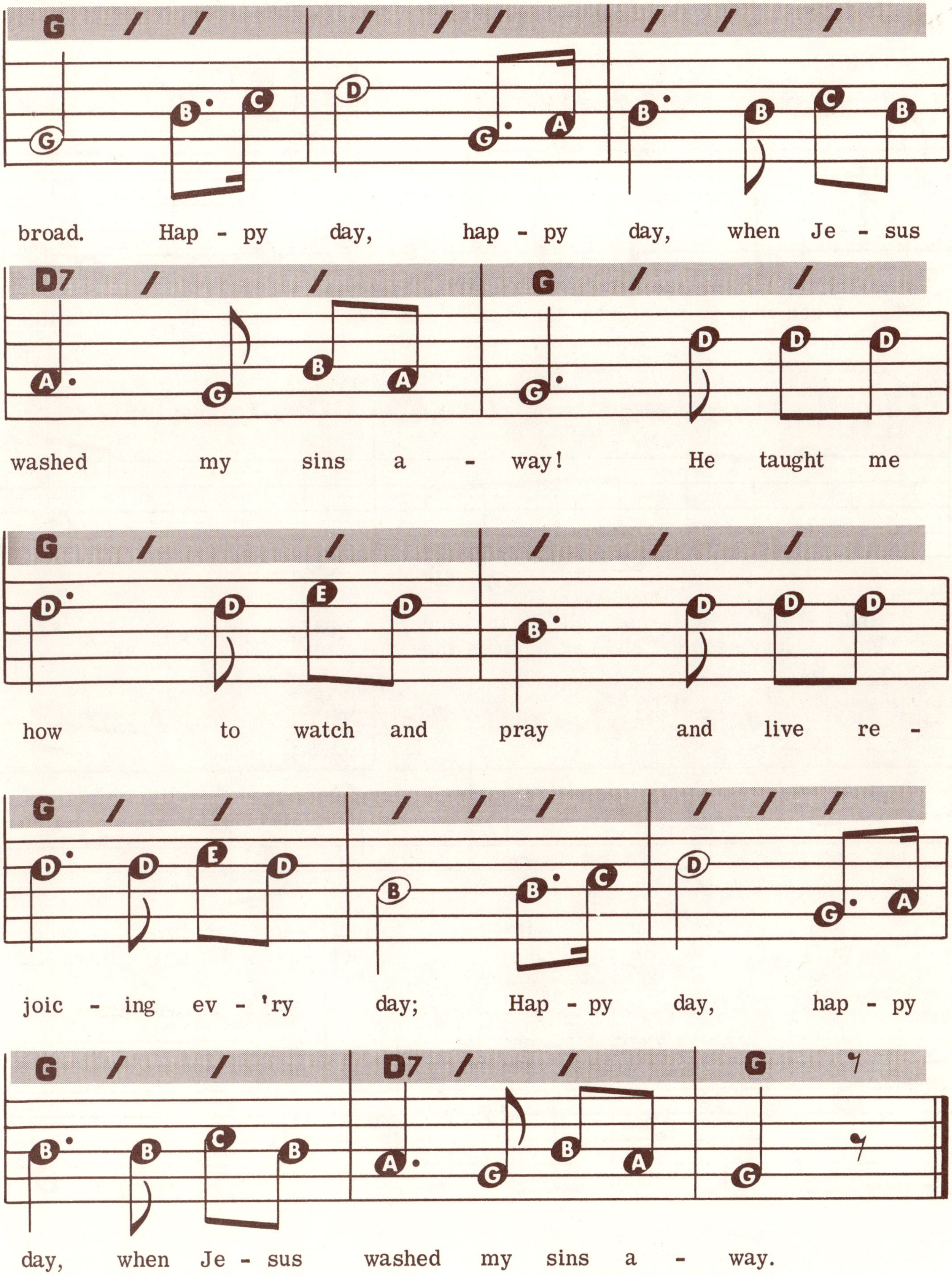

broad.  Hap - py  day,  hap - py  day,  when  Je - sus

washed  my  sins  a - way!  He  taught  me

how  to  watch  and  pray  and  live  re -

joic - ing  ev - 'ry  day;  Hap - py  day,  hap - py

day,  when  Je - sus  washed  my  sins  a - way.

Oh Happy Day -2 -2

*From the Paramount Picture "THE ONE AND ONLY"*

# THE ONE AND ONLY

Words by ALAN and MARILYN BERGMAN
Music by PATRICK WILLIAMS

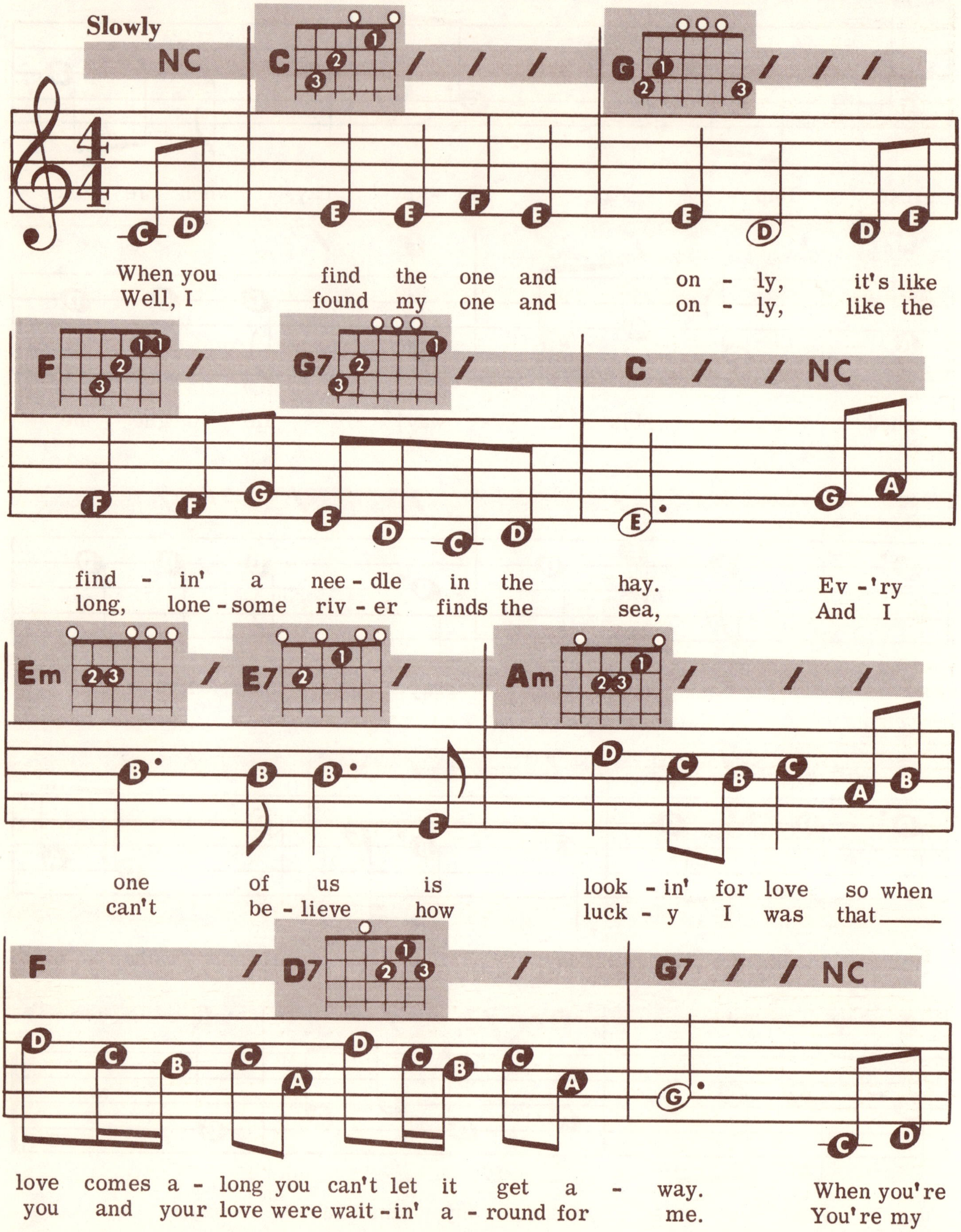

When you find the one and on - ly, it's like
Well, I found my one and on - ly, like the

find - in' a nee - dle in the hay. Ev - 'ry
long, lone - some riv - er finds the sea, And I

one of us is look - in' for love so when
can't be - lieve how luck - y I was that_____

love comes a - long you can't let it get a - way. When you're
you and your love were wait - in' a - round for me. You're my

some-one's one and on - ly, and she says that she's noth -in' with -out
dar - lin' one and on - ly, I've got no more＿＿ look -in' left to

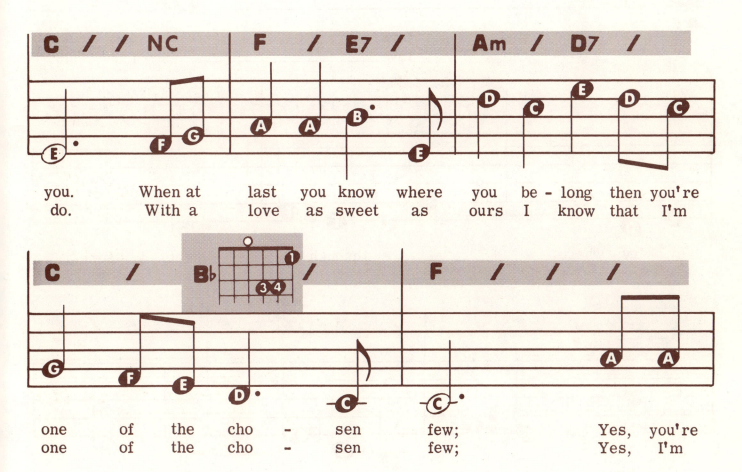

you. When at last you know where you be - long then you're
do. With a love as sweet as ours I know that I'm

one of the cho - sen few; Yes, you're
one of the cho - sen few; Yes, I'm

*D.C.*

one of the cho - sen＿＿＿ few.
one of the cho - sen＿＿＿ few.

The One And Only -2 -2

# OUR LOVE
## (Based on Tchaikovsky's "Romeo And Juliet")

Words and Music by
LARRY CLINTON, BUDDY BERNIER
and BOB EMMERICH

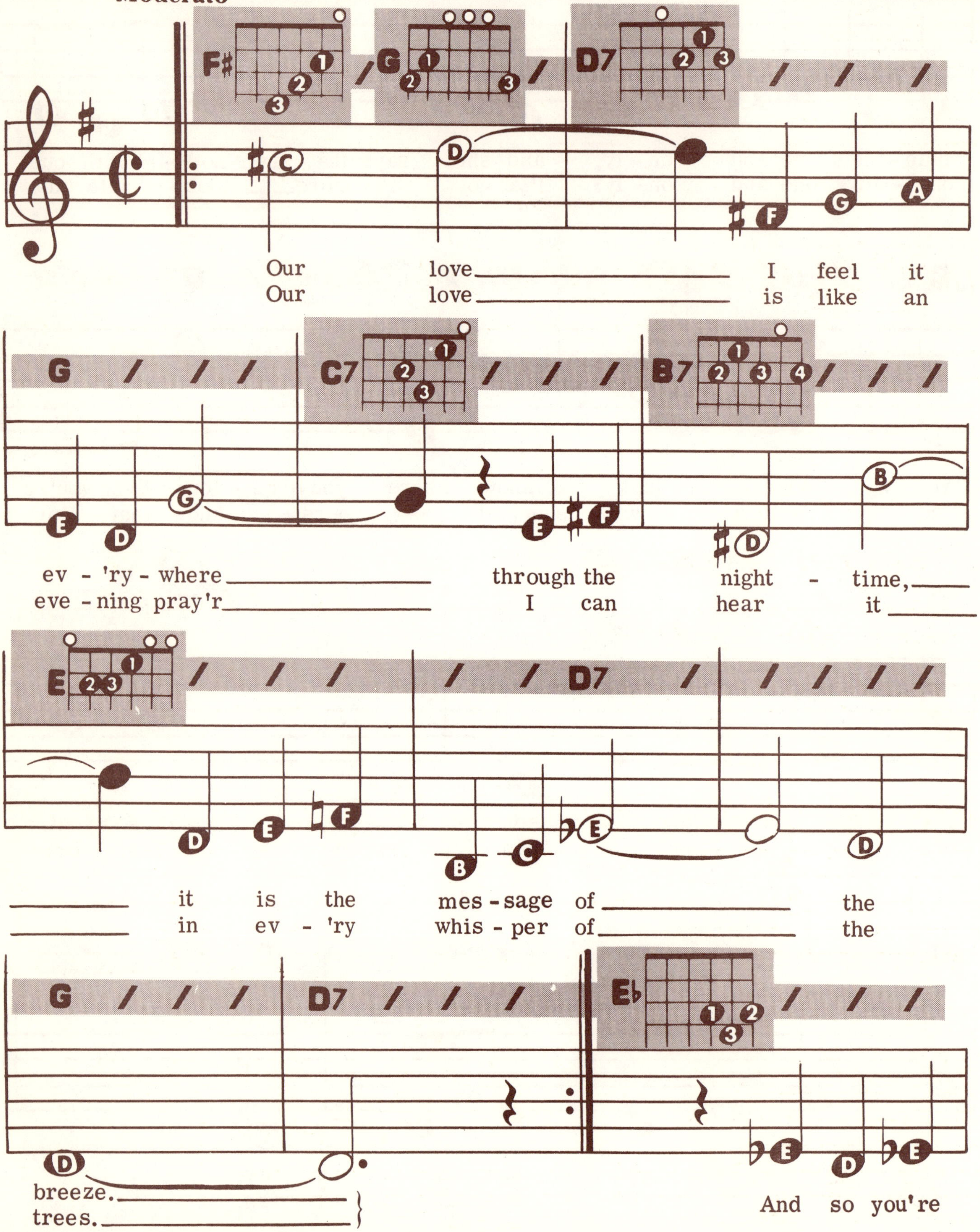

Our love_____ I feel it
Our love_____ is like an

ev - 'ry - where_____ through the night - time,_____
eve - ning pray'r_____ I can hear it_____

_____ it is the mes - sage of _____ the
_____ in ev - 'ry whis - per of _____ the

breeze._____
trees._____

And so you're

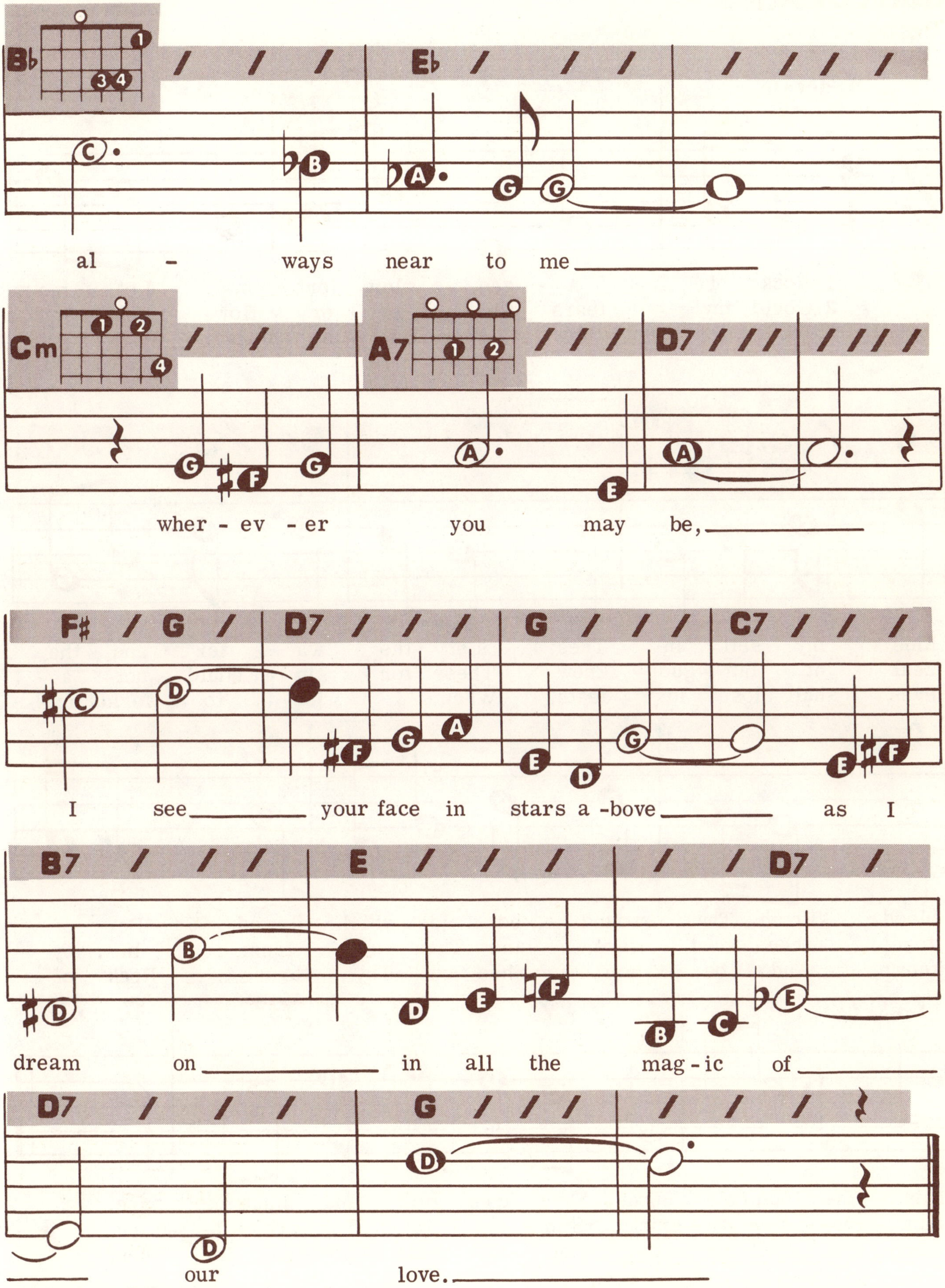

al – ways   near   to   me _____

wher – ev – er   you   may   be, _____

I   see _____ your face   in   stars a –bove _____ as   I

dream   on _____ in   all   the   mag - ic   of _____

_____ our   love. _____

Our Love-2-2

# ROCK OF AGES

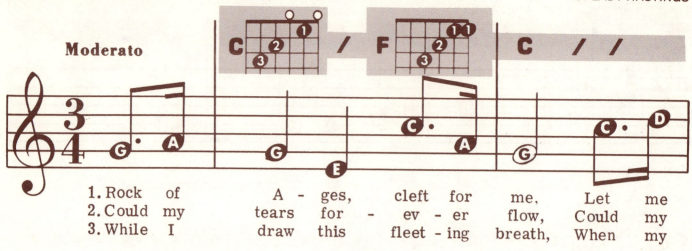

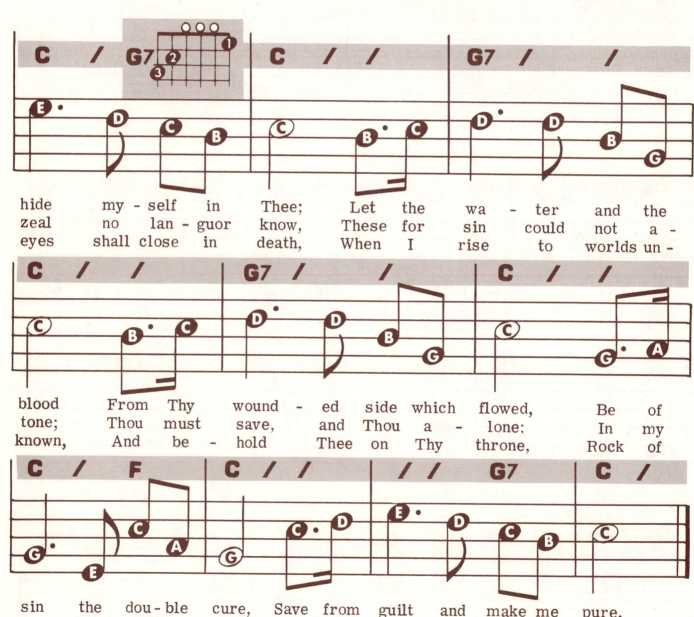

1. Rock of A - ges, cleft for me, Let me hide my - self in Thee; Let the wa - ter and the blood From Thy wound - ed side which flowed, Be of sin the dou - ble cure, Save from guilt and make me pure.

2. Could my tears for - ev - er flow, Could my zeal no lan - guor know, These for sin could not a - tone; Thou must save, and Thou a - lone; In my hand no price I bring; Sim - ply to Thy cross I cling.

3. While I draw this fleet - ing breath, When my eyes shall close in death, When I rise to worlds un - known, And be - hold Thee on Thy throne, Rock of A - ges, cleft for me, Let me hide my - self in Thee.

# ROCKY TOP

Words and Music by
BOUDLEAUX BRYANT
AND FELICE BRYANT

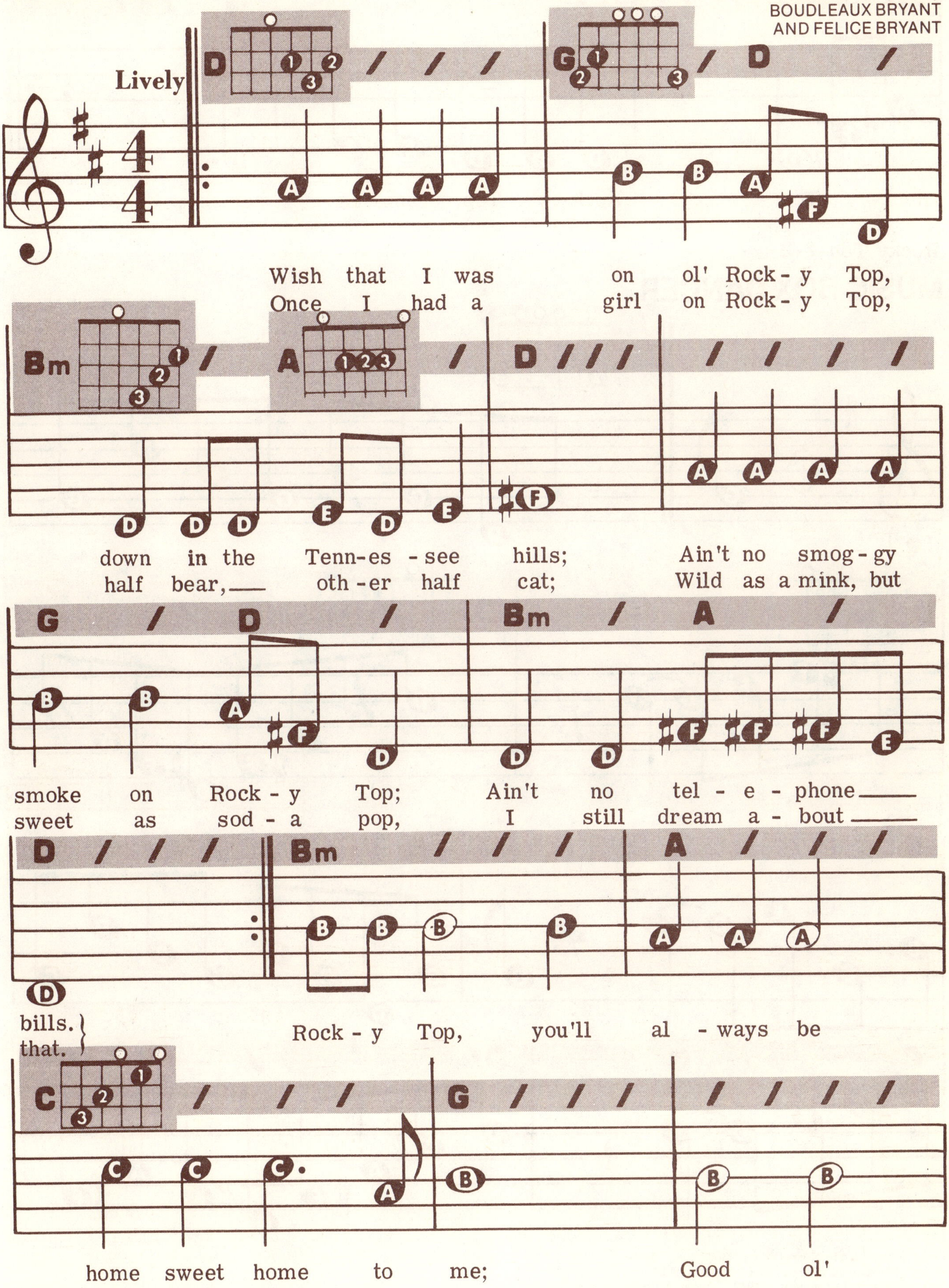

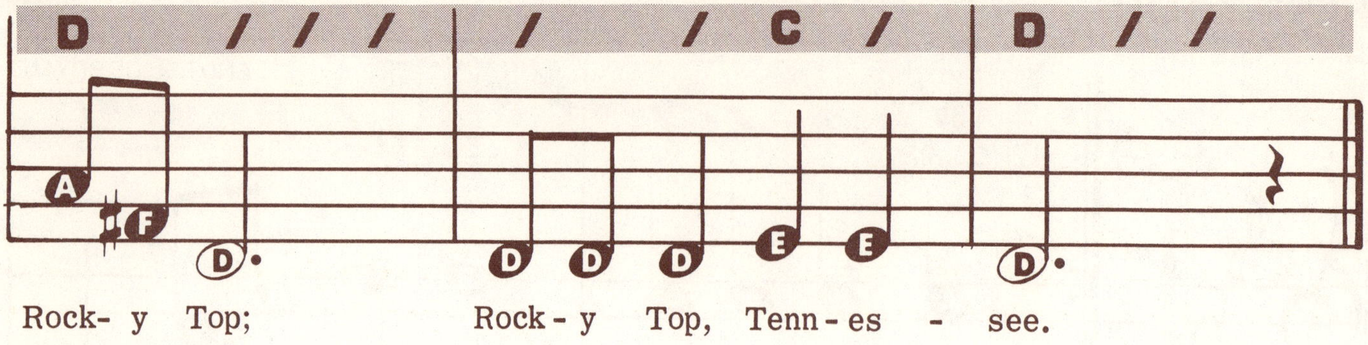

Rock- y Top;        Rock- y Top, Tenn - es - see.

Rocky Top-2-2

# MUSIC BOX DANCER

By FRANK MILLS

Lively

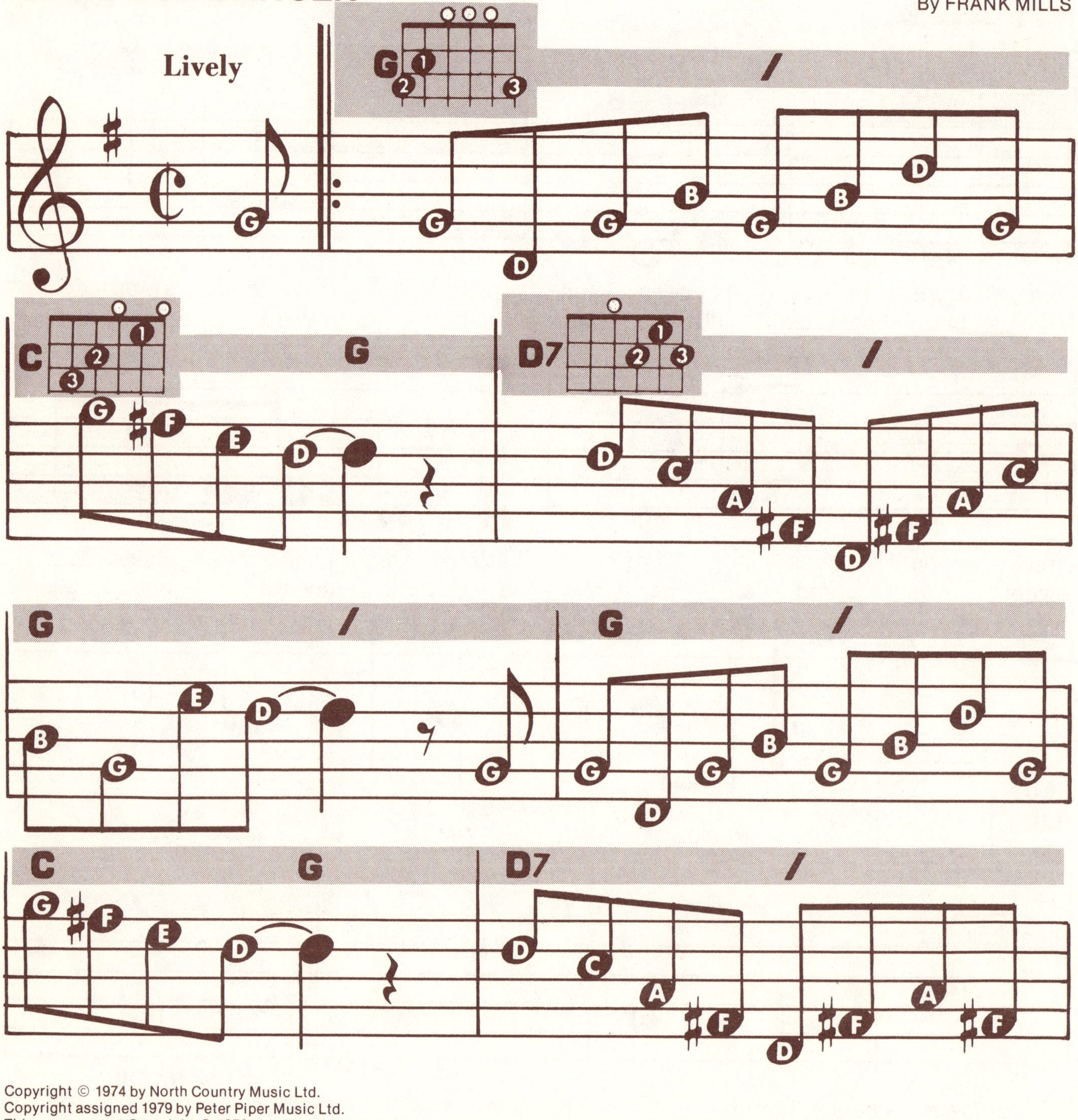

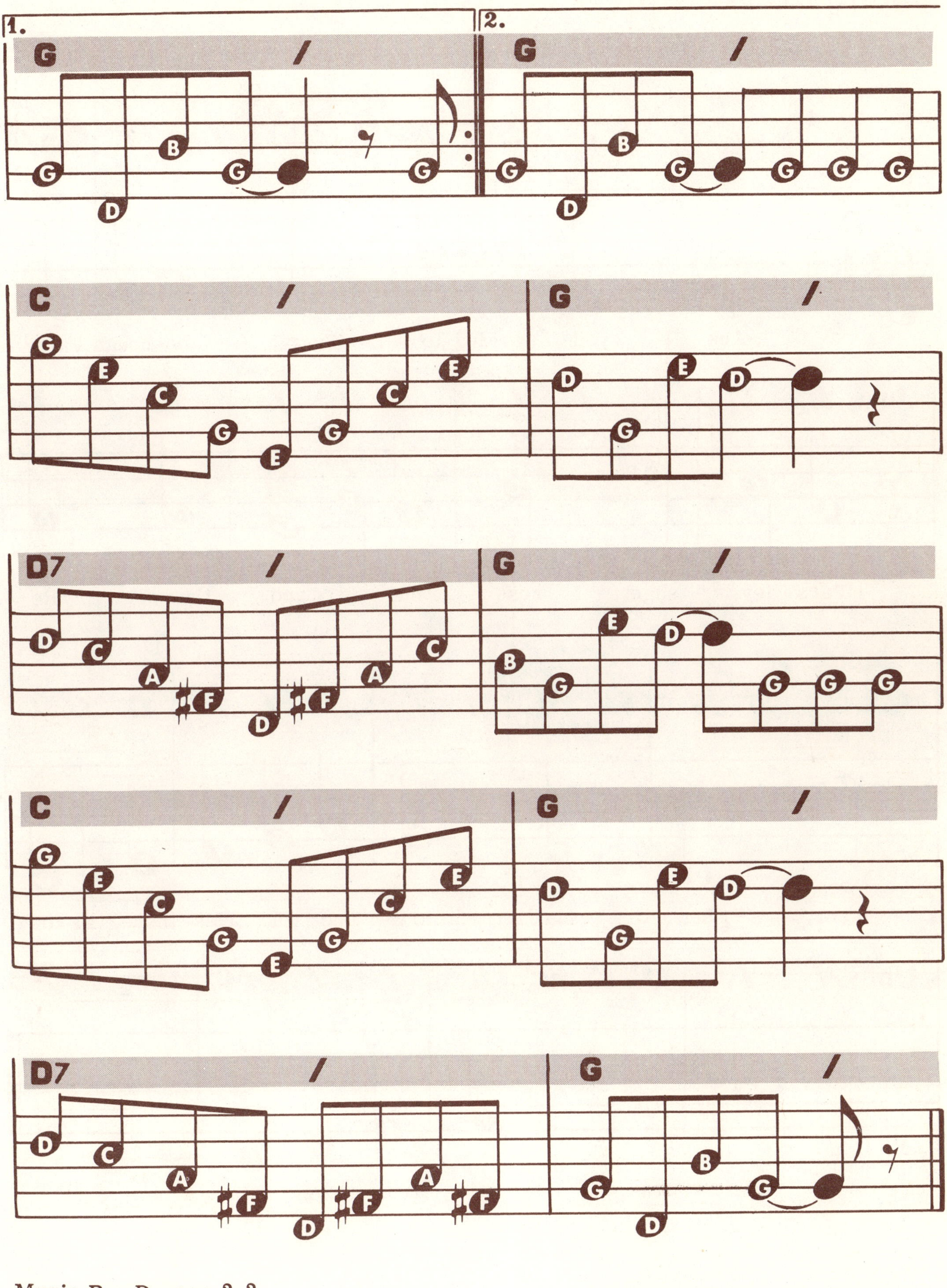

Music Box Dancer-2-2

# SCARBOROUGH FAIR

TRADITIONAL

**Moderato**

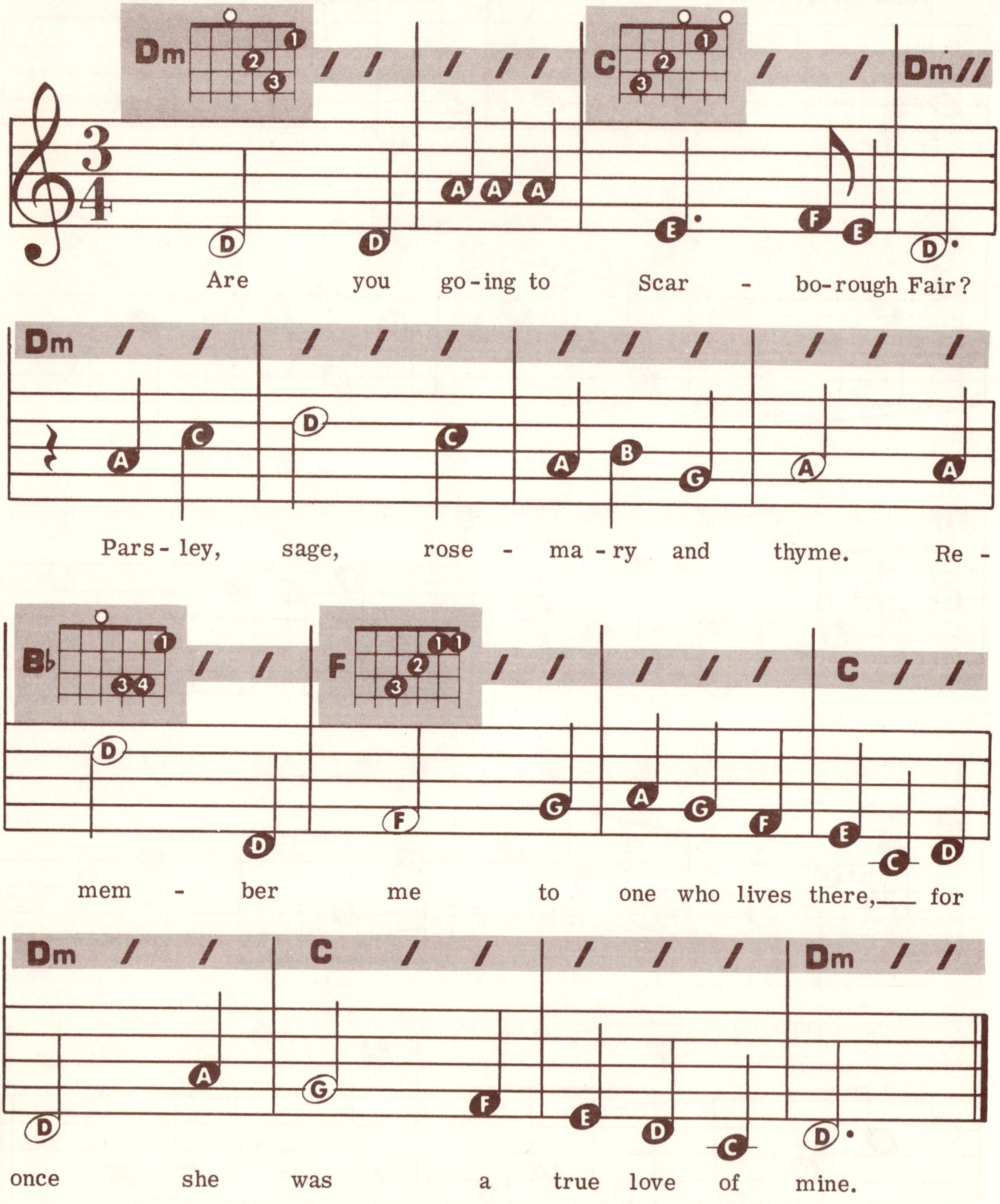

Are you go-ing to Scar - bo-rough Fair?

Pars - ley, sage, rose - ma - ry and thyme. Re -

mem - ber me to one who lives there, ___ for

once she was a true love of mine.

# SHE'LL BE COMIN' ROUND THE MOUNTAIN

TRADITIONAL

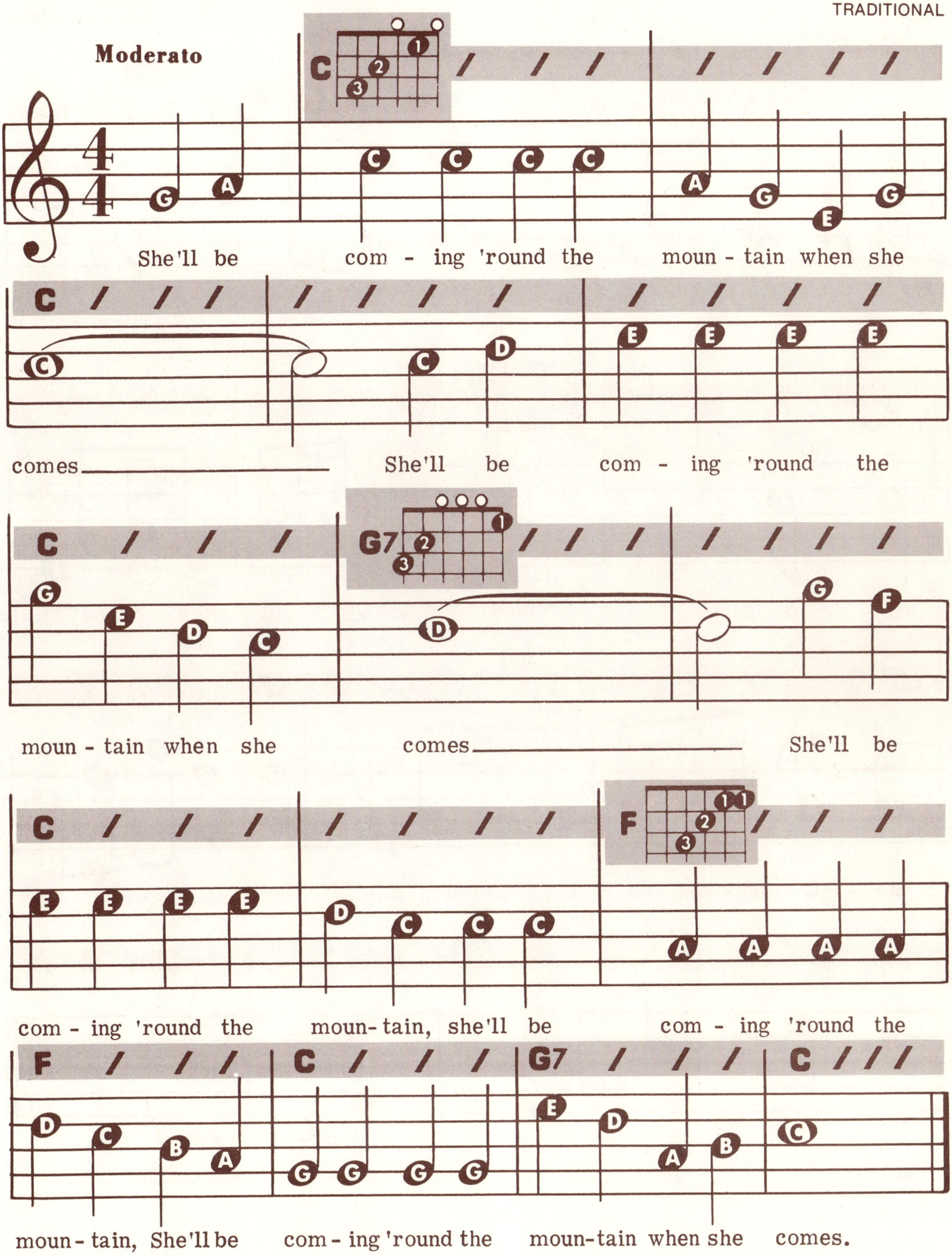

# SILENT NIGHT

F. GRUBER

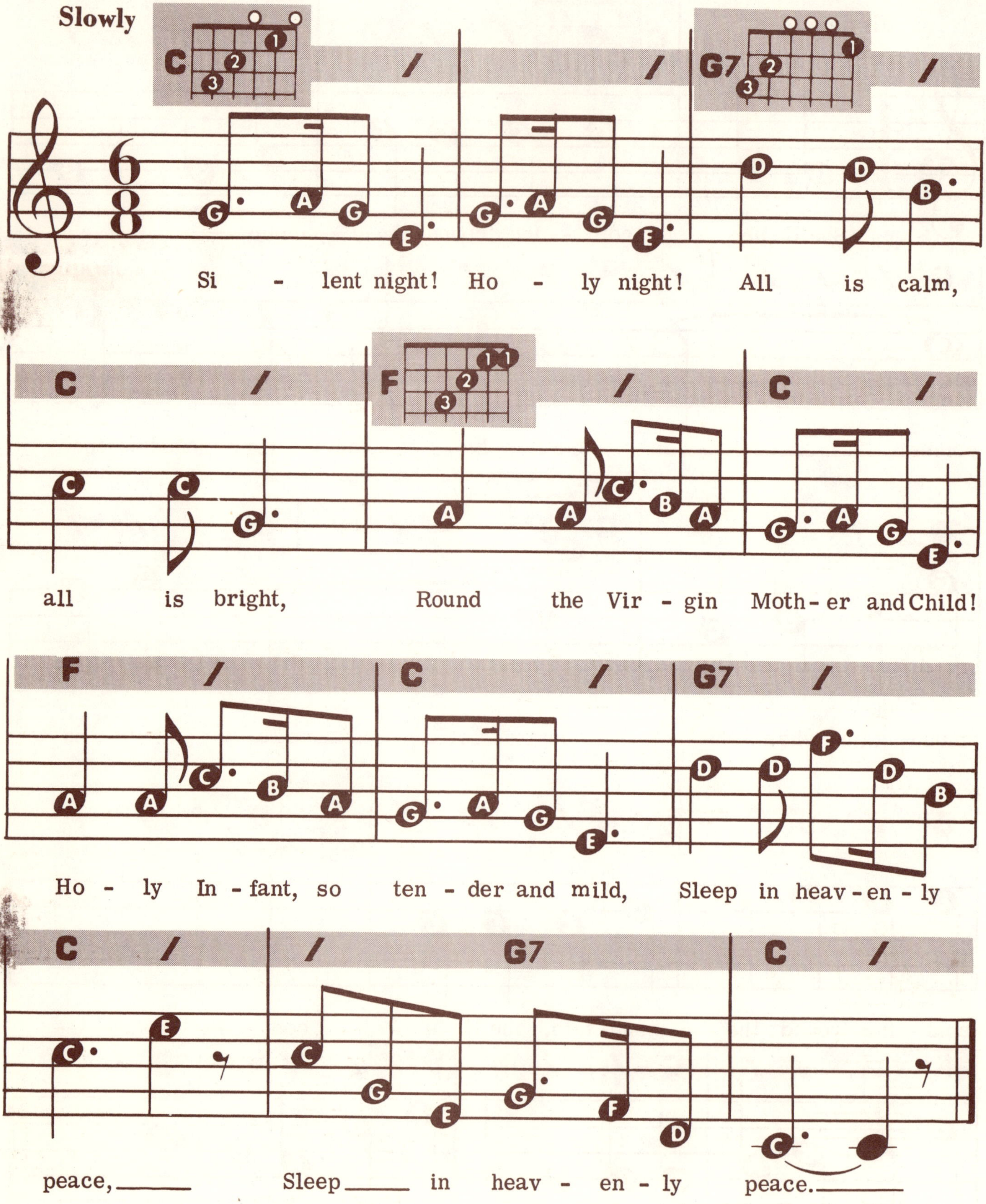

# SOMETIMES I FEEL LIKE A MOTHERLESS CHILD

SPIRITUAL

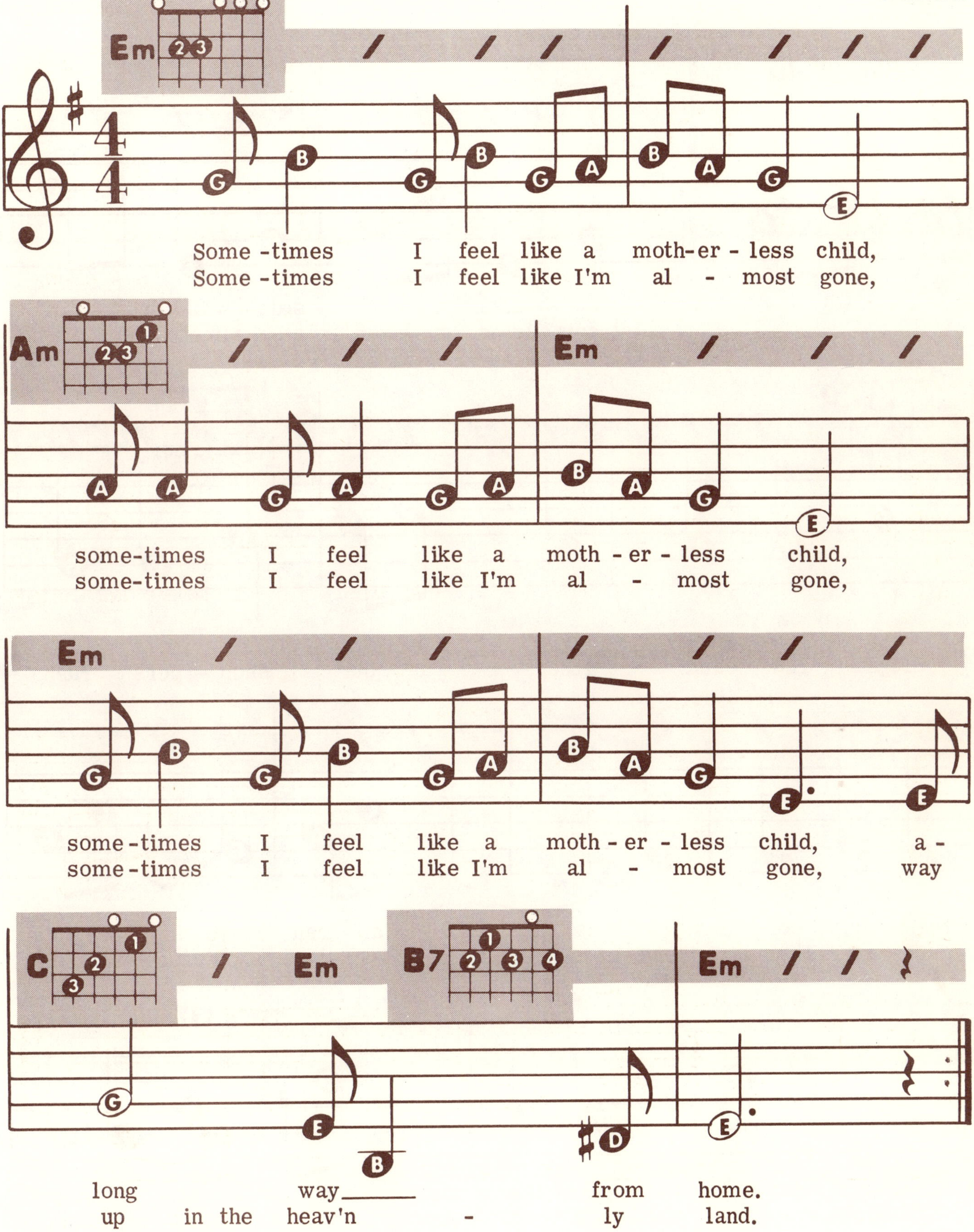

Some-times I feel like a moth-er-less child,
Some-times I feel like I'm al-most gone,

some-times I feel like a moth-er-less child,
some-times I feel like I'm al-most gone,

some-times I feel like a moth-er-less child, a-
some-times I feel like I'm al-most gone, way

long way_____ from home.
up in the heav'n - ly land.

*From the Paramount Picture "THE LEMON DROP KID"*

# SILVER BELLS

By JAY LIVINGSTON
and RAY EVANS

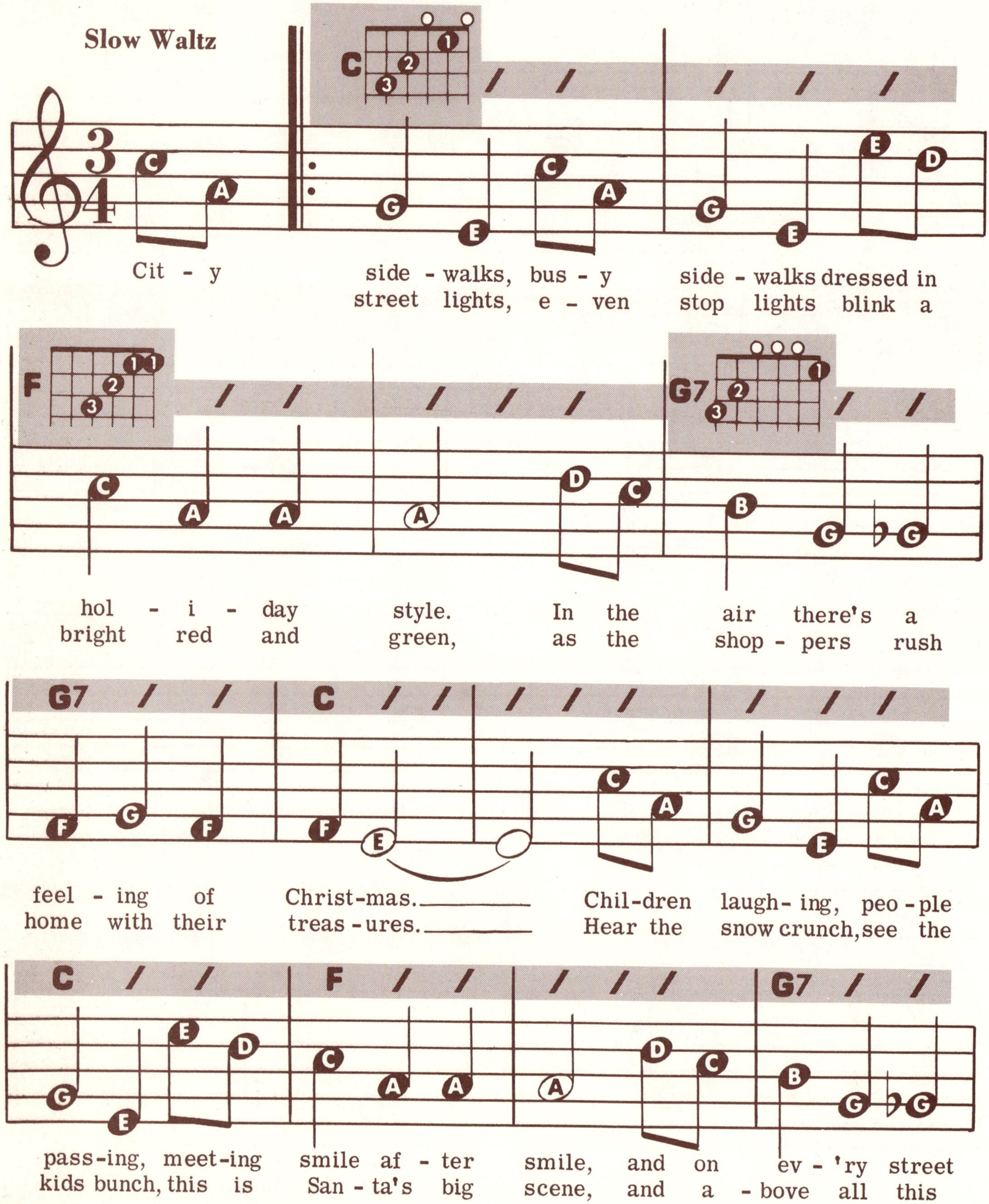

**Slow Waltz**

Cit - y side - walks, bus - y side - walks dressed in
street lights, e - ven stop lights blink a

hol - i - day style. In the air there's a
bright red and green, as the shop - pers rush

feel - ing of Christ-mas._____ Chil-dren laugh- ing, peo - ple
home with their treas - ures._____ Hear the snow crunch, see the

pass - ing, meet - ing smile af - ter smile, and on ev - 'ry street
kids bunch, this is San - ta's big scene, and a - bove all this

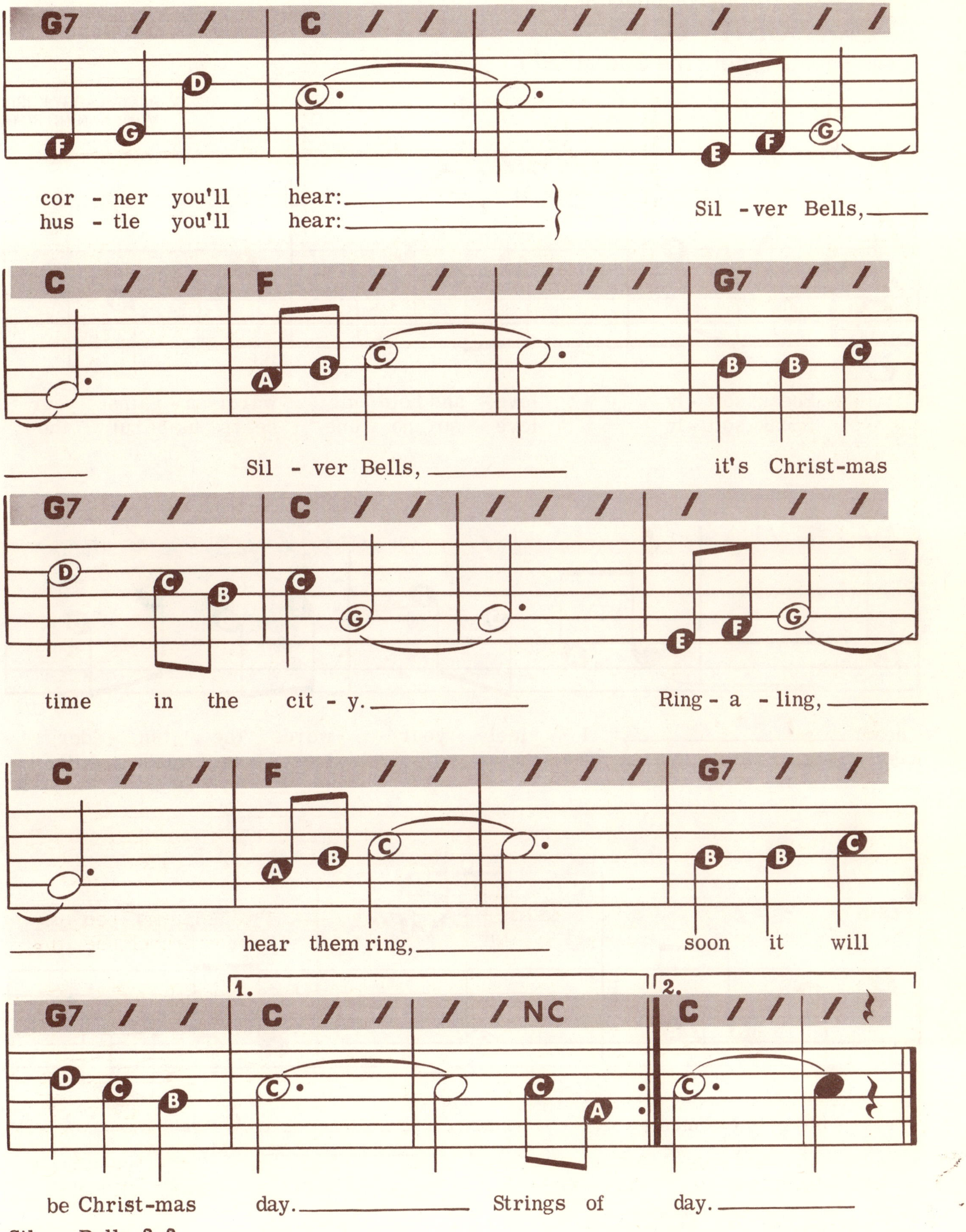
G7 C G7 C F G7 C G7 C F G7 G7 C NC C
cor - ner you'll hear:
hus - tle you'll hear:
Sil - ver Bells,
Sil - ver Bells,
it's Christ-mas
time in the cit - y.
Ring - a - ling,
hear them ring,
soon it will
be Christ-mas day.
Strings of
day.
1.
2.

*From the Paramount Picture "THE GODFATHER"*

# SPEAK SOFTLY LOVE
## (Love Theme From "The Godfather")

Words by LARRY KUSIK
Music by NINO ROTA

**Slowly**

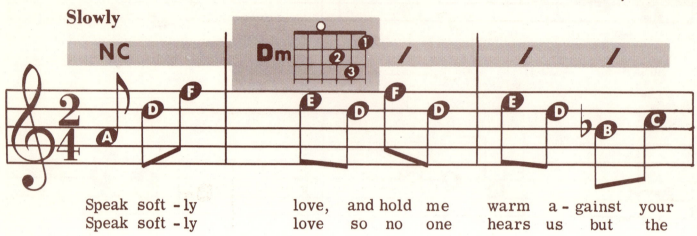

Speak soft - ly love, and hold me warm a - gainst your
Speak soft - ly love so no one hears us but the

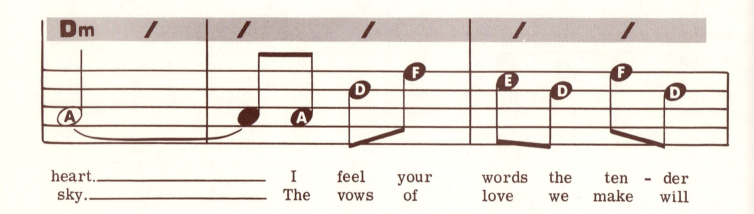

heart._____ I feel your words the ten - der
sky._____ The vows of love we make will

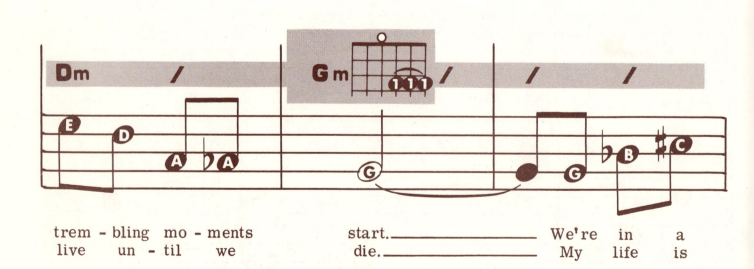

trem - bling mo - ments start._____ We're in a
live un - til we die._____ My life is

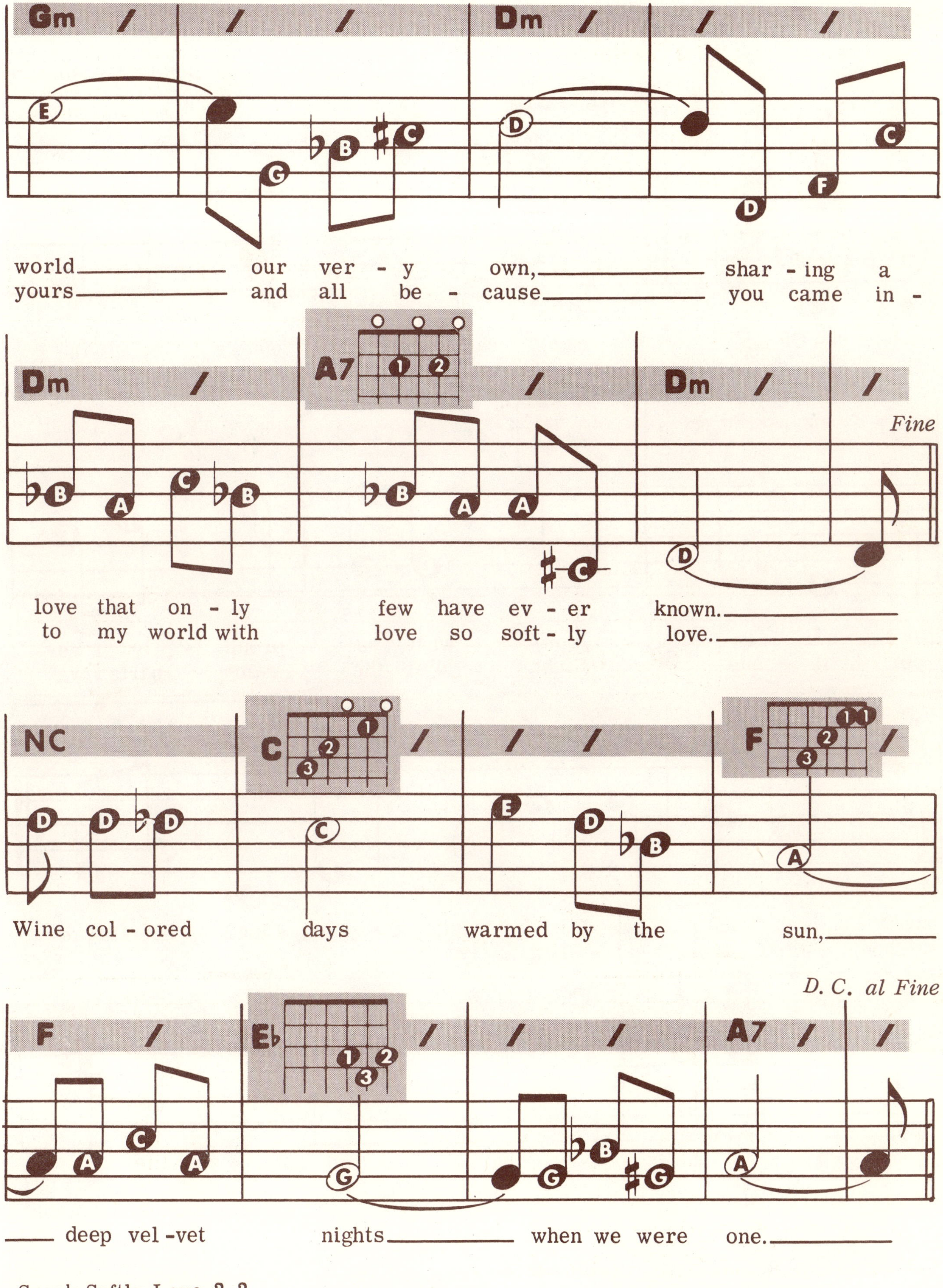

world_____ our ver - y own,_____ shar - ing a
yours_____ and all be - cause_____ you came in -

love that on - ly few have ev - er known._____
to my world with love so soft - ly love._____

Wine col - ored days warmed by the sun,_____

deep vel - vet nights_____ when we were one._____

Speak Softly Love -2 -2

# STAR-SPANGLED BANNER

FRANCIS SCOTT KEY
JOHN STAFFORD SMITH

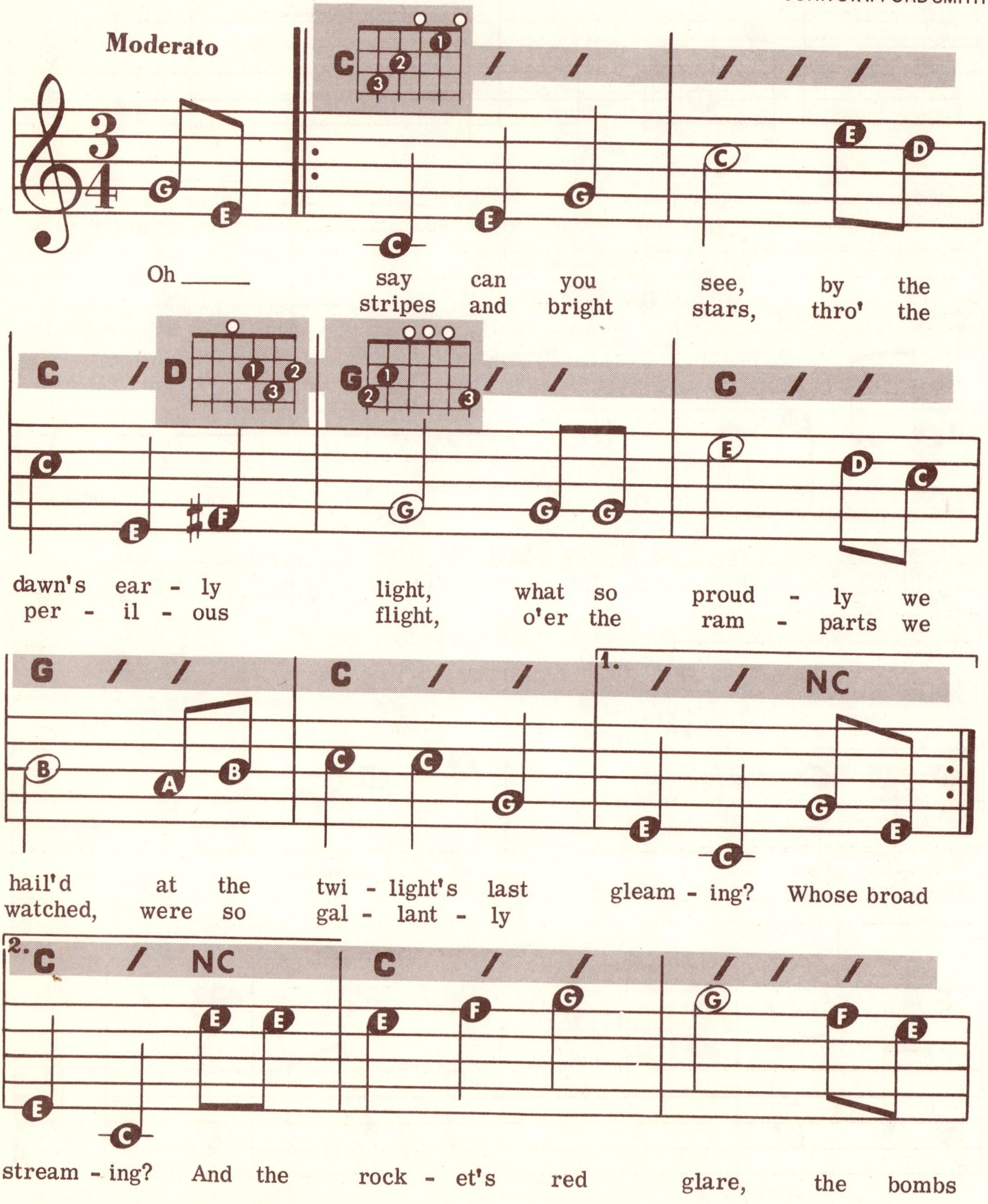

Oh _____ say can you see, by the
stripes and bright stars, thro' the

dawn's ear - ly light, what so proud - ly we
per - il - ous flight, o'er the ram - parts we

hail'd at the twi - light's last gleam - ing? Whose broad
watched, were so gal - lant - ly

stream - ing? And the rock - et's red glare, the bombs

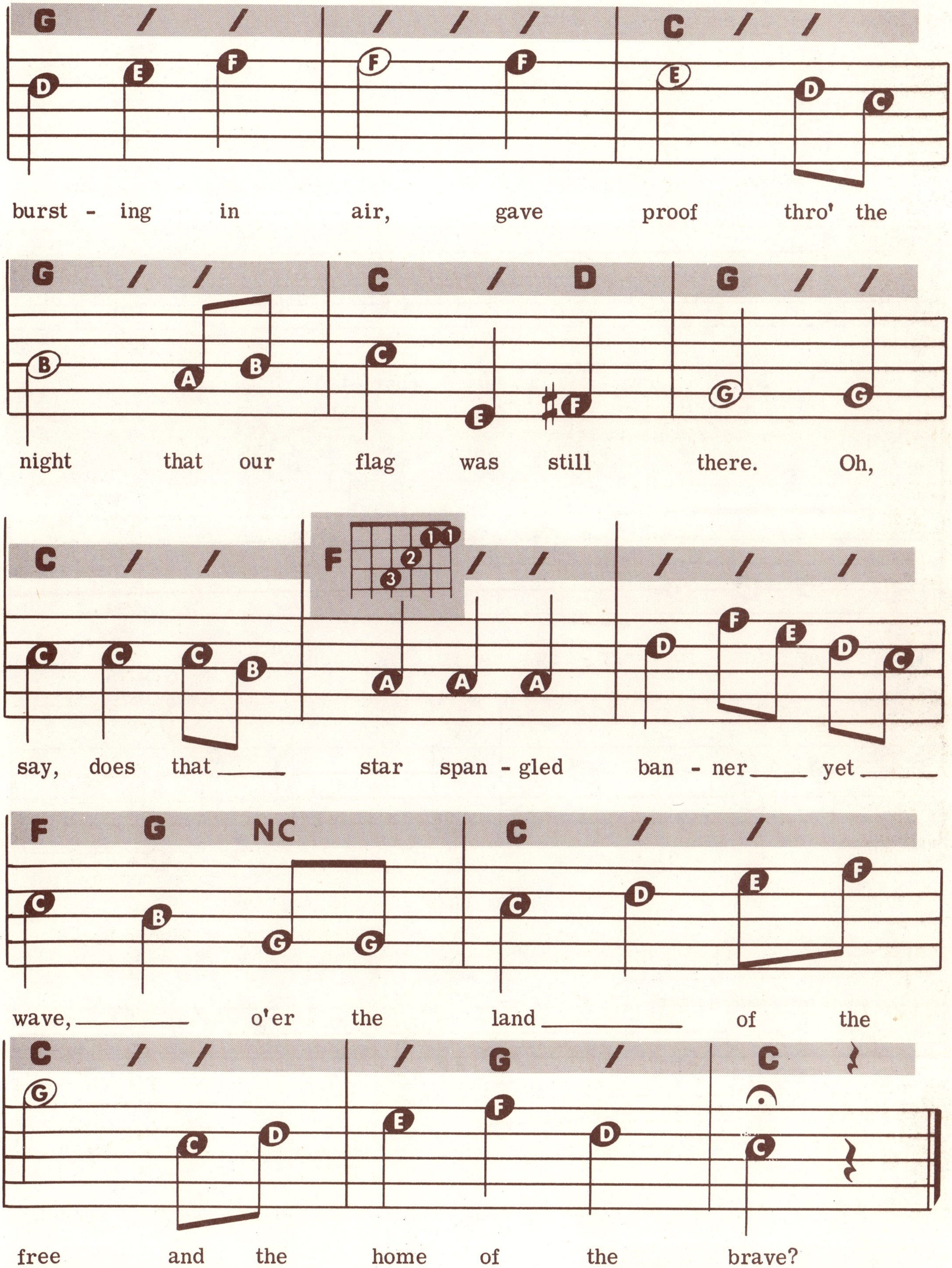

burst - ing in air, gave proof thro' the

night that our flag was still there. Oh,

say, does that _____ star span - gled ban - ner_____ yet _____

wave,_____ o'er the land _____ of the

free and the home of the brave?

Star-Spangled Banner-2 -2

# SWING LOW, SWEET CHARIOT

TRADITIONAL

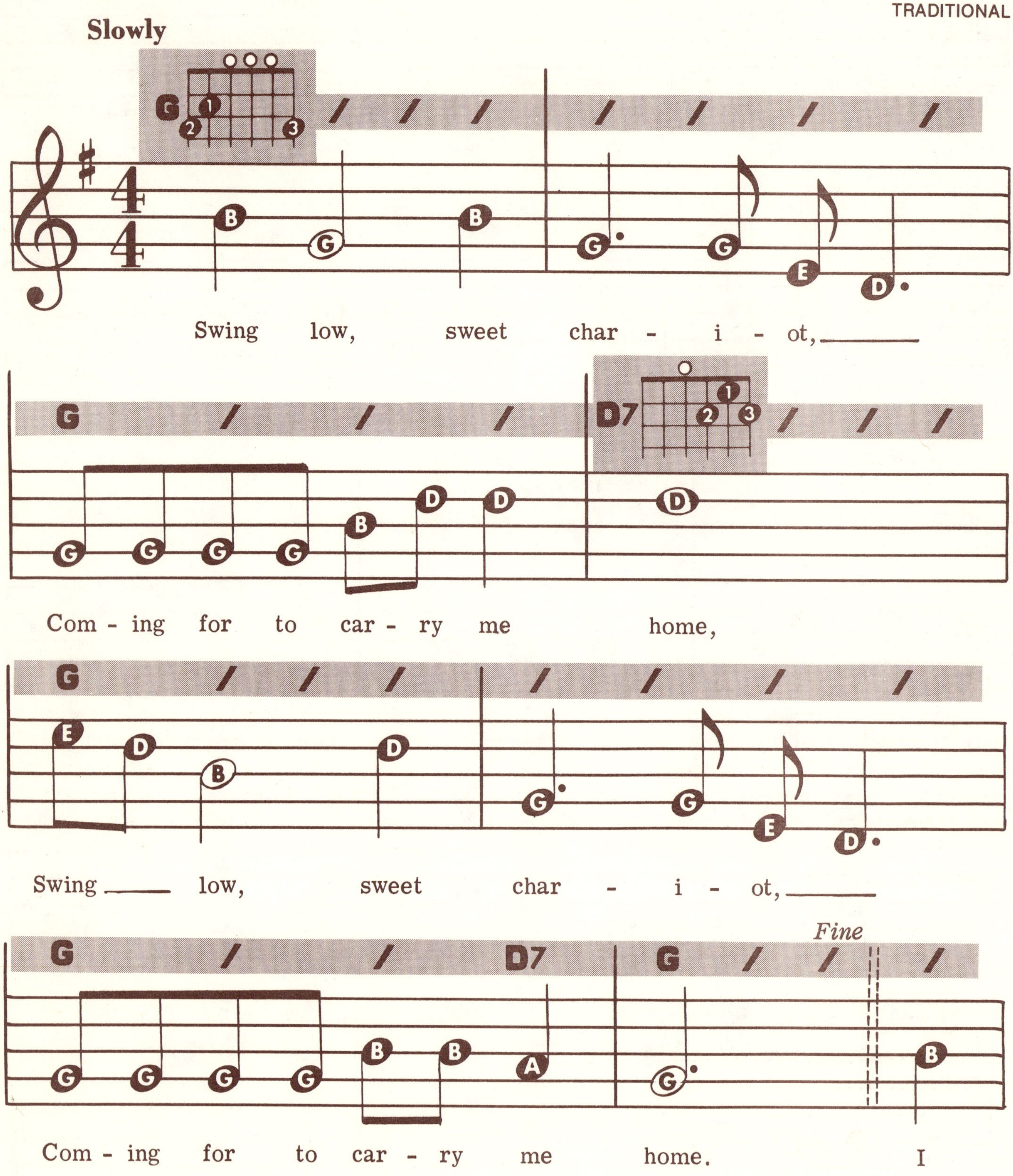

Swing low, sweet char - i - ot, ___

Com - ing for to car - ry me home,

Swing ___ low, sweet char - i - ot, ___

Com - ing for to car - ry me home. I

157

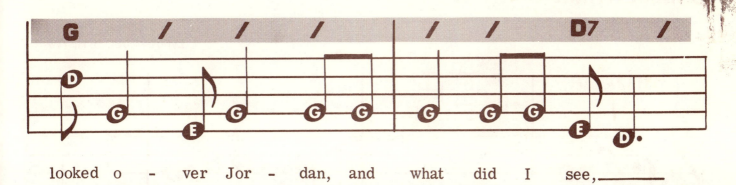

looked o - ver Jor - dan, and what did I see,_____

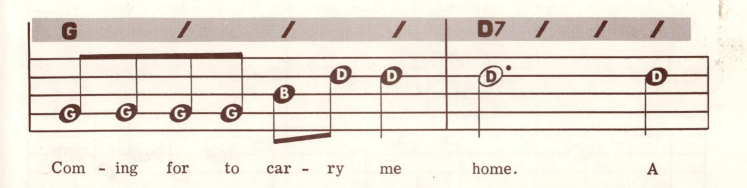

Com — ing for to car — ry me home. A

*D.C. al Fine*

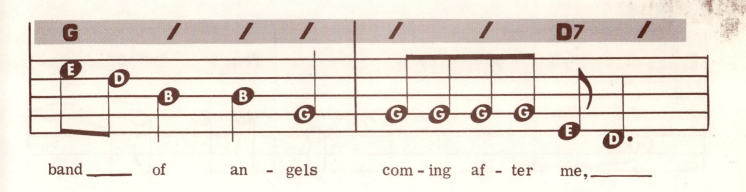

band_____ of an - gels com - ing af - ter me,_____

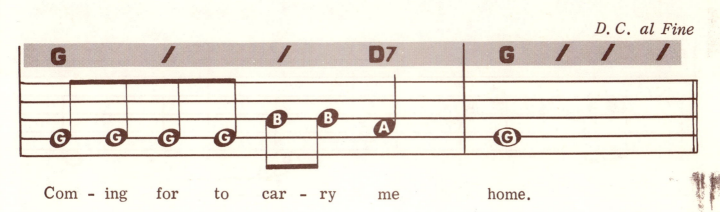

Com — ing for to car — ry me home.

Swing Low, Sweet Chariot-2-2

# SUMMERTIME

Music by GEORGE GERSHWIN
Lyric by DuBOSE HEYWARD

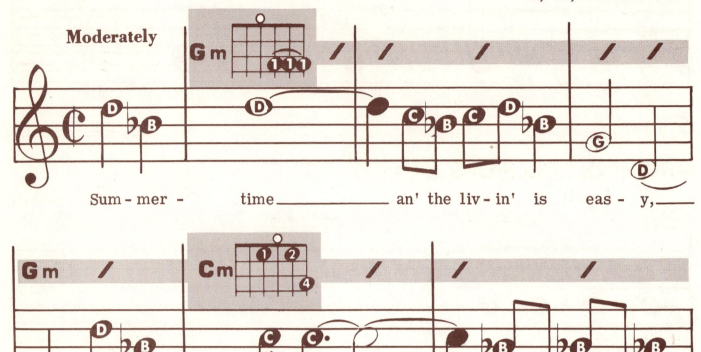

Sum - mer - time _____ an' the liv - in' is eas - y, _____

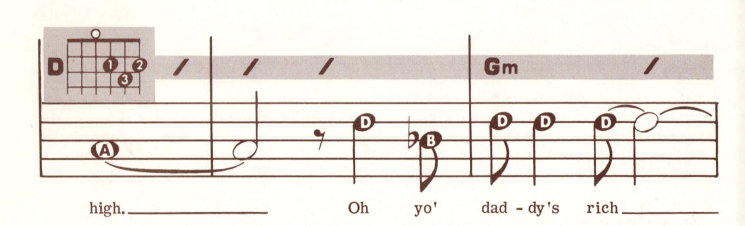

_____ fish are jump - in', _____ an' the cot - ton is

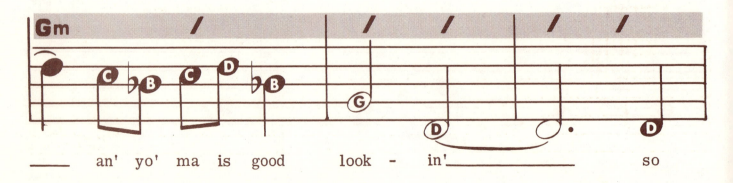

high. _____ Oh yo' dad - dy's rich _____

_____ an' yo' ma is good look - in' _____ so

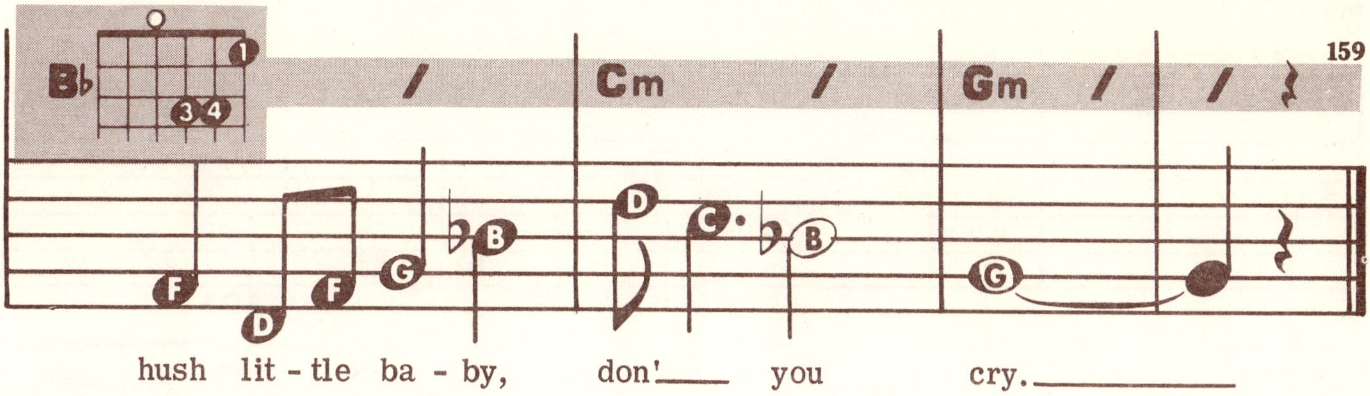

hush lit-tle ba-by, don'___ you cry._____

Summertime-2-2

# SUNSHINE, LOLLIPOPS AND RAINBOWS

Lively, with a beat

Words by HOWARD LIEBLING
Music by MARVIN HAMLISCH

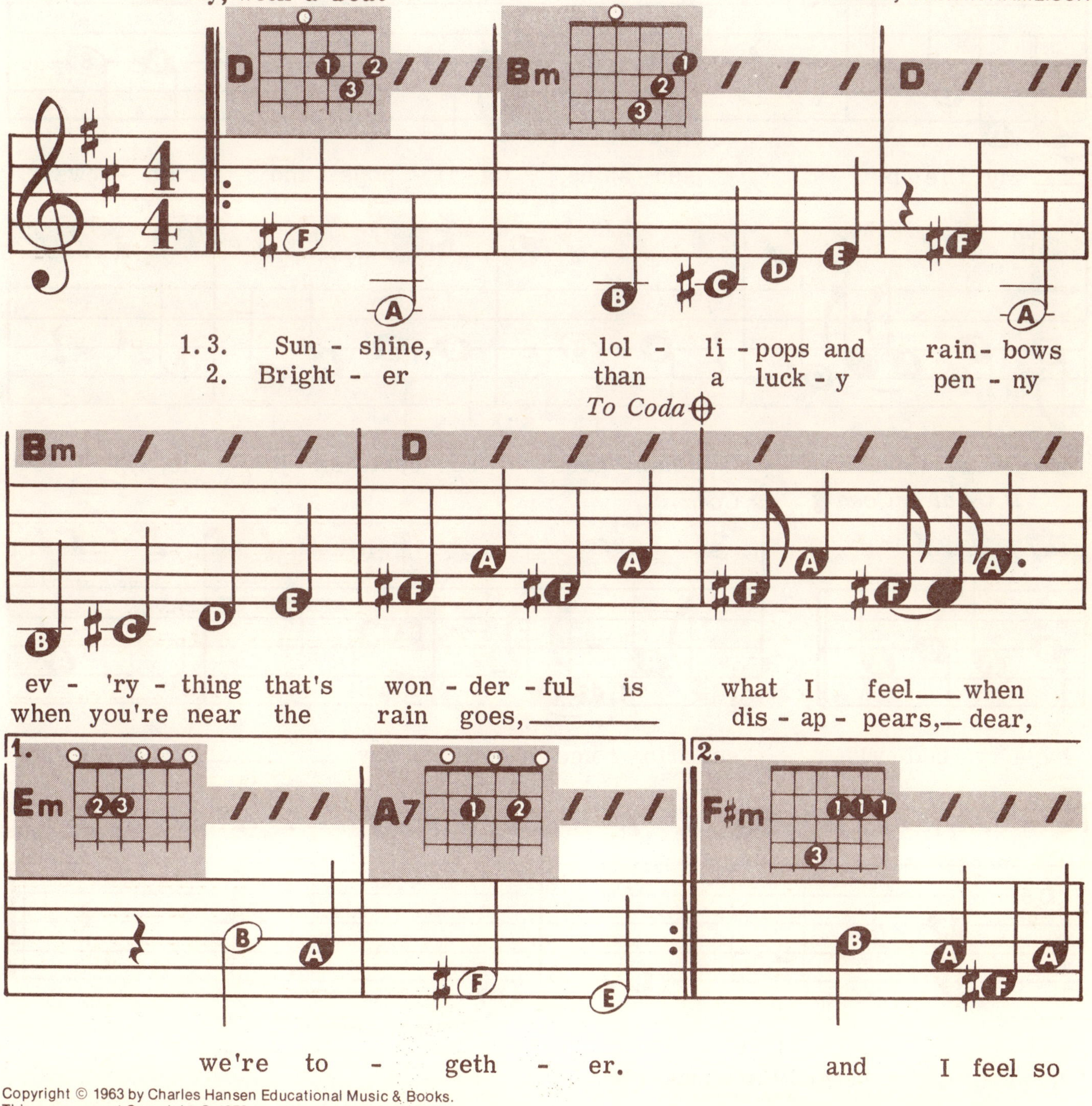

1. 3.   Sun - shine,        lol - li -pops and   rain - bows
2.   Bright - er        than   a   luck - y   pen - ny

To Coda ⊕

ev - 'ry - thing that's   won - der - ful   is      what I   feel___ when
when you're near   the   rain goes, _____   dis - ap - pears,— dear,

we're to - geth - er.                  and   I   feel so

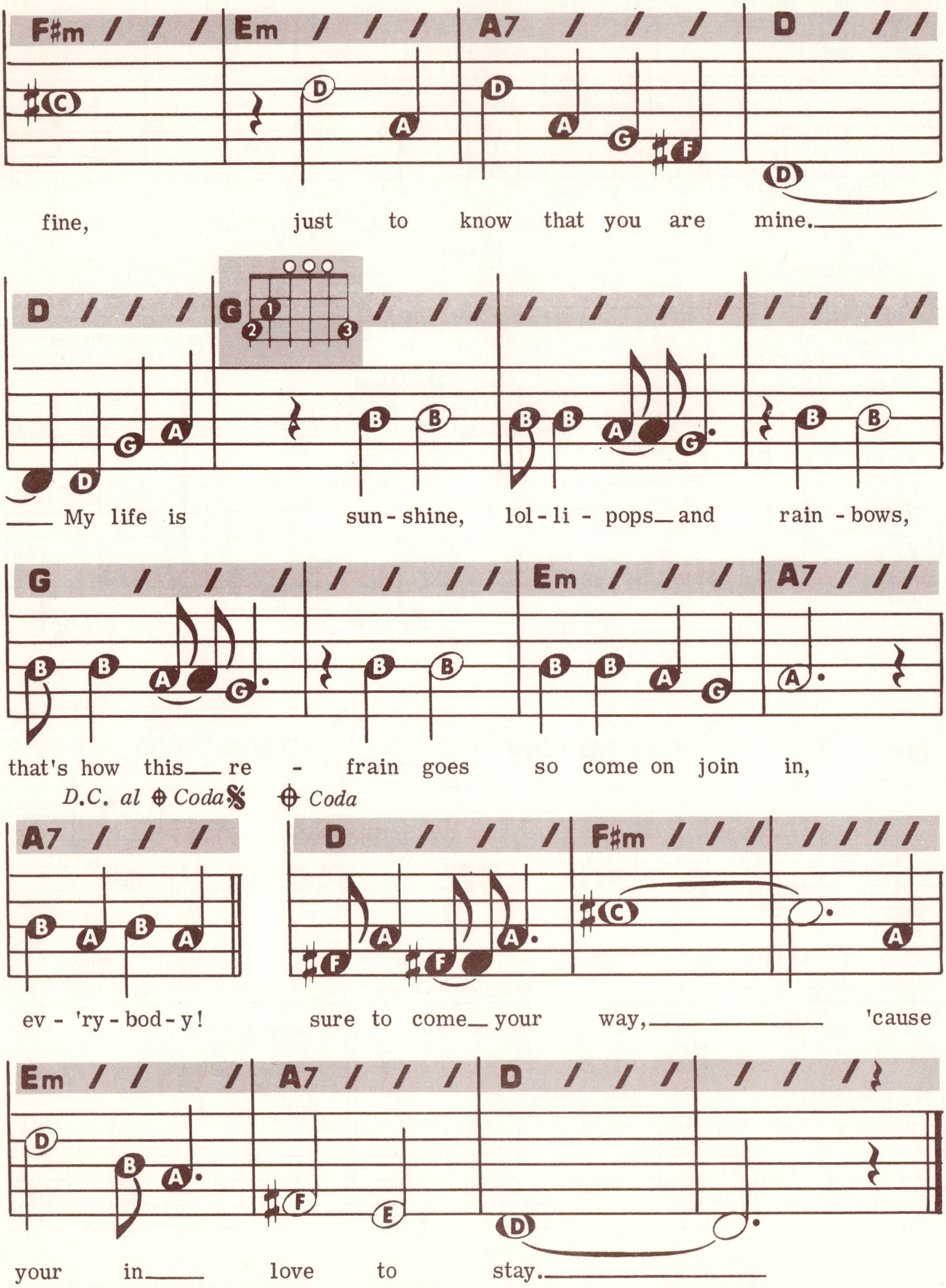

fine, just to know that you are mine.____

____ My life is sun-shine, lol-li-pops__ and rain-bows,

that's how this__ re - frain goes so come on join in,
*D.C. al ⊕ Coda* 𝄋 ⊕ *Coda*

ev-'ry-bod-y!

sure to come__ your way,_____ 'cause

your in____ love to stay.____

Sunshine, Lollipops And Rainbows-2-2

# TAKE ME HOME, COUNTRY ROADS

Words and Music by
BILL DANOFF, TAFFY NIVERT
and JOHN DENVER

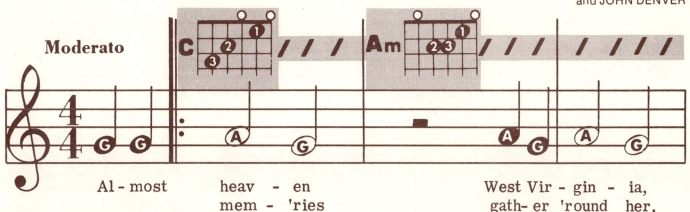

Al - most    heav - en    West Vir - gin - ia,
mem - 'ries    gath - er 'round her,

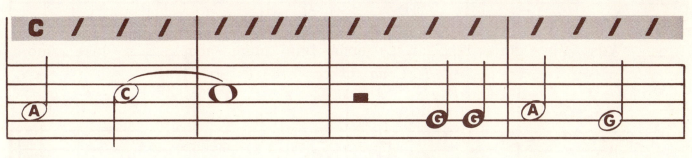

Blue Ridge    Moun - tains,    Shen - an - do - ah
min - er's    la - dy,    stran - ger to blue

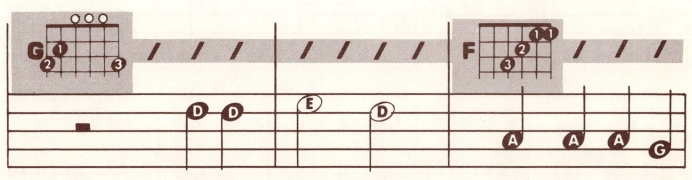

Riv - er,_____    life is    old    there,
wa - ter,_____    dark and    dust - y,

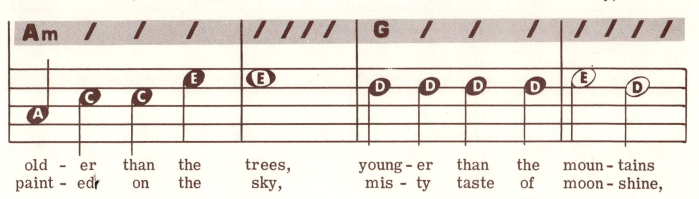

old - er    than the    trees,    young - er    than the    moun - tains
paint - ed    on the    sky,    mis - ty    taste of    moon - shine,

45853

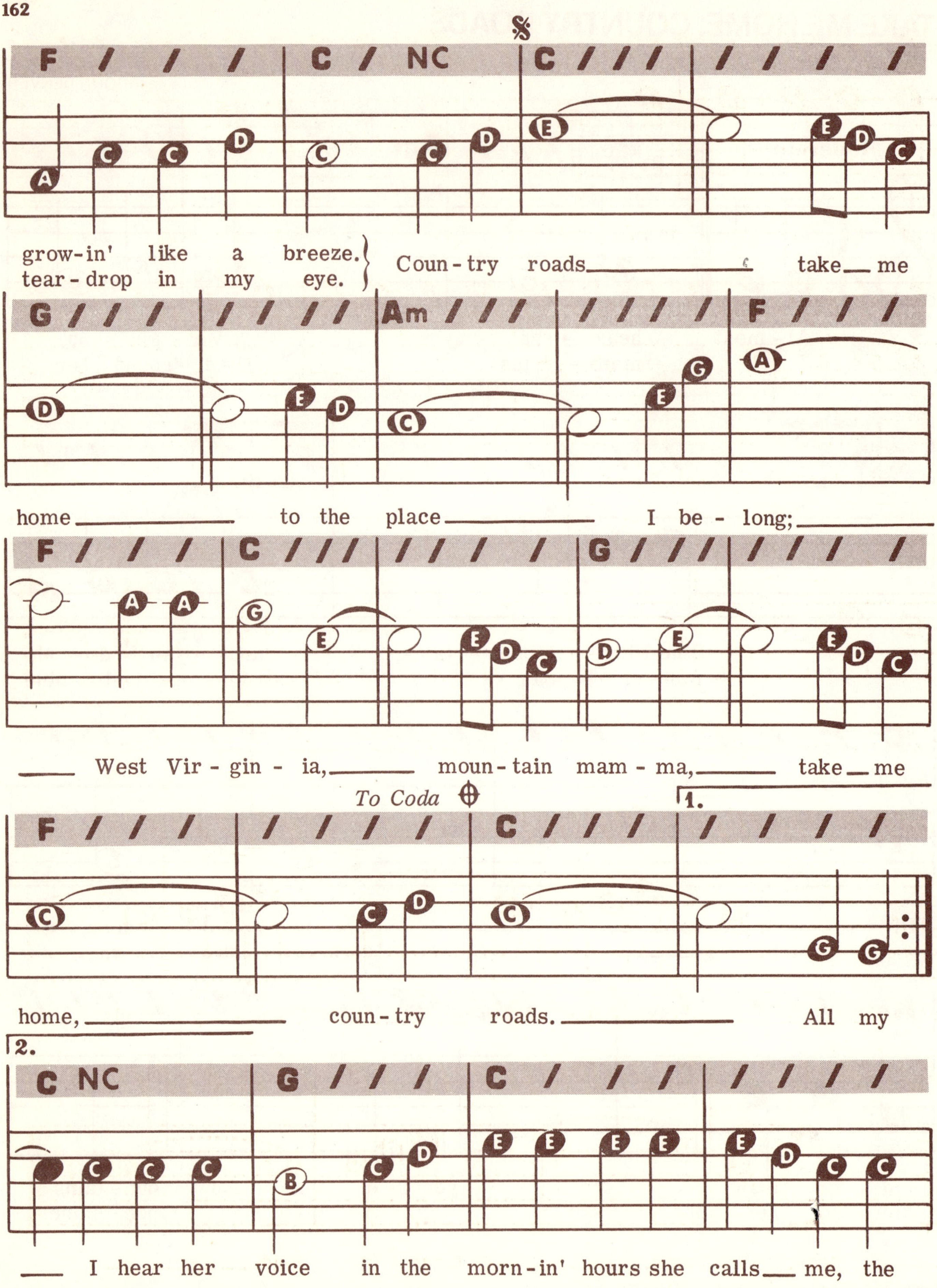

grow-in' like a breeze.
tear-drop in my eye.
Coun-try roads_____ take_ me

home_____ to the place_____ I be-long;_____

___ West Vir-gin-ia,_____ moun-tain mam-ma,_____ take_ me

*To Coda* ⊕

**1.**

home,_____ coun-try roads._____ All my

**2.**

___ I hear her voice in the morn-in' hours she calls_ me, the

Take Me Home, Country Roads-3-2

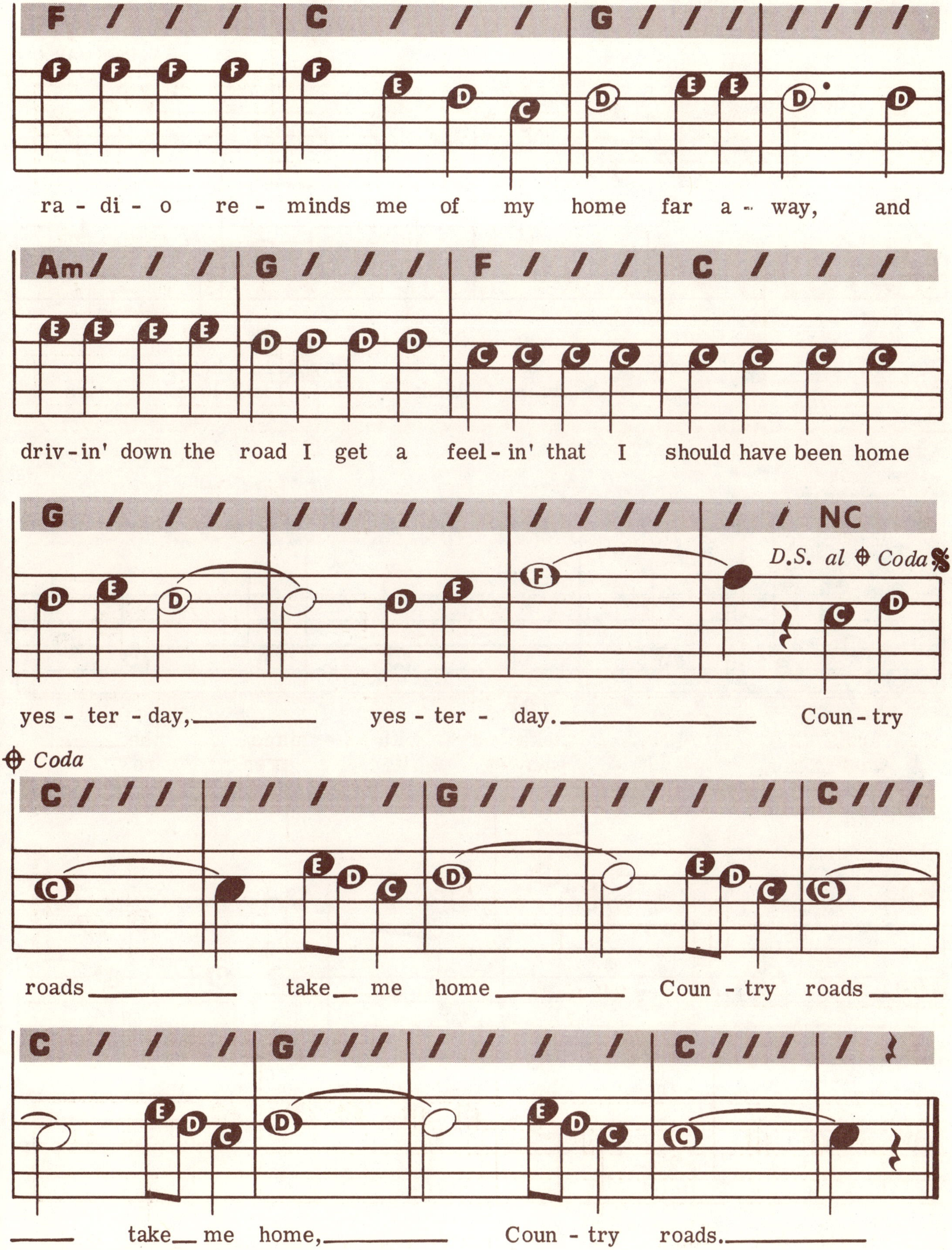
F / / / / C / / / / G / / / / / / / /
ra - di - o re - minds me of my home far a - way, and
Am / / / / G / / / / F / / / / C / / / /
driv - in' down the road I get a feel - in' that I should have been home
G / / / / / / / / / / / / / / NC
D.S. al Coda
yes - ter - day, yes - ter - day. Coun - try
Coda
C / / / / / / / / G / / / / / / / / C / / /
roads take me home Coun - try roads
C / / / / G / / / / / / / / C / / / / /
take me home, Coun - try roads.

# A TASTE OF HONEY

By RICK MARLOW
and BOBBY SCOTT

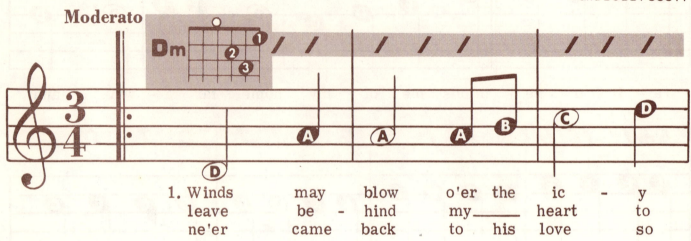

1. Winds may blow o'er the ic - y
leave be - hind my___ heart to
ne'er came back my to his love so

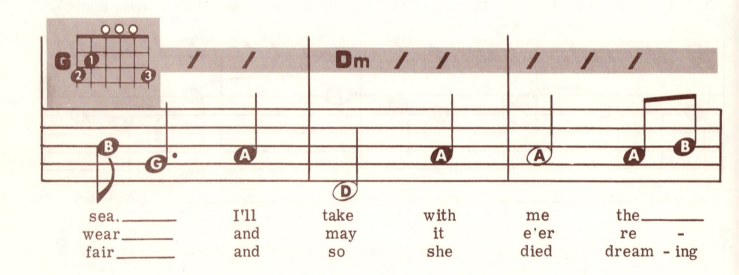

sea.___ I'll take with me the___
wear___ and may it e'er re -
fair___ and so she died dream - ing

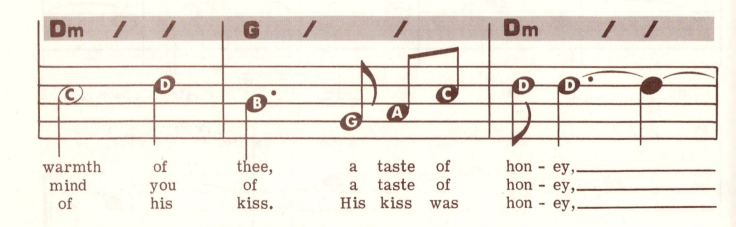

warmth of thee, a taste of hon - ey,___
mind you of a taste of hon - ey,___
of his kiss. His kiss was hon - ey,___

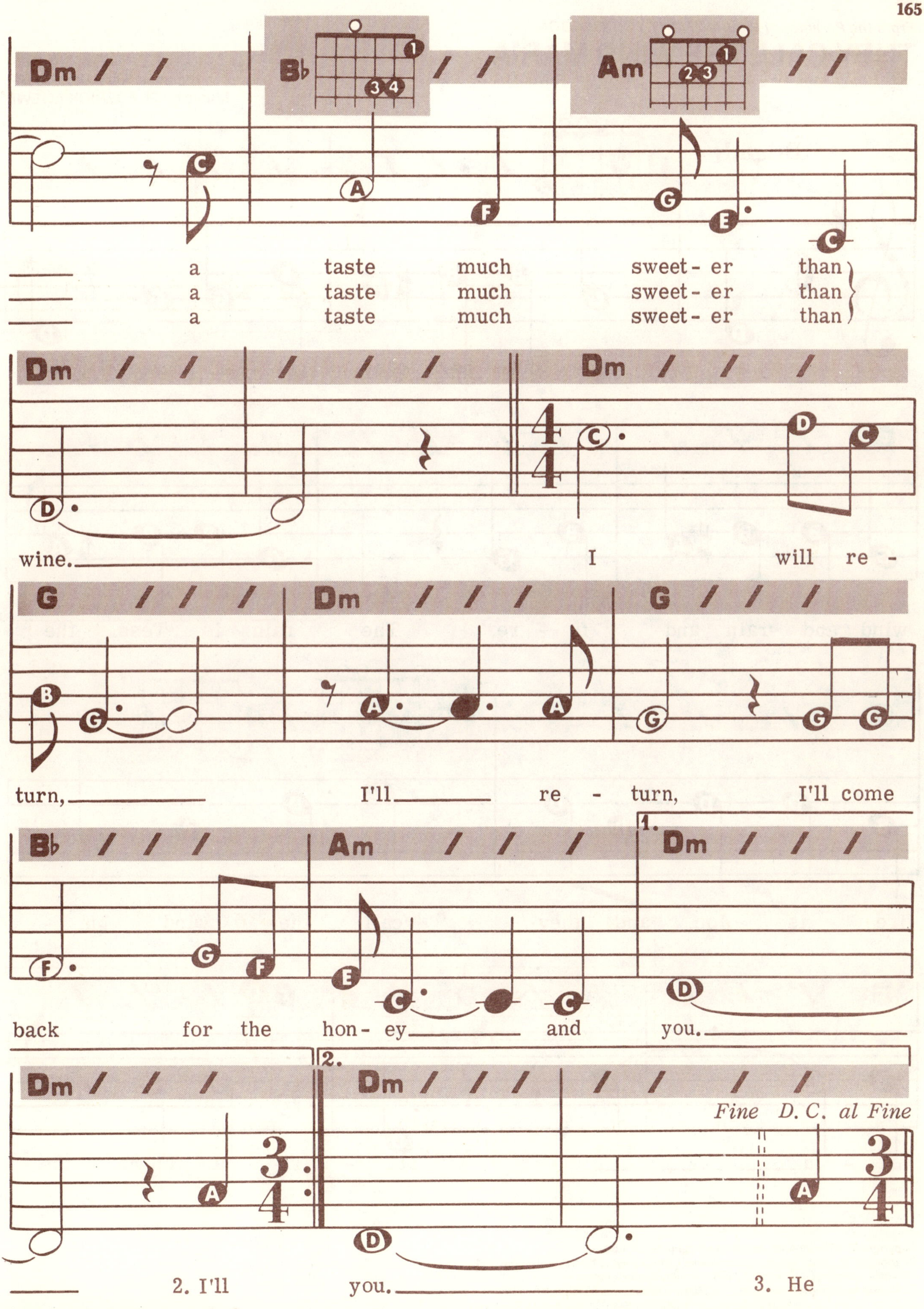

A Taste Of Honey-2-2

45853

*From the Paramount Picture "PAINT YOUR WAGON"*

# THEY CALL THE WIND MARIA

Lyric by ALAN JAY LERNER
Music by FREDERICK LOEWE

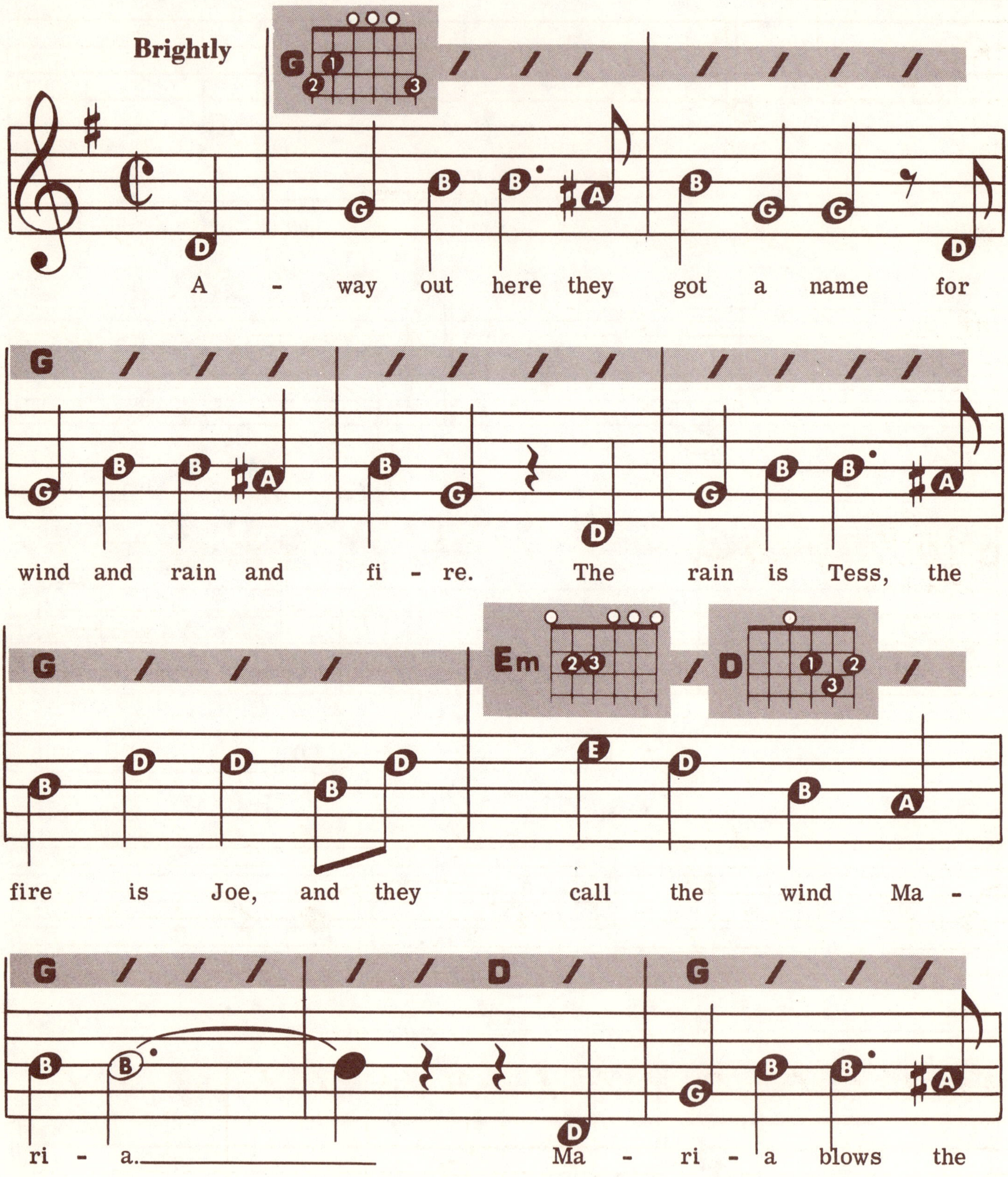

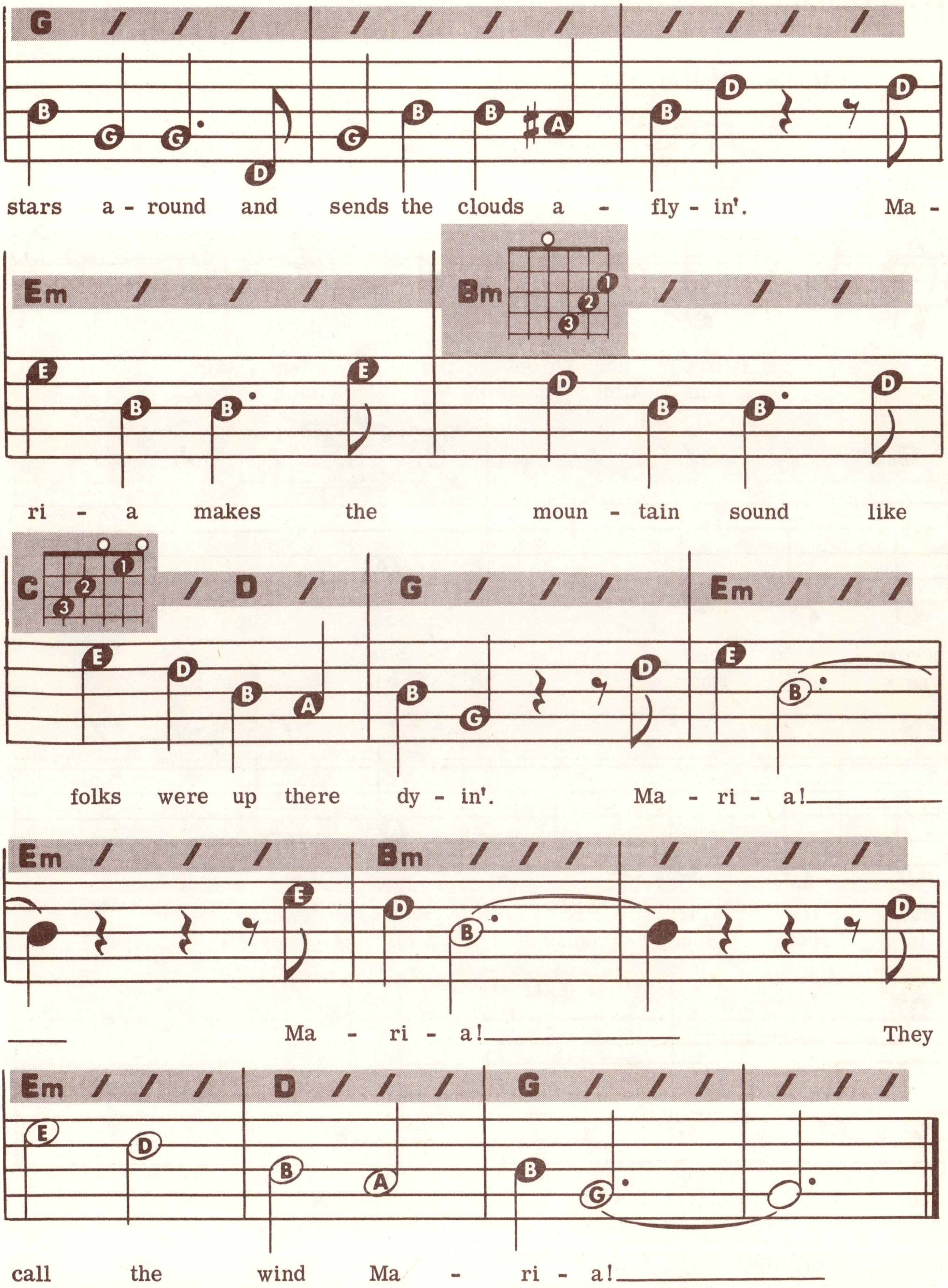

stars   a - round   and   sends   the   clouds   a - fly - in'.   Ma -

ri - a   makes   the   moun - tain   sound   like

folks   were   up   there   dy - in'.   Ma - ri - a!_____

_____   Ma - ri - a!_____   They

call   the   wind   Ma - ri - a!_____

They Call The Wind Maria-2-2

# TOM DOOLEY

**Medium Ballad**

FOLK SONG

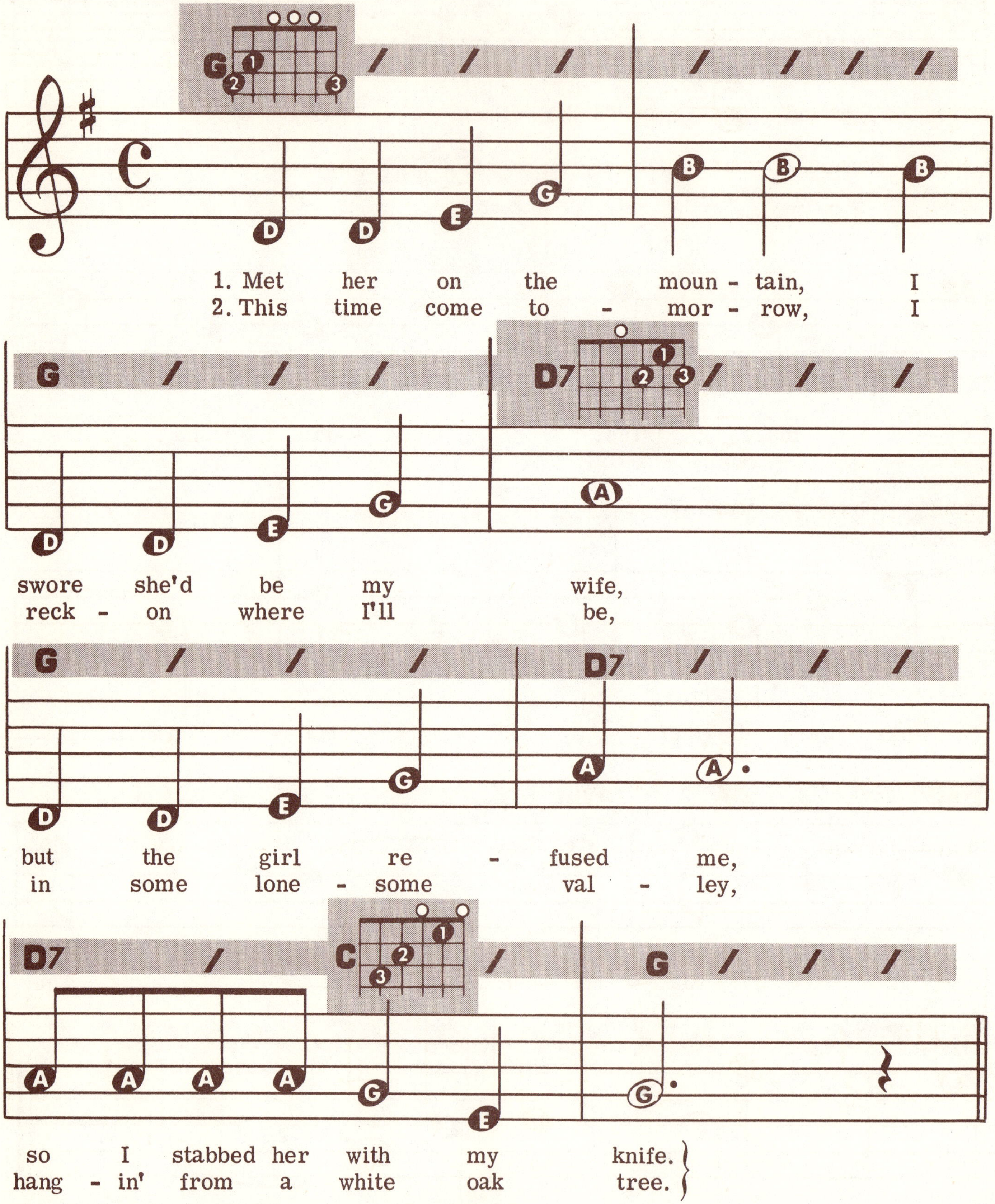

1. Met her on the moun - tain, I
2. This time come to - mor - row, I

swore she'd be my wife,
reck - on where I'll be,

but the girl re - fused me,
in some lone - some val - ley,

so I stabbed her with my knife.
hang - in' from a white oak tree.

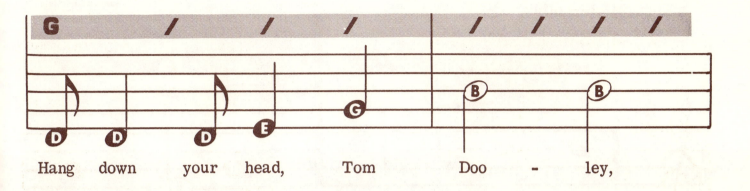

Hang    down    your    head,    Tom    Doo  -  ley,

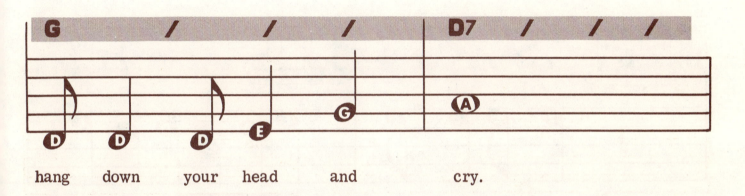

hang    down    your    head    and    cry.

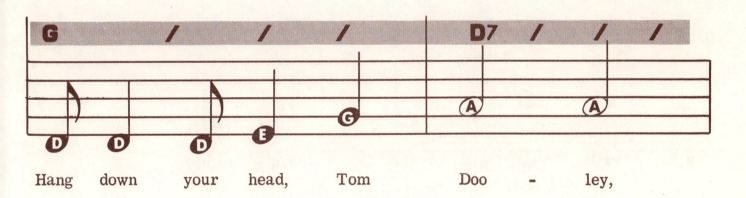

Hang    down    your    head,    Tom    Doo  -  ley,

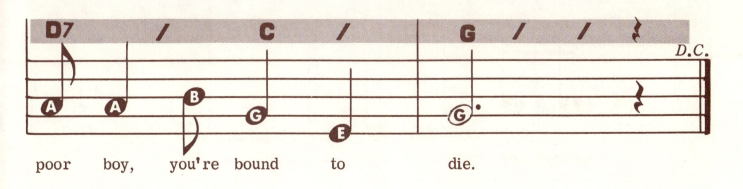

poor    boy,    you're    bound    to    die.

Tom Dooley -2 -2

# WE'LL SING IN THE SUNSHINE

GALE GARNETT

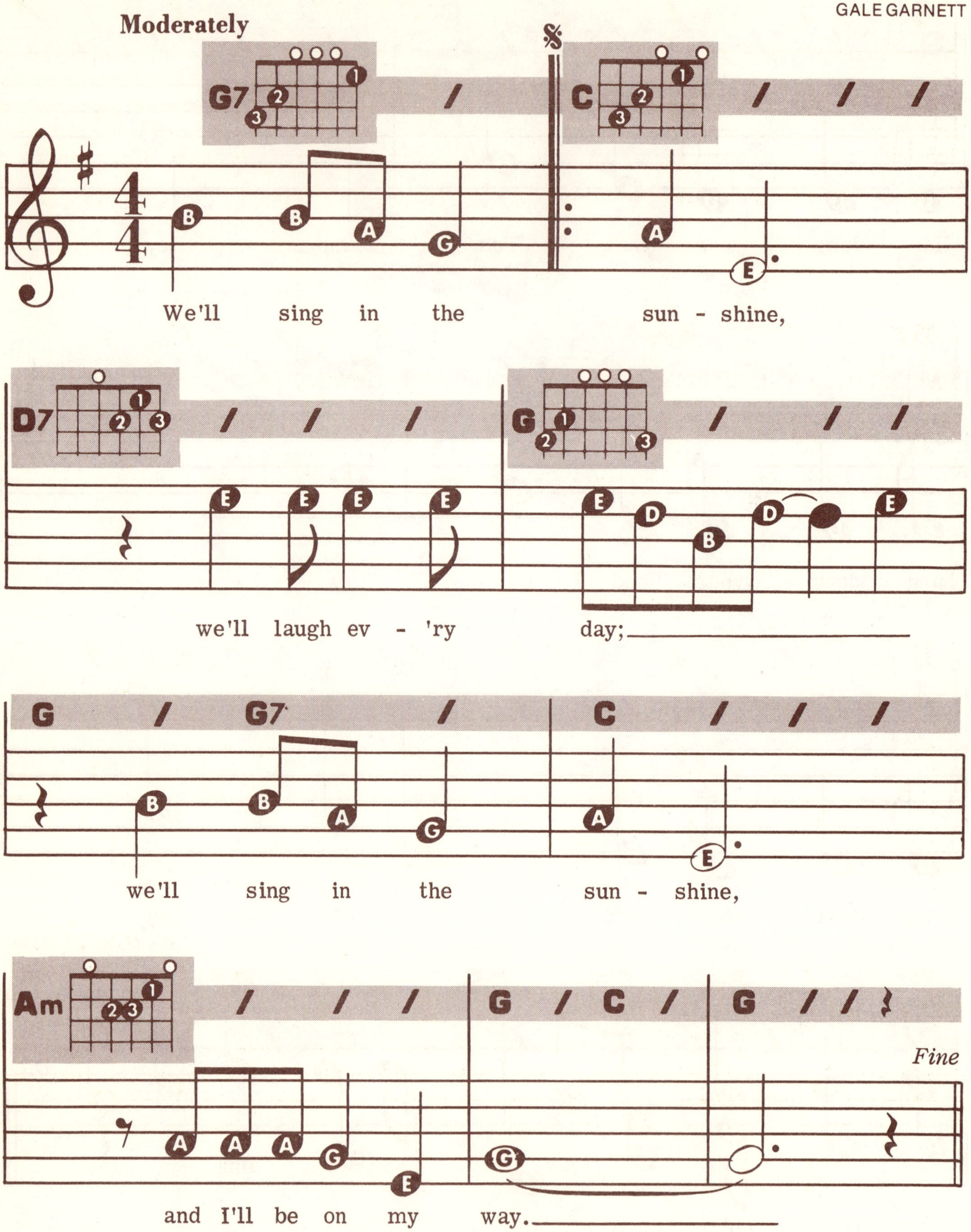

We'll sing in the sun-shine, we'll laugh ev-'ry day;____ we'll sing in the sun-shine, and I'll be on my way.____

*Fine*

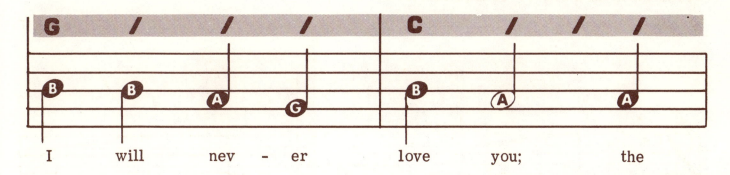

I will nev - er love you; the

cost of love's too dear, but

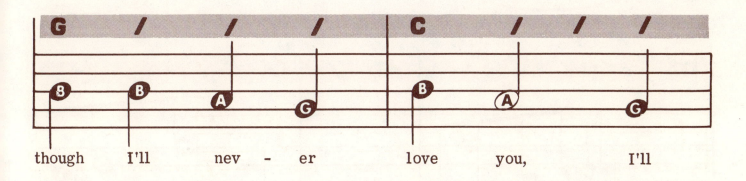

though I'll nev - er love you, I'll

*D.S. al Fine*

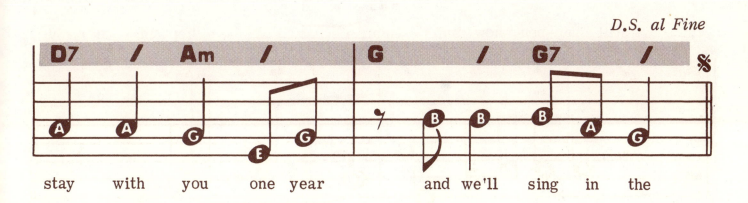

stay with you one year and we'll sing in the

We'll Sing In The Sunshine-2-2

# WELCOME TO MY WORLD

By RAY WINKLER and JOHN HATHCOCK

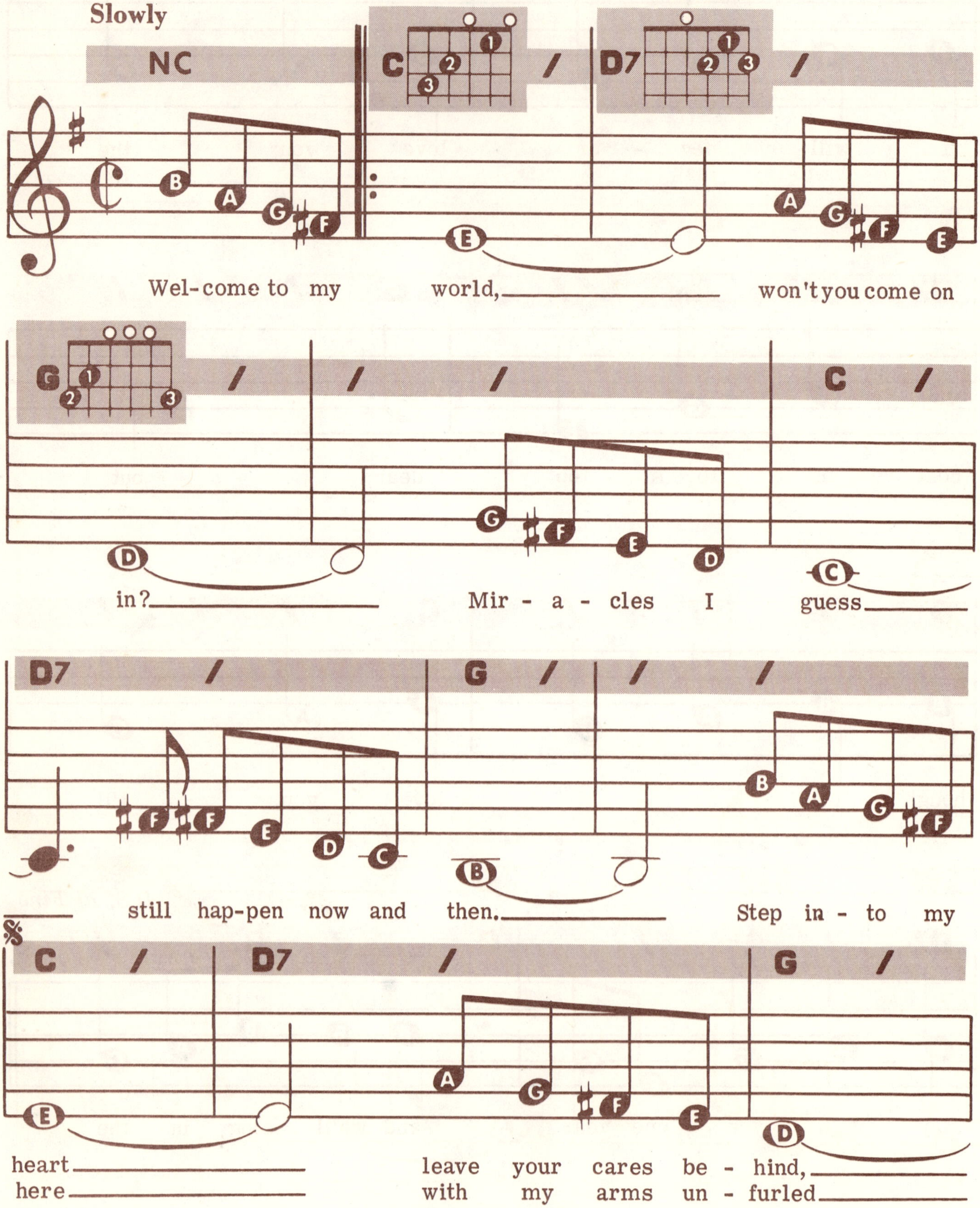

Wel-come to my world,_____ won't you come on in?_____ Mir - a - cles I guess_____ still hap-pen now and then._____ Step in - to my heart_____ leave your cares be - hind, here_____ with my arms un - furled_____

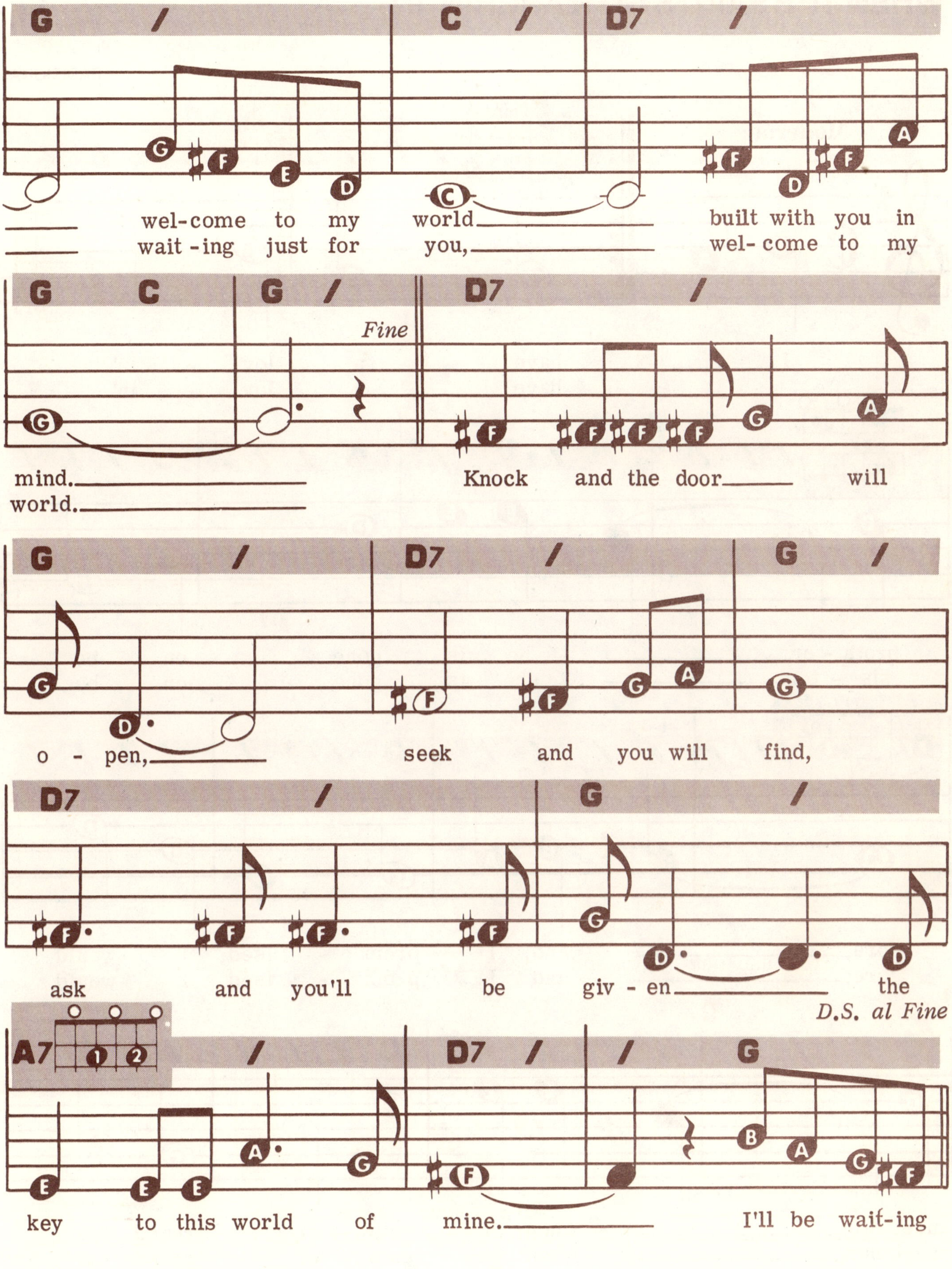
G / C / D7 /
wel-come to my world built with you in
wait-ing just for you, wel-come to my
G C G / Fine D7 /
mind.
world.
Knock and the door will
G / D7 / G /
o - pen, seek and you will find,
D7 / G /
ask and you'll be giv - en the
D.S. al Fine
A7 / D7 / / G
key to this world of mine. I'll be wait-ing

# WHEN THE SAINTS GO MARCHIN' IN

TRADITIONAL

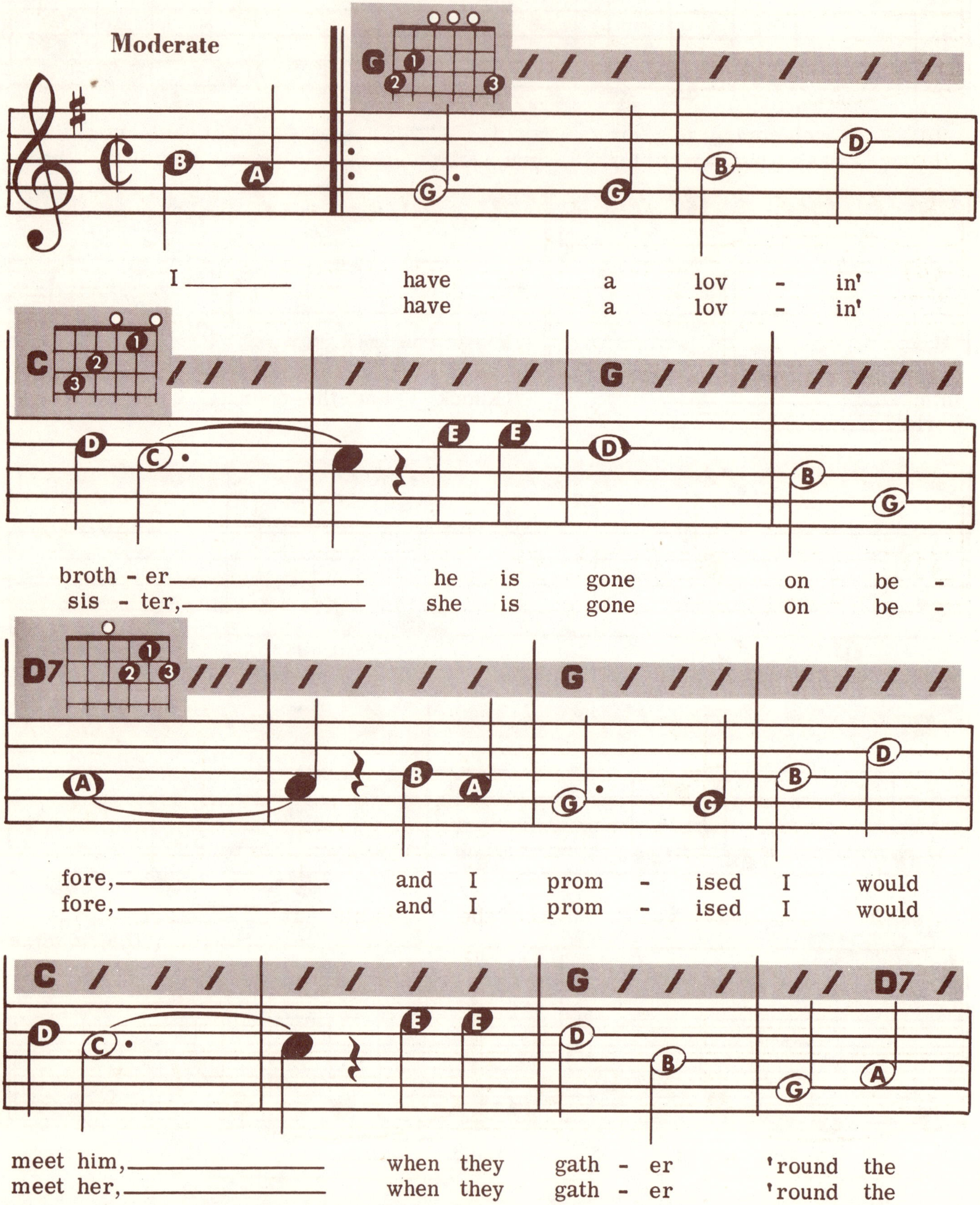

I _____ have a lov - in'
have a lov - in'

broth - er_____ he is gone on be -
sis - ter,_____ she is gone on be -

fore,_____ and I prom - ised I would
fore,_____ and I prom - ised I would

meet him,_____ when they gath - er 'round the
meet her,_____ when they gath - er 'round the

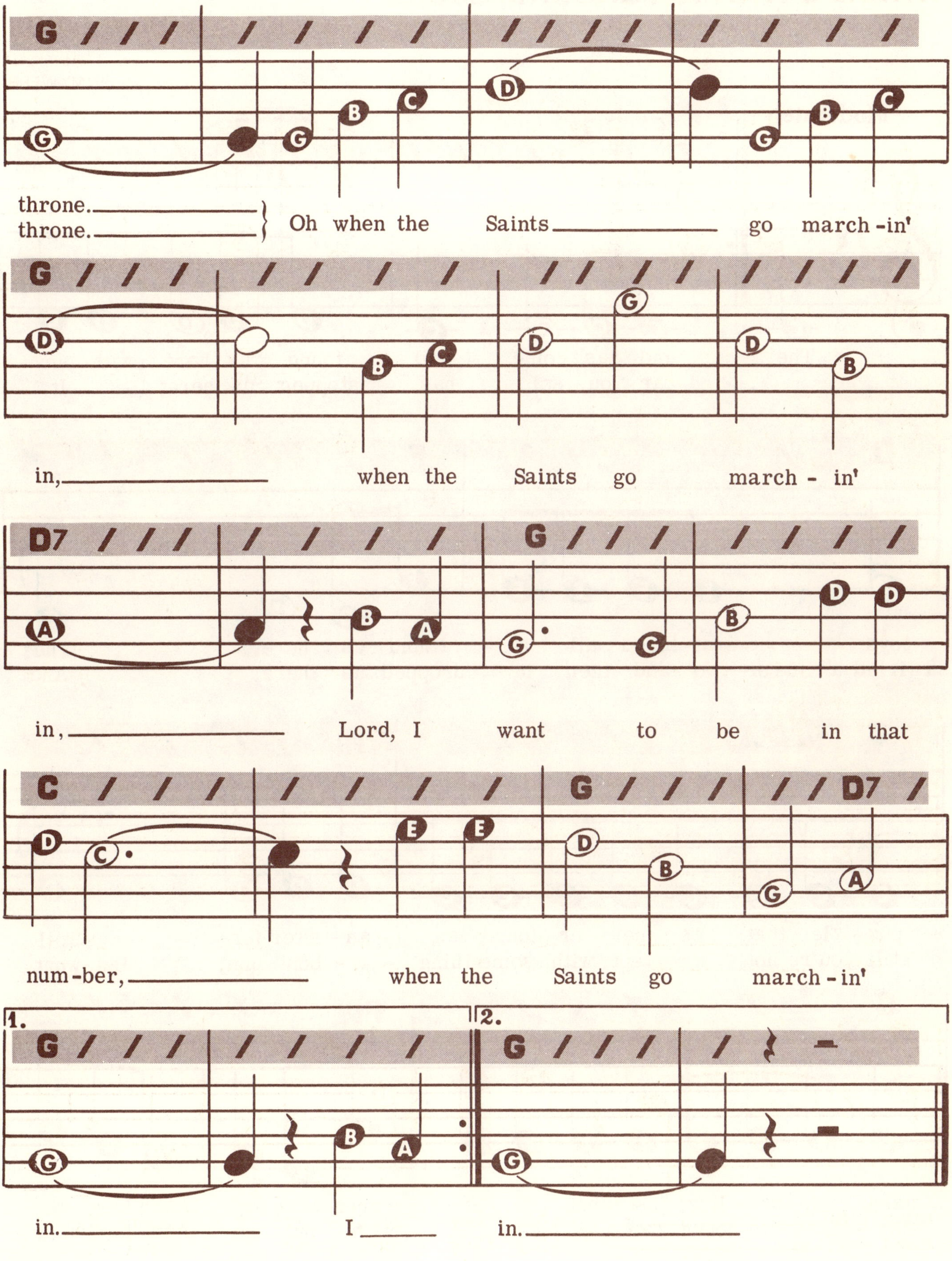
throne.
throne.
Oh when the Saints go march-in'
in, when the Saints go march - in'
in, Lord, I want to be in that
num-ber, when the Saints go march-in'
1.
2.
in. I in.

# WHERE'S THE PLAYGROUND, SUSIE?

By JIMMY WEBB

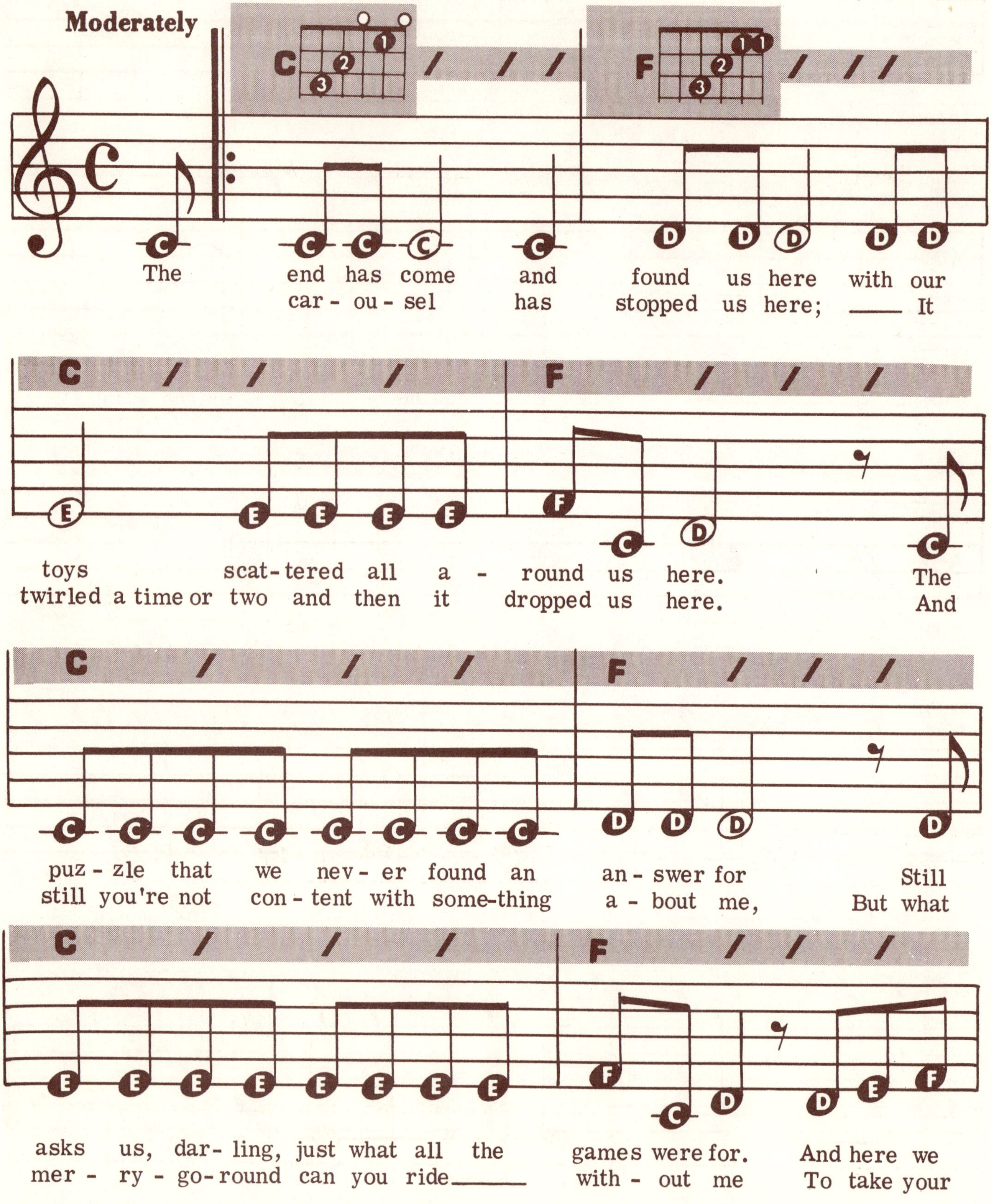

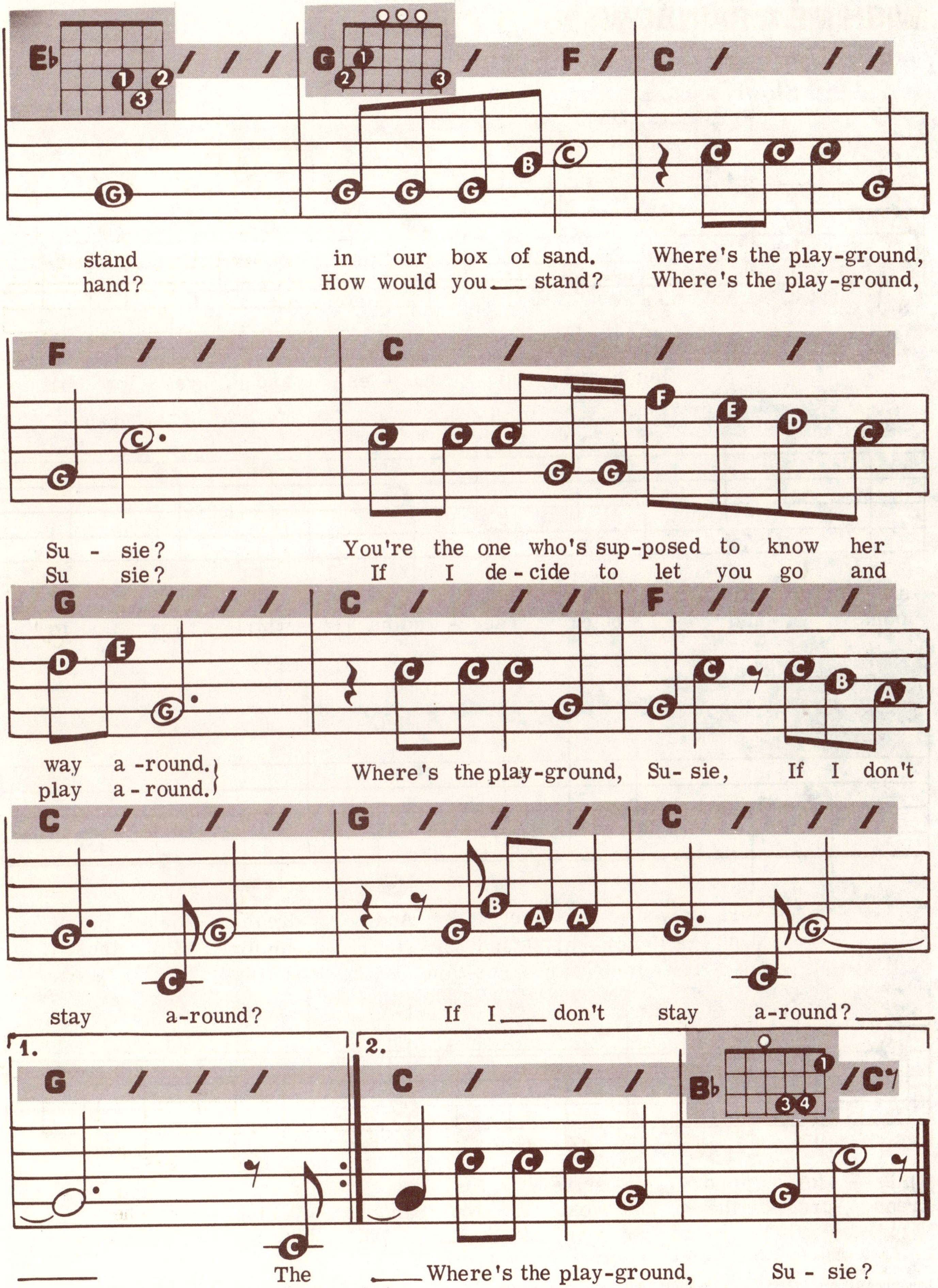
E♭ G F C
stand in our box of sand. Where's the play-ground,
hand? How would you ___ stand? Where's the play-ground,
F C
Su - sie? You're the one who's sup-posed to know her
Su sie? If I de-cide to let you go and
G C F
way a-round.
play a-round.
Where's the play-ground, Su-sie, If I don't
C G C
stay a-round? If I ___ don't stay a-round? ___
1. G 2. C B♭ /C7
___ The ___ Where's the play-ground, Su - sie?

*From the Paramount Picture "THIS PROPERTY IS CONDEMNED"*

# WISH ME A RAINBOW

By JAY LIVINGSTON
and RAY EVANS

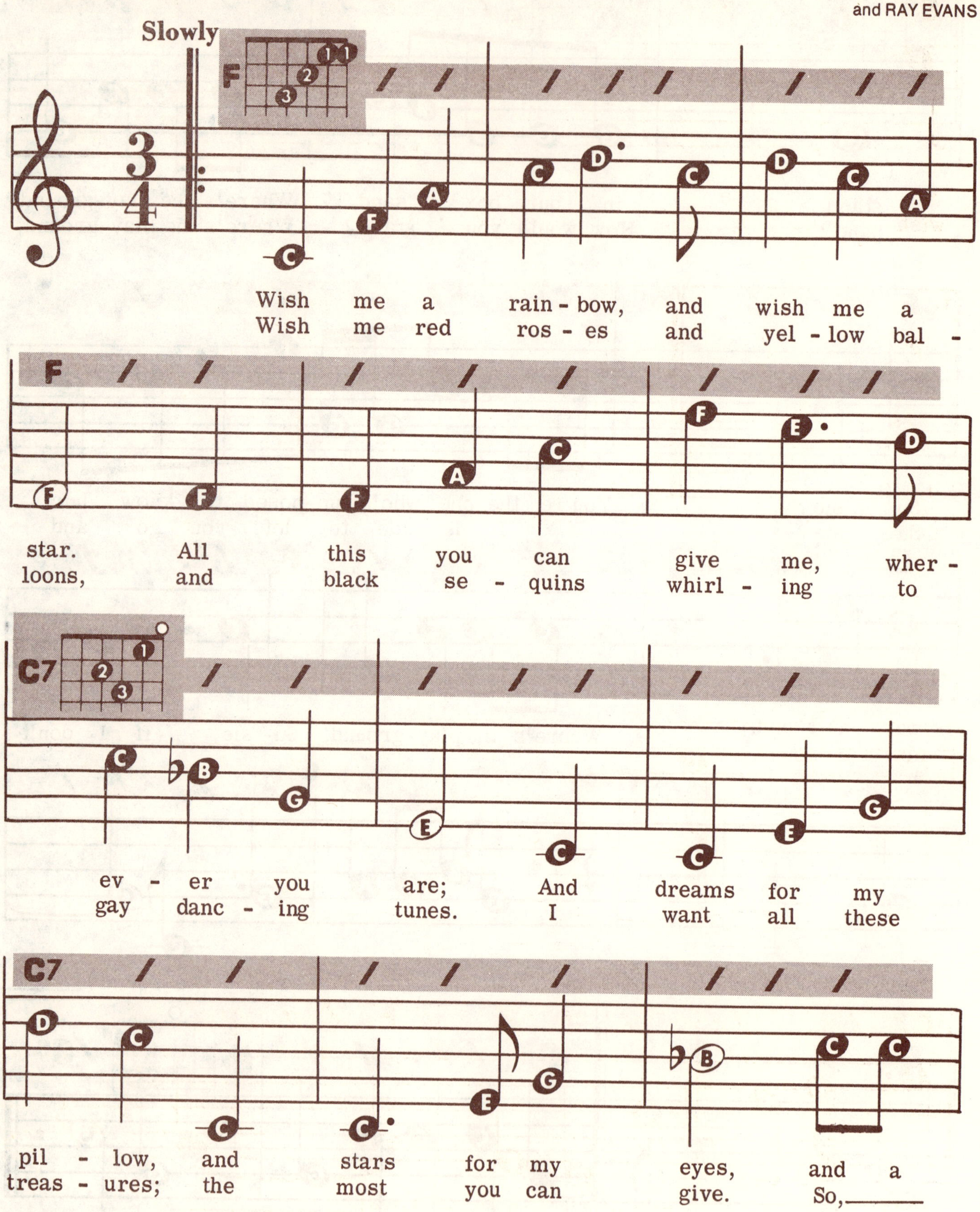

Wish me a rain-bow, and wish me a star.
Wish me red ros-es and yel-low bal-loons,

All this you can give me, wher-ev-er you are;
And I
And and this black se-quins give whirl-ing to gay danc-ing tunes. I want

dreams for my pil-low, and stars for my eyes, and a
treas-ures; the most you can give. So,____

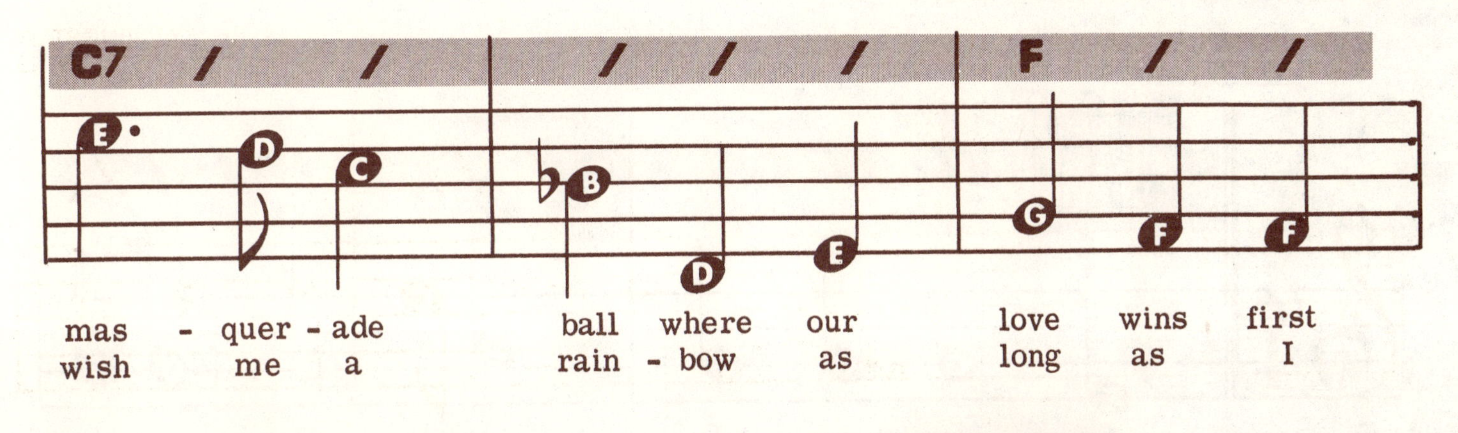

mas - quer - ade       ball   where   our       love   wins   first
wish       me   a       rain - bow   as       long   as   I

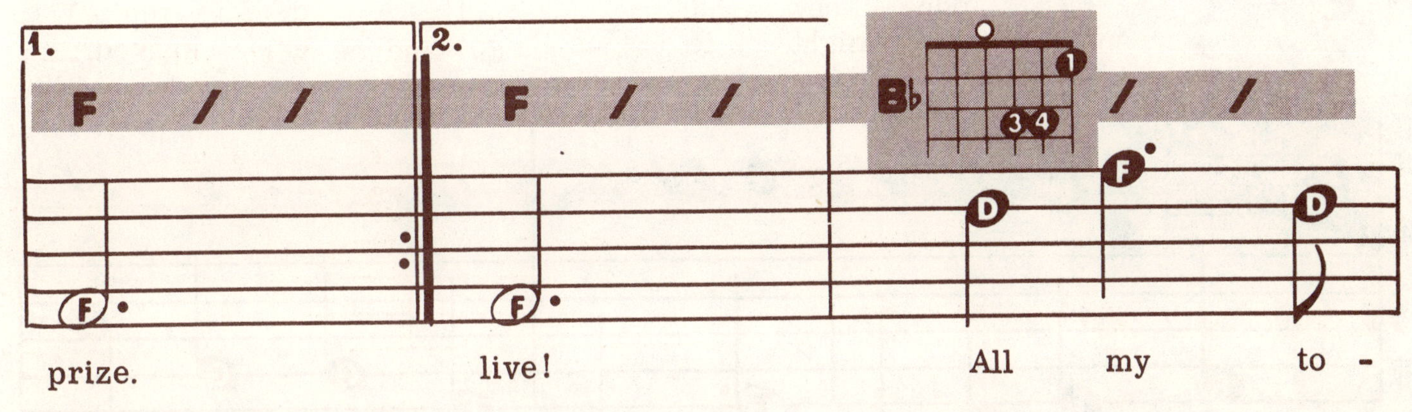

prize.              live!                       All   my   to -

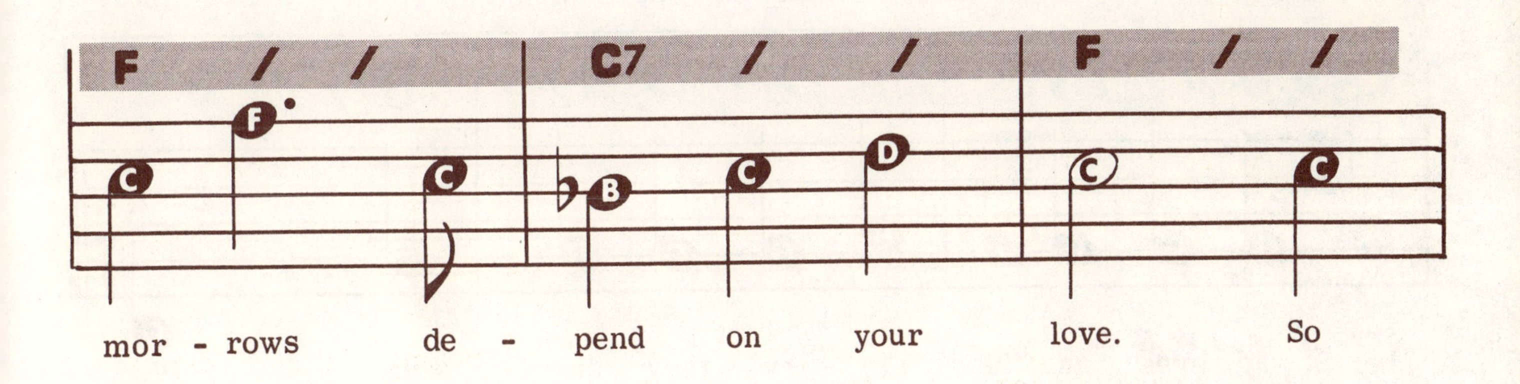

mor - rows       de - pend   on   your       love.       So

wish   me   a       rain - bow   a - bove!_____

Wish Me A Rainbow -2 -2

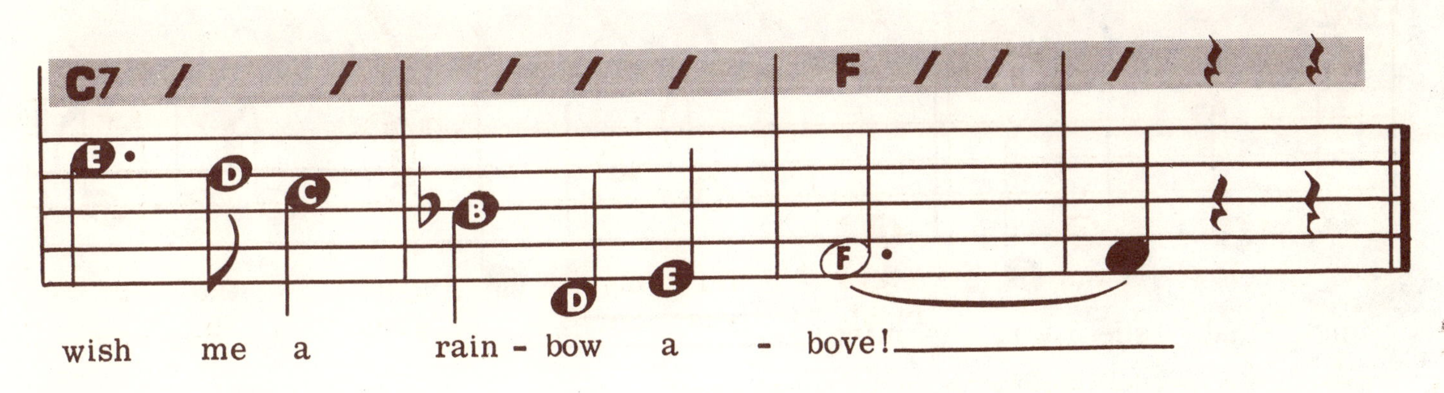

# A WOMAN IN NEED OF SOMEONE

By CHARLONA (Charley) JACOBSON

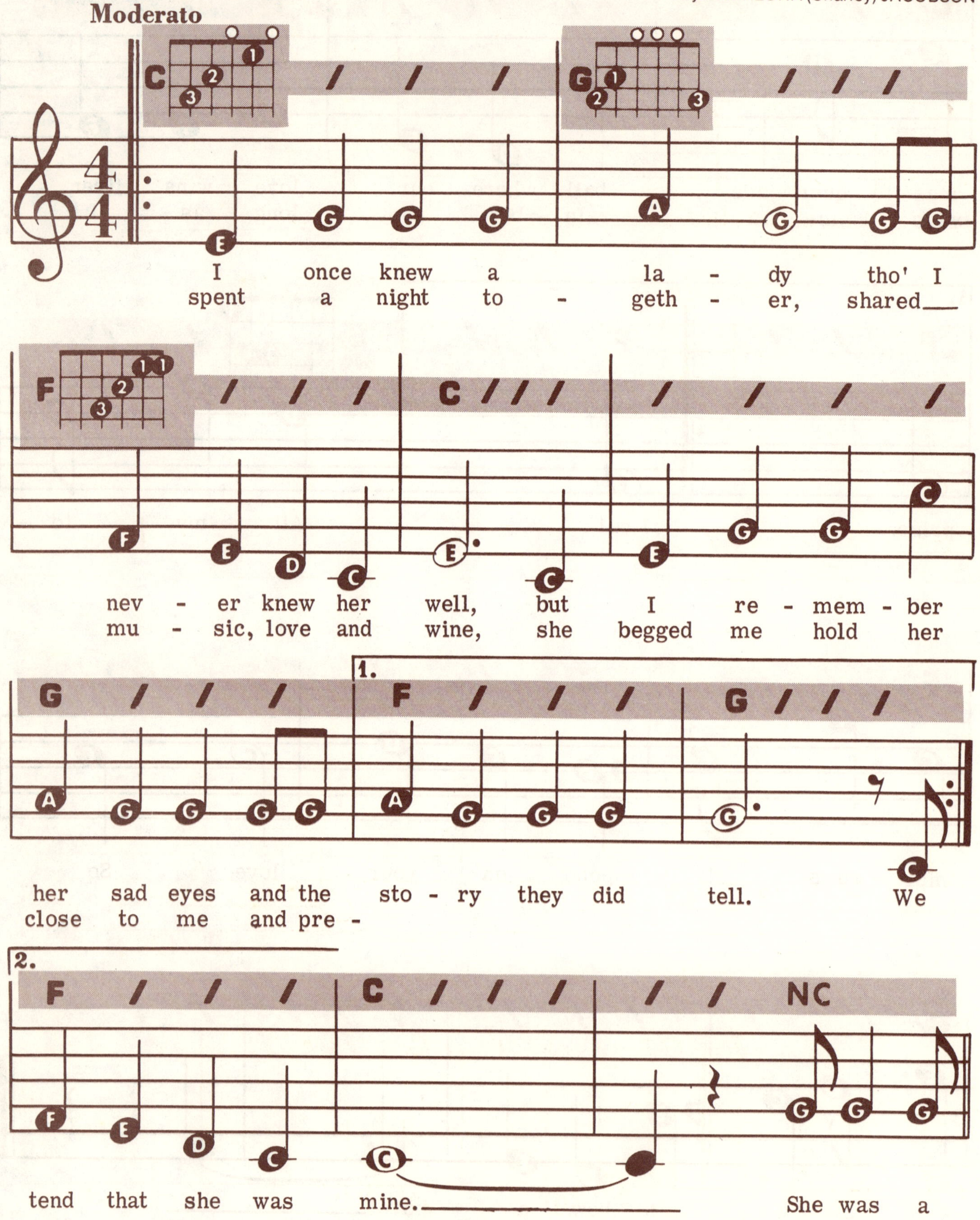

I once knew a la - dy tho' I
spent a night to - geth - er, shared___

nev - er knew her well, but I re - mem - ber
mu - sic, love and wine, but she begged me hold her

her sad eyes and the sto - ry they did tell. We
close to me and pre -

tend that she was mine.___ She was a

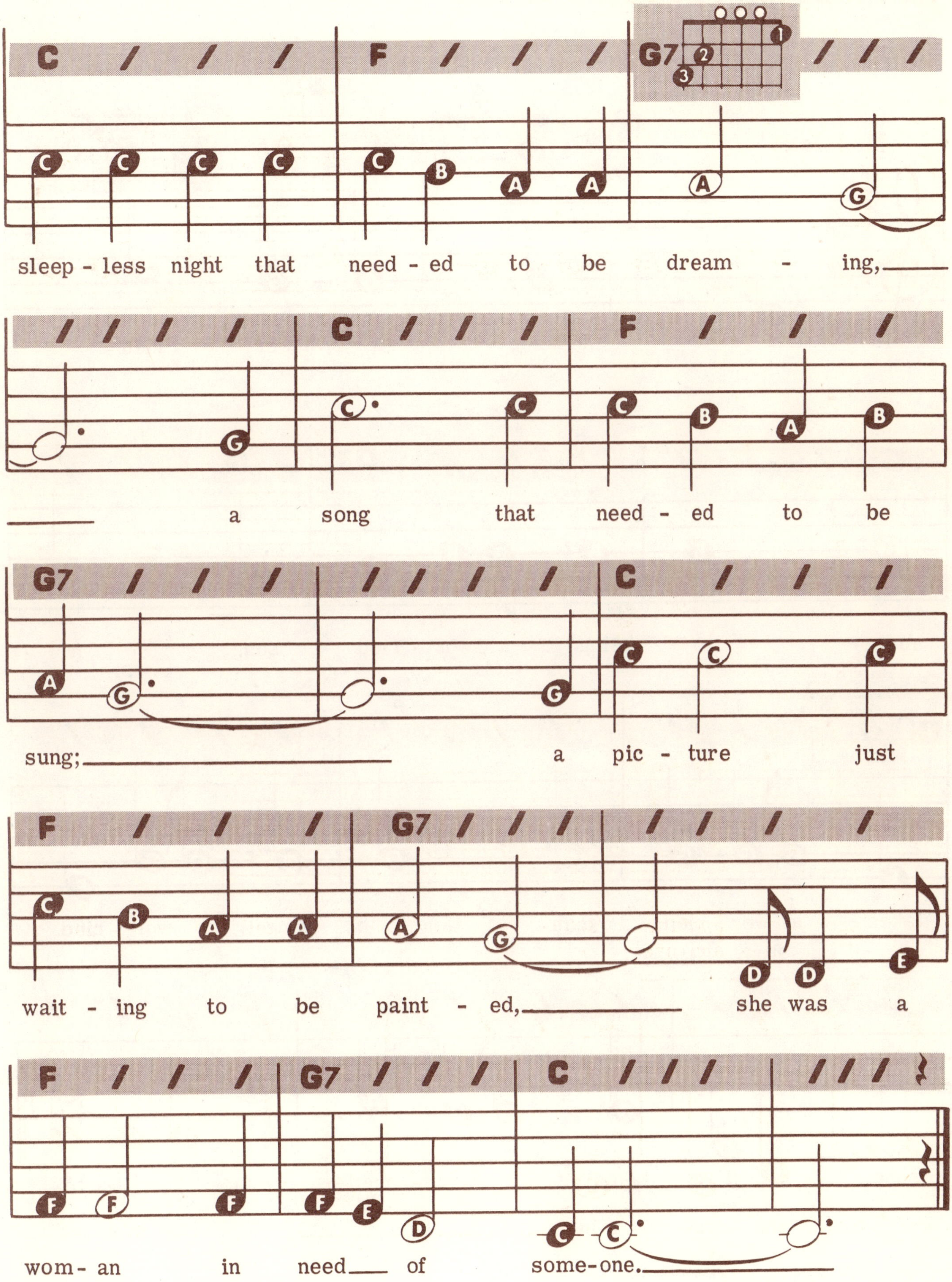

sleep - less night that need - ed to be dream - ing,____

____ a song that need - ed to be

sung;____ a pic - ture just

wait - ing to be paint - ed,____ she was a

wom - an in need__ of some-one.____

A Woman In Need Of Someone-2-2

# WORRIED MAN BLUES

TRADITIONAL

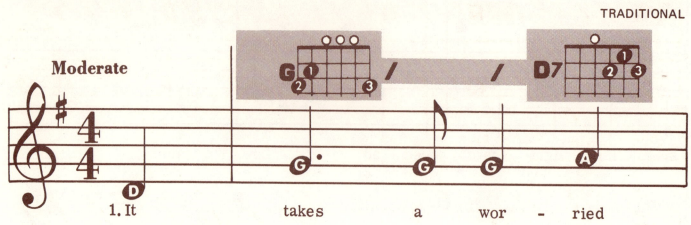

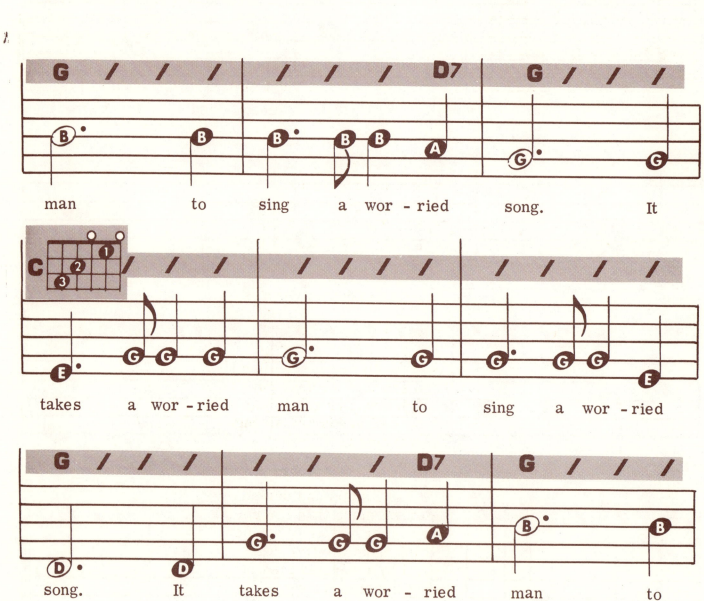

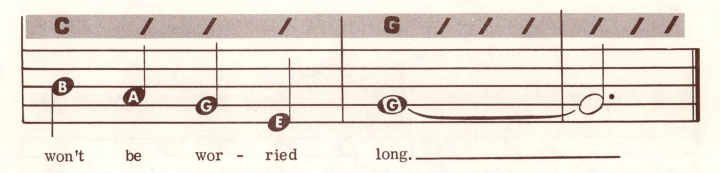

sing    a    wor – ried    song,   I'm   wor – ried    now         but    I

won't    be    wor – ried        long._____

2. When everything goes wrong,
I sing a worried song,
When everything goes wrong,
I sing a worried song,
When everything goes wrong,
I sing a worried song,
I'm worried now,
But I won't be worried long.

3. I saved a thousand bucks,
Then I met Jennie Bly,
She took me for ev'ry dime
Then she took another guy,
Though now I've got no job,
My pair of hands are strong.
I'm worried now,
But I won't be worried long.

4. Life has its ups and downs,
I'm down more than I'm up,
When others drank the wine,
I drank from a bitter cup.
Yes, I'm a worried man,
I sing a worried song,
I'm worried now,
But I won't be worried long.

Worried Man Blues-2-2

# YELLOW ROSE OF TEXAS

TRADITIONAL

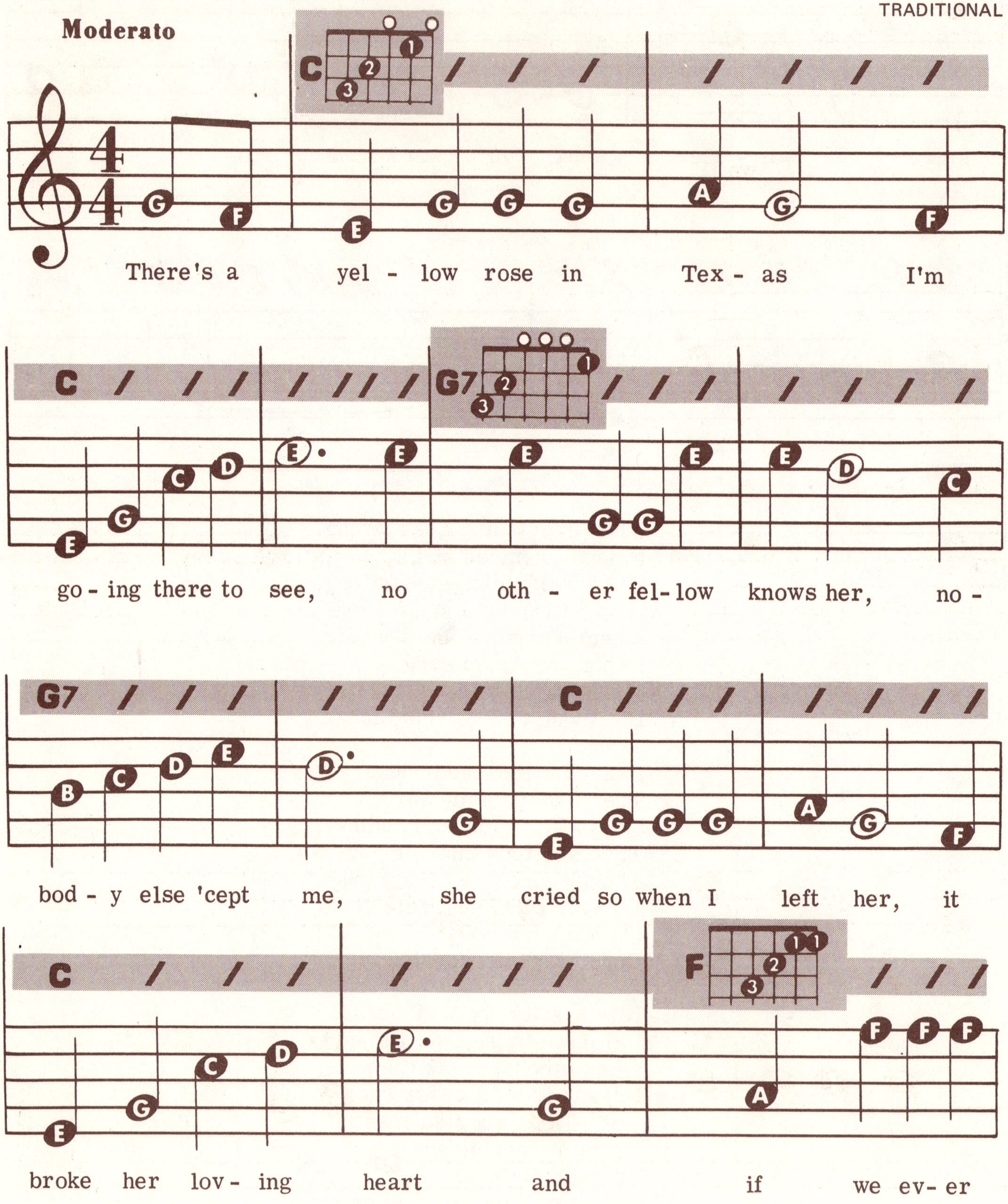

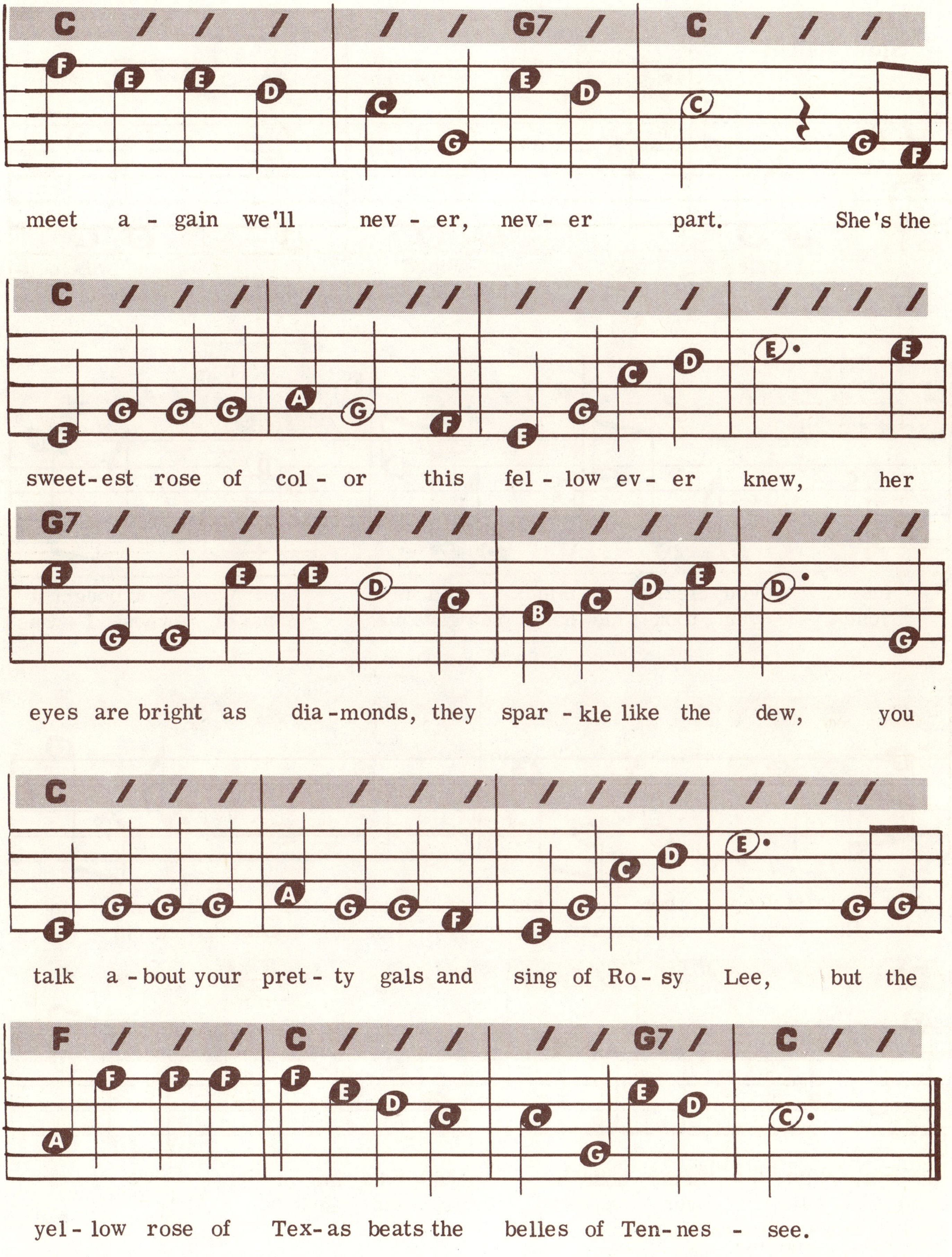

meet a - gain we'll nev - er, nev - er part. She's the

sweet-est rose of col - or this fel - low ev - er knew, her

eyes are bright as dia -monds, they spar - kle like the dew, you

talk a -bout your pret - ty gals and sing of Ro - sy Lee, but the

yel - low rose of Tex-as beats the belles of Ten - nes - see.

Yellow Rose Of Texas-2-2

# YOU NEEDED ME

Words and Music by
RANDY GOODRUM

**Slow Ballad**

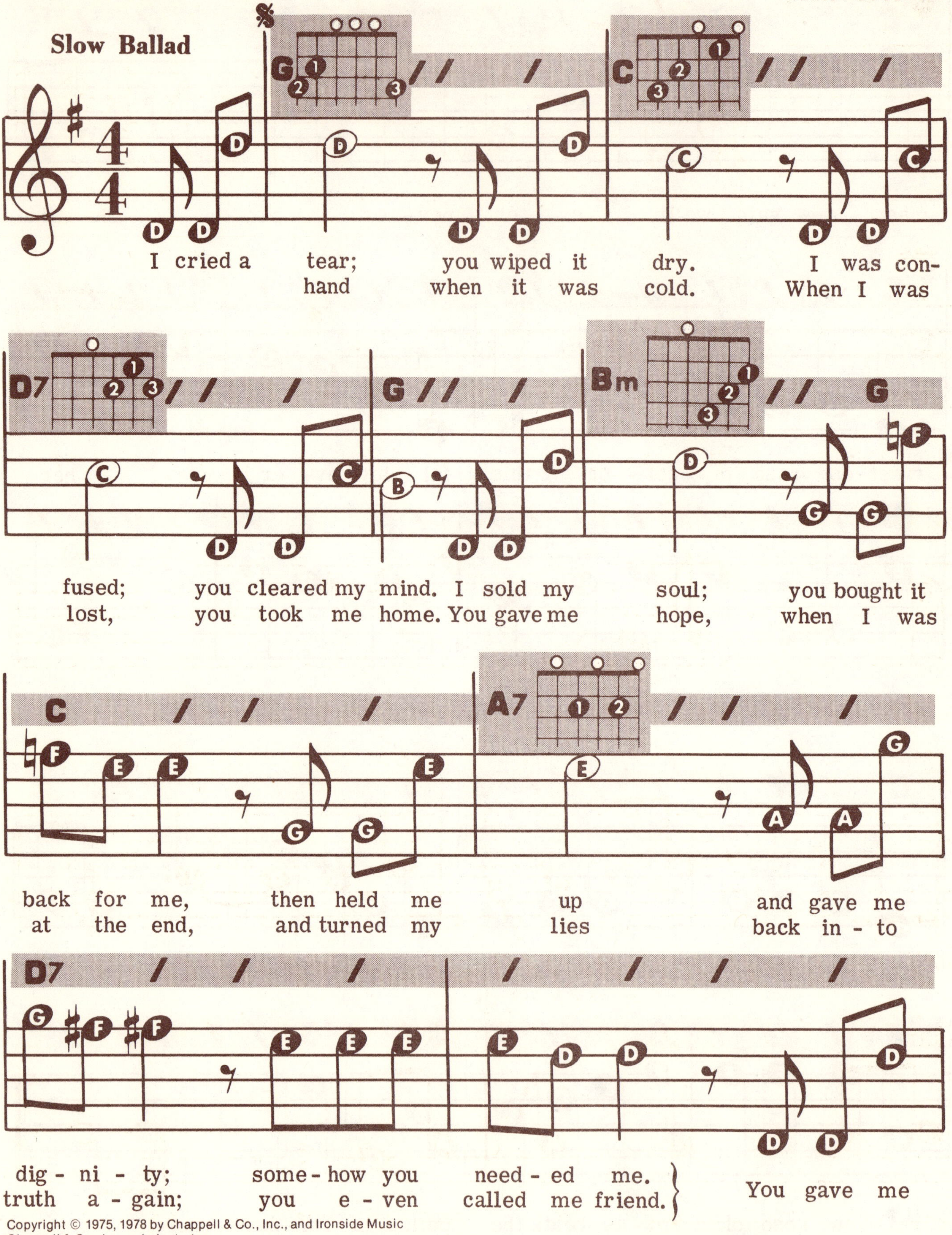

I cried a tear; you wiped it dry. I was con-
hand when it was cold. When I was

fused; you cleared my mind. I sold my soul; you bought it
lost, you took me home. You gave me hope, when I was

back for me, then held me up and gave me
at the end, and turned my lies back in - to

dig - ni - ty; some - how you need - ed me.
truth a - gain; you e - ven called me friend. } You gave me

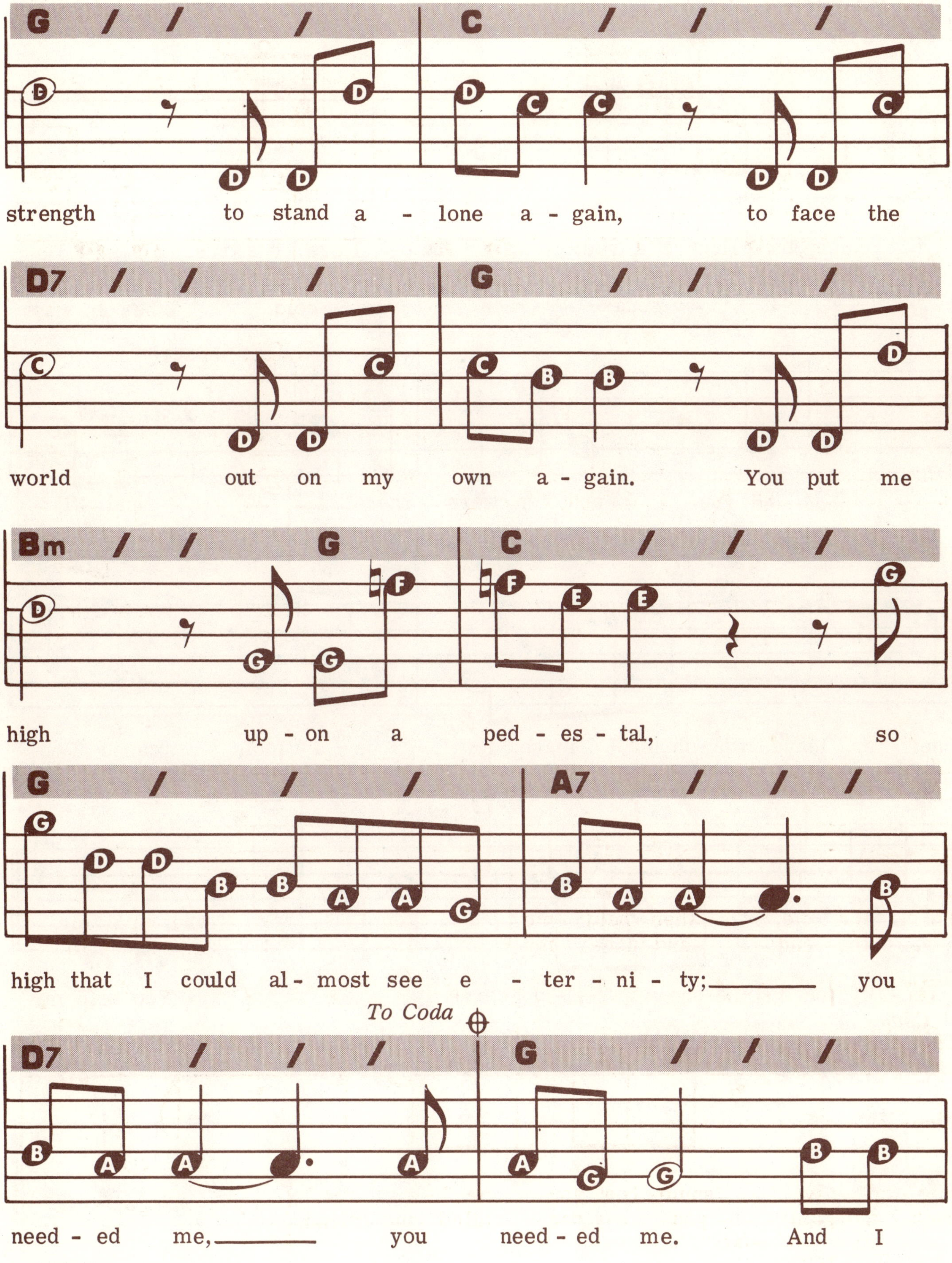

strength     to stand a - lone a - gain,     to face the

world     out on my own a - gain.     You put me

high     up - on a ped - es - tal,     so

high that I could al - most see e - ter - ni - ty; _____ you

*To Coda* ⊕

need - ed me, _____ you need - ed me. And I

You Needed Me-3-2

188

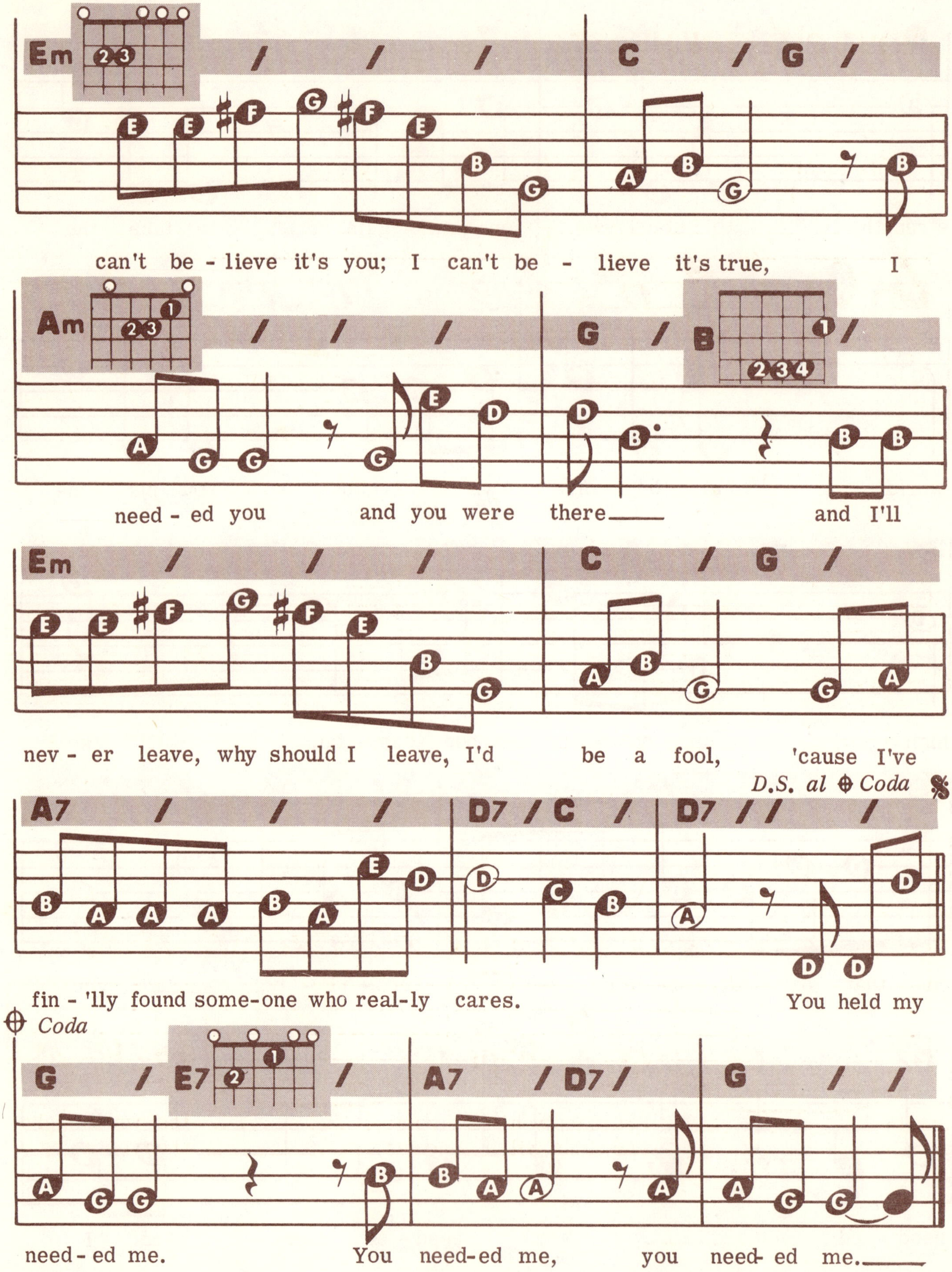

can't be - lieve it's you; I can't be - lieve it's true, I

need - ed you and you were there_____ and I'll

nev - er leave, why should I leave, I'd be a fool, 'cause I've

*D.S. al ⊕ Coda*

fin - 'lly found some-one who real-ly cares. You held my

⊕ *Coda*

need - ed me. You need-ed me, you need- ed me._____

You Needed Me-3-3

# YOUR CHEATIN' HEART

By HANK WILLIAMS

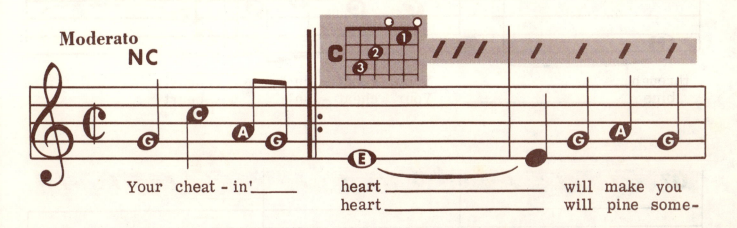

Your cheat-in'____ heart_____ will make you
heart_____ will pine some-

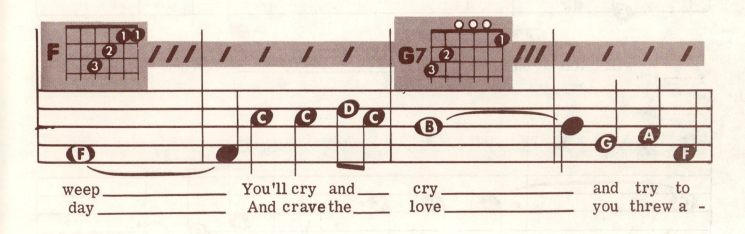

weep_____ You'll cry and____ cry_____ and try to
day_____ And crave the____ love_____ you threw a-

sleep_____ But sleep won't____ come_____ the whole night
way._____ The time will____ come_____ when you'll be

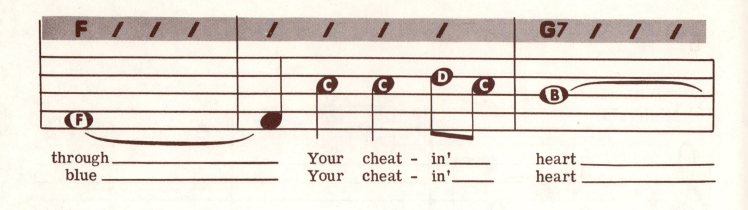

through _____ Your cheat - in'_____ heart _____
blue _____ Your cheat - in'_____ heart _____

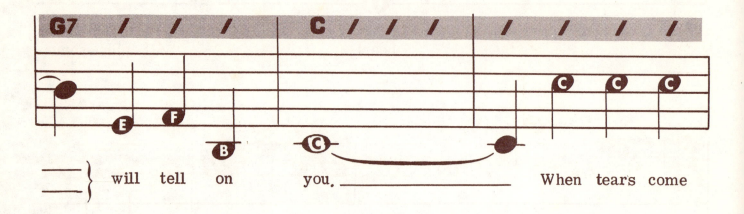

_____ } will tell on you. _____ When tears come

down _____ like fall - in' rain _____

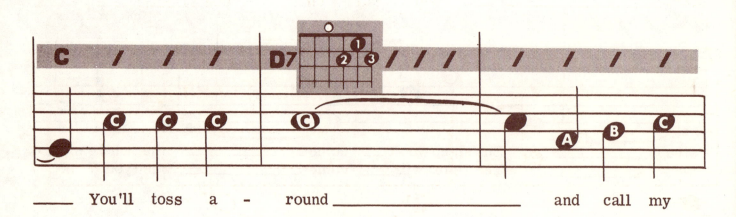

_____ You'll toss a - round _____ and call my

Your Cheatin' Heart-3-2

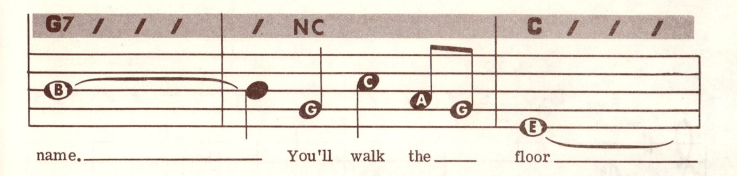

name._____ You'll walk the\_\_\_\_ floor_____

\_\_\_\_ the way I do _____ Your cheat - in'\_\_\_\_

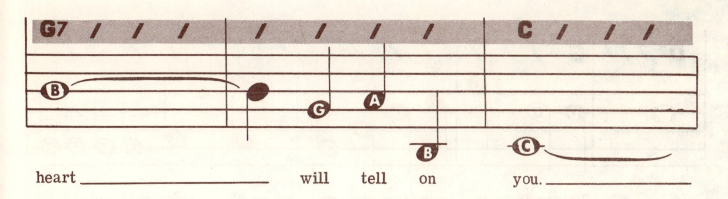

heart _____ will tell on you.\_\_\_\_

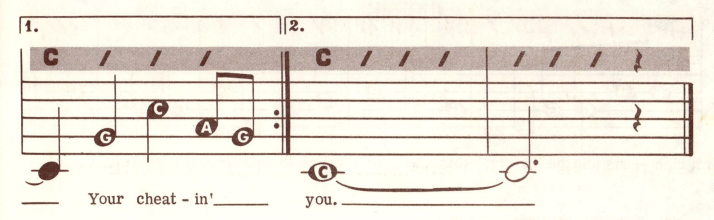

\_\_\_\_ Your cheat - in'\_\_\_\_ you._____

Your Cheatin' Heart-3-3

# THIS TRAIN IS BOUND FOR GLORY

SPIRITUAL

This train is bound for glo-ry, this train.

This train is bound for glo-ry, this train.

This train is bound for glo-ry, won't ride noth-in' but the

right-eous and the ho-ly, this train is bound for glo-ry, this train.